CHEMISTRY
for AQA

Ann and Patrick Fullick

Heinemann

Heinemann Educational Publishers,
Halley Court, Jordan Hill, Oxford, OX2 8EJ
Part of Harcourt Education

Heinemann is a registered trademark
of Harcourt Education Ltd

First published 2001

ISBN 0 435 583913
05 04 03
10 9 8 7 6 5 4

Edited by Linda Moore

Designed and typeset by Gecko Ltd

Illustrated by Gecko Ltd, Martin Fish, Paul McCaffry
and Geoff Ward

Printed and bound in Italy by Printer Trento S.r.l.

Acknowledgements

The authors and publishers would like to thank the
following for permission to use photographs:

2: TR SPL/NASA/GSFC, ML SPL/Klaus Guldbrandsen, M
Andrew Lambert, BR Robert Harding; 4: SPL/Philippe
Plailly; 5: TR SPL, M Mary Evans; 7: SPL; 8: SPL/Michael
Gilbert; 10: Ace Photo Library; 12: TR Stock Market, M
Andrew Lambert, B SPL; 13: Andrew Lambert; 14: Andrew
Lambert; 15: SPL/Charles D Winters; 16: Robert Harding;
18: SPL/Charles D. Winters; 19: Robert Harding; 22: TR
SPL/Sheila Terry, four pictures at bottom Andrew Lambert;
24: Andrew Lambert; 26: TR Andrew Lambert, B Corbis; 27:
TL Andrew Lambert, TM Andrew Lambert, TR Andrew
Lambert, ML Andrew Lambert, M Andrew Lambert, MR
Andrew Lambert, BR Roger Scruton; 29: SPL/Colin
Cuthbert; 30: GSF; 31: Robert Harding; 32: TR Andrew
Lambert, BR Andrew Lambert, MR Andrew Lambert, BL Peter
Gould; 33: Ace Photos; 34: SPL; 35: Andrew Lambert; 38:
Robert Harding; 39: Environmental Images; 41: Popperfoto;
42: SPL/David Halpern; 43: SPL/Y.Hamel, Publiphoto
Diffusion; 44: TR Corbis, MR Roger Scruton; 45: Ace Photos;
46: Environmental Images; 48: TR SPL/Francoise Sauze, BR
Collections; 49: TL Advertising Archives, TR Topham
Picturepoint; 52: TR Colorific, BR AA & A, BL
SPL/Maximilian Stock Ltd; 53: AA & A; 54: TR Peter Gould,
MR Andrew Lambert, BR Andrew Lambert; 57:
SPL/Maximilian Stock Ltd; 58: SPL; 60: Corbis; 61: TR
SPL/Rosenfield Images Ltd, ML Robert Harding; 62: Ace
Photos; 64: TR Ace Photos, MR Ace Photos, BL Collections;
65: Robert Harding; 66: OSF; 68: BASF; 69: TR
Environmental Images, M Robert Harding, MR Robert
Harding; 72: TR OSF, BL SPL; 73: TR SPL, MR SPL; 74: GSF;
75: SPL; 76: Robert Harding; 78: M SPL, B GSF, TM SPL; 79:
BL GSF, M GSF; 82: TR SPL, M GSF, B GSF; 83: TR SPL, M SPL;
86: TR SPL, BR Royal Society of Chemistry; 87: M SPL, TR G.
T. Woods; 89: TR Andrew Lambert, MR Andrew Lambert; 90:
M Roger Scruton, MR Andrew Lambert; 92: BL Peter Gould,
three pictures at bottom right Andrew Lambert; 93: Peter
Gould; 94: MR Andrew Lambert, M SPL; 96: MR Peter Gould,
B Andrew Lambert; 99: Collections; 101: SPL; 102:TR Mark
Powell, M GSF, MR SPL; 103: Environmental Images; 106: TR
West Sussex Police, MR Peter Gould; 108: TR Peter Gould, BR
SPL; 109: SPL; 110: TR Andrew Lambert, MR Andrew
Lambert, BR Peter Gould; 111: M Robert Harding, MR Roger
Scruton; 112: four pictures left to right Peter Gould, far
right Andrew Lambert; 113: TM Roger Scruton, TR Roger
Scruton, MR SPL, BR SPL; 114: TR OSF, M ECON, BR Salt
Union; 116: M Mary Evans, TR Ace Photos, B Gerstenburg;
120: TR SPL, B Peter Gould; 121: T Peter Gould, M Peter
Gould; 122: T SPL, B SPL; 124: TR Robert Harding, M
Andrew Lambert, MR Andrew Lambert, B Corbis; 126: TR
Peter Gould, B SPL; 128: TR AA & A, ML Anthony Blake, M
Anthony Blake, B Peter Gould; 129: SPL; 130: SPL; 131:
Roger Scruton; 132: M SPL, BL SPL; 136: M Robert Harding,
R OSF; 137: R Ann Fullick, M OSF; 139: TR SPL, ML Peter
Gould; 140: GSF; 141: SPL; 142: Peter Gould; 143: Ace
Photos; 144: TR Peter Gould, BR Mark Powell; 150: TM
Robert Harding, TR SPL/Volker Steger/Siemens, BR GSF;
151: Peter Morris; 154: SPL; 156: TR Oxford Scientific
Films, MTR Oxford Scientific Films; 158: TR Anthony Blake
Photo Library, R Cumulus/Roger Scruton, BL SPL/P. Nieto,
Jerrican; 159: Oxford Scientific Films; 160: ML Roger
Scruton, MR Roger Scruton; 161: TR SPL, R SPL/Jeremy
Walker; 162: Ace; 163: TR SPL/Charles D. Winters, TM
Anthony Blake Photo Library; 164: SPL; 165: Anthony Blake
Photo Library; 166: T SPL, B SPL; 167: Roger Scruton; 168:
Gareth Boden; 169: TR Roger Scruton, MR Roger Scruton;
172: TR Environmental Picture Library, MR SPL; 174:
SPL/Martin Bond; 175: TR Mark Powell, ML Mark Powell, MR
Mark Powell; 176: TR Anthony Blake Photo Library, BR
Mansfield Anodisers Ltd; 177: Paul Brierley; 178: TR Robert
Harding, BR Corbis; 180: Environmental Picture Library;
181: Ace Photo Agency; 182: TR SPL, MR SPL, ML Empics, BR
SPL; 186: Robert Harding; 187: Robert Harding; 188:
Andrew Lambert; 190: Keith Gibson; 191: OSF; 192: TR
Roger Scruton, BR Mary Evans Picture Library; 193: Peter
Gould; 194: Ace Photo Agency; 196: (all) Andrew Lambert;
198: Mark Powell; 202: TR Mary Evans Picture Library, MR
Andrew Lambert, BR Andrew Lambert; 204: Mark Powell;
205: Andrew Lambert; 206: SPL; 207: TR SPL, MR
SPL/Custom Medical Stock Photo.

Picture research by Thelma Gilbert

Tel: 01865 888058 www.heinemann.co.uk

Introduction

Chemistry – the science which looks at matter and the way it behaves. The world of chemistry is intriguing and absorbing, and full of possibilities. In this book you will find out more about the behaviour of atoms and molecules, and how this behaviour affects and influences everything around us.

This book has been written to support you as you study the AQA Separate Science GCSE. As well as lots of facts and clear explanations with diagrams and photos to illustrate the science, there are some other features which will add interest and depth to your learning.

- ⊙ **Science people** introduces you to some of the scientists who have worked out the science we now take for granted.
- ⊙ **Ideas and evidence** looks at the way ideas about chemistry have developed and grown over the years.

At the end of each double page spread there are questions to help you check that you have understood the material you have just read, and at the end of each chapter there are GCSE style questions which will allow you to test your knowledge for the exams ahead.

Studying chemistry will give you an increased understanding of the world of materials – their properties, their uses and how new materials can be made. We hope this book will help you in your studies, and help you enjoy chemistry throughout your course.

Contents

Chapter 1: Classifying materials

1.1	The atomic universe	2
1.2	Ideas about atoms	4
1.3	Atomic structure	6
1.4	The electronic structure of atoms	8
1.5	The states of matter	10
1.6	Chemical reactions	12
1.7	Ionic bonding	14
1.8	Covalent bonding	16
1.9	Giant structures (H)	18
1.10	End of chapter questions	20

Chapter 2: Chemical accounting

2.1	Representing chemicals	22
2.2	Using chemical equations	24
2.3	Hazard!	26
2.4	The masses of atoms and compounds	28
2.5	Using relative atomic mass (I)	30
2.6	Using relative atomic mass (II)	32
2.7	Finding the mole (H)	34
2.8	End of chapter questions	36

Chapter 3: Useful products from oil

3.1	What is oil?	38
3.2	Separating crude oil	40
3.3	Using oil products	42
3.4	Chemicals from oil	44
3.5	Hydrocarbon chemistry (H)	46
3.6	Polymerisation (H)	48
3.7	End of chapter questions	50

Chapter 4: Resources from the Earth

4.1	The metal link	52
4.2	Ways of extracting metals	54
4.3	Iron	56
4.4	Electrolysis	58
4.5	Using electrolysis	60

Chapter 4: continued

4.6	More electrolysis (H)	62
4.7	Limestone	64
4.8	Nitrogen from the air	66
4.9	The pros and cons of using nitrogen	68
4.10	End of chapter questions	70

Chapter 5: The changing Earth

5.1	The history of the atmosphere	72
5.2	Life, oxygen and the planet	74
5.3	The atmosphere today	76
5.4	The record of the rocks	78
5.5	The restless Earth	80
5.6	The changing surface	82
5.7	End of chapter questions	84

Chapter 6: The periodic table

6.1	The structure of the periodic table	86
6.2	Patterns in the periodic table	88
6.3	Group 1 – the alkali metals	90
6.4	Reactions of the alkali metals	92
6.5	Group 7 – the halogens	94
6.6	Reactions of the halogens	96
6.7	Group 0 – the noble gases	98
6.8	The transition metals	100
6.9	More about transition metals	102
6.10	End of chapter questions	104

Chapter 7: Acids, bases and salts

7.1	Acids and bases	106
7.2	Neutralisation	108
7.3	Making salts	110
7.4	More about salts	112
7.5	Sodium chloride – the best known salt	114
7.6	Using brine products	116
7.7	End of chapter questions	118

Chapter 8: Reaction rates

8.1	Rates of reactions	120
8.2	Factors affecting reaction rates	122
8.3	More about reaction rates	124
8.4	Enzymes	126
8.5	Reactions in living cells	128
8.6	Enzymes in industry	130
8.7	Using enzymes successfully Ⓗ	132
8.8	End of chapter questions	134

Chapter 9: Energy and equilibria

9.1	Energy in reactions	136
9.2	Making and breaking bonds Ⓗ	138
9.3	Activation energy and catalysts Ⓗ	140
9.4	Bond energy calculations Ⓗ	142
9.5	Reversible reactions	144
9.6	Reversible reactions, equilibrium and industry Ⓗ	146
9.7	End of chapter questions	148

Chapter 10: Organic chemistry

10.1	Introducing organic chemistry	150
10.2	Burning fossil fuels	152
10.3	Homologous series Ⓗ	154
10.4	Isomers Ⓗ	156
10.5	Ethanol – the best known alcohol	158
10.6	The alcohols Ⓗ	160
10.7	The reactions of the alcohols Ⓗ	162
10.8	The carboxylic acids Ⓗ	164
10.9	Cardiac chemistry Ⓗ	166
10.10	Polymer chemistry Ⓗ	168
10.11	End of chapter questions	170

Chapter 11: Industrial processes

11.1	Making sulphuric acid	172
11.2	Using sulphuric acid	174
11.3	Using aluminium	176
11.4	Making the most of iron	178
11.5	More about steel	180
11.6	Titanium	182
11.7	End of chapter questions	184

Chapter 12: Aqueous chemistry

12.1	Water, water, everywhere …	186
12.2	Hard water, soft water	188
12.3	Solubility in water	190
12.4	Water, acids and bases	192
12.5	Acids, bases and salts	194
12.6	Titrations Ⓗ	196
12.7	Titrations and calculations Ⓗ	198
12.8	End of chapter questions	200

Chapter 13: Detection & identification

13.1	Investigating the unknown	202
13.2	More chemical detection	204
13.3	High-tech analysis	206
13.4	End of chapter questions	208

| Data | 210 |
| Index | 212 |

1.1 The atomic universe

Everywhere we look we are surrounded by materials of different types – wood, paper, plastics, metals, wool, skin, glass … the list seems almost endless. Look around the Earth on which we live, and the number and type of materials becomes mind-boggling.

Material make-up

All substances are made of **atoms**. As far as we know there are about 100 different types of atom which occur naturally in the universe, and all of the matter which exists is based on combinations of these different types of atom.

Some substances are made up of only one type of atom. These substances are known as **elements**. As there are only about 100 different types of atom, there are only about 100 different elements.

Elements show an enormous range in properties. For example metals like copper, silver, zinc and gold are shiny solids with properties which are easily recognised. Other elements, like oxygen, nitrogen and chlorine, are non-metals and gases.

↑ **Figure 1:** The range of materials on Earth is vast. Chemistry helps us to make sense of it all!

aluminium

← **Figure 2:** A substance which contains only one sort of atom is an element.

bromine

↓ **Figure 3:** Almost everything in this picture is a compound, made up of a combination of atoms from several different elements.

Compounds

The vast majority of substances around us and in the universe are not pure elements. Most substances are made up of combinations of different types of atoms and are known as **compounds**. These range from simple combinations of two different elements such as water (hydrogen and oxygen combined) through to huge compounds made up of many atoms such as plastics and the genetic material, DNA. The arrangement of nearly 100 elements in different combinations means that there is an almost infinite variety of materials.

The structure of atoms

All elements are made up of atoms. Because compounds are made up of elements, it follows that all compounds are made up of atoms too. In the middle of an atom is a small nucleus which contains two types of particles, called protons and neutrons. A third type of particle is found orbiting the nucleus – the electron. Every atom has the same number of electrons orbiting its nucleus as it has protons in its nucleus.

The mass of a proton and a neutron are the same. Another way of putting this is to say that the **relative mass** of a neutron compared to a proton is 1. Electrons are far, far smaller than protons and neutrons – their relative mass is negligible. Because of this, the mass of an atom is concentrated in its nucleus – the electrons in an atom just do not matter when it comes to thinking about its mass!

However, the electrons are important when it comes to thinking about charge. Protons have a positive charge while neutrons have no charge – they are neutral – so the nucleus itself has an overall positive charge. The electrons orbiting the nucleus are negatively charged. The size of the negative charge on an electron is exactly the same as the size of the positive charge on a proton. (In other words, the **relative charge** on a proton is $+1$, while the relative charge on an electron is -1.) Because any atom contains equal numbers of protons and electrons, the overall charge on any atom is exactly zero. For example, a carbon atom has six protons, so we know it also has six electrons. Similarly oxygen has eight protons and therefore eight electrons.

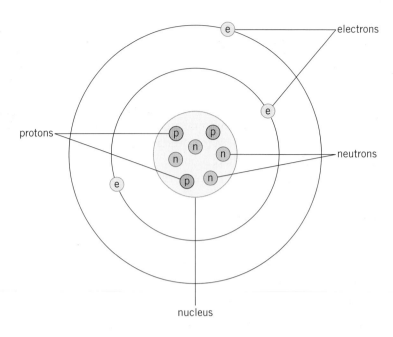

↑ **Figure 4:** Understanding the structure of an atom gives us vital clues to the way chemicals react together.

Type of sub-atomic particle	Relative mass	Relative charge
proton	1	$+1$
neutron	1	0
electron	negligible	-1

Questions

1 What is an element?

2 a What is the difference between an element and a compound?

   b Why are there so many more compounds than there are elements?

3 a An atom has two protons and two neutrons in its nucleus. Draw a diagram of this atom to show protons, neutrons and electrons.

   b How do you know how many electrons to draw in orbit around this atom?

4 a Iron atoms have 26 protons. How many electrons would you expect?

   b Zinc atoms have 30 electrons moving around the nucleus. How many protons would you expect there to be in the nucleus?

   c A special type of atom known as carbon-14 has six protons and eight neutrons. How many electrons would you expect?

Key Ideas

⊙ All matter is made up of atoms.

⊙ Elements are substances made up of only one type of atom.

⊙ Atoms have a central nucleus which contains protons and neutrons.

⊙ Electrons move in orbits around the nucleus.

⊙ Protons have a relative mass of 1 and a positive charge.

⊙ Neutrons have a relative mass of 1 and are neutral.

⊙ Electrons have negligible mass and a negative charge.

All substances are made up of atoms. We all accept this, yet no one has ever seen an atom in detail. Atoms are so small it would take billions of them to cover a single full stop! The closest we come to seeing atoms is when a scanning electron microscope is used to magnify metal structures many thousands of times.

How did our model of the atom evolve?

We take the existence of atoms for granted – yet for centuries no one believed in them. Around 2500 years ago a Greek philosopher called Leucippus and his pupil Demokritos put forward the idea that the universe is made up of tiny indivisible particles, which they called atoms. Unfortunately the great Greek philosopher Aristotle did not agree with them. As Aristotle's views were accepted throughout Europe for almost 2000 years the idea of atoms was shelved for centuries to come.

The problem with the idea of atoms is that there is no easily available evidence for their existence. In fact, common sense says that solids are solid and liquids are liquid, not lots of tiny particles which no one can see.

John Dalton's atomic theory

About 200 years ago an English scientist named John Dalton was working on the nature of gases and chemical compounds. As a result of observations he had made during his experiments he published a ground-breaking theory on the nature of matter. He suggested that:

- All matter is made up of indivisible particles called atoms.
- Atoms of the same element are similar in mass and shape but differ from the atoms of other elements.
- Atoms cannot be created or destroyed.
- Atoms join together to form compound atoms (what we now call molecules) in simple ratios.

Dalton's statements were backed up with much research. Even though not all of it was accurate – for example he thought that one hydrogen atom combined with one oxygen atom to form water – most of it reflected the same results as other scientists of the time were getting. Dalton's atomic theory explained much of what scientists were seeing, and so this time around the idea of atoms was accepted relatively quickly. Some scientists even made wooden models of atoms of different elements, to show their different relative sizes.

Not everyone was an immediate fan however – one critic wrote 'Atoms are round bits of wood invented by Mr Dalton'! But by 1850, the atomic theory of matter was almost universally accepted and virtually all opposition had disappeared. Dalton's atomic theory was the basis of much of the chemistry done in the rest of the 19th and early 20th century.

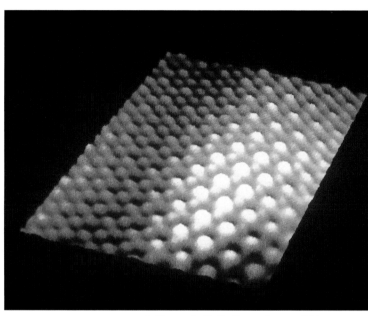

↑ **Figure 1:** Palladium atoms within the crystal lattice structure of the metal. These fuzzy blobs are the closest we have yet come to seeing individual atoms. This photograph was taken using a scanning electron microscope.

John Dalton was born in 1766 in the Lake District in England. His father was a weaver, and he taught John before sending him to a Quaker school in Eaglesfield, the town where they lived. John was incredibly bright, and was teaching other people by the time he was 12 years old! His interests were far ranging. He made many original observations on the weather – over 57 years he built up around 200 000 observations and measurements of the weather in the Manchester area! He was also the first person to identify and study colour blindness – his interest stemmed from the fact that he was colour blind himself. But Dalton is best remembered for his ideas in chemistry, particularly his atomic theory of matter which was published in 1808 in a book titled 'A New System of Chemical Philosophy'. Although his work was not perfectly accurate, it became the basis of the modern periodic table. Dalton also discovered a law governing the behaviour of a mixture of gases – he was indeed a worthy winner of the Gold Medal given by the Royal Society in 1882.

↑ **Figure 2:** John Dalton – the man who gave us atoms!

Ideas and Evidence

Developing the atomic model

Clear ideas of what an atom might actually be didn't start to emerge until around the beginning of the 20th century. In 1897 Joseph John Thompson showed that electrons were found in all matter. He also came up with a model for the atom, suggesting that the negative electrons were embedded in a sphere of positive charge like dried fruit in a 'plum pudding'. Then in 1911 Ernest Rutherford and his colleagues showed that the plum pudding model was wrong. Rutherford's model atom had a nucleus with electrons moving around it in orbits like the planets orbiting the sun.

In 1932 the British scientist James Chadwick carried out experiments which showed that neutrons, the final atomic particle to be discovered, actually existed. The changes that have been made to the model in the 70-odd years since are all relatively minor – our working model of the atom comes from almost a century ago.

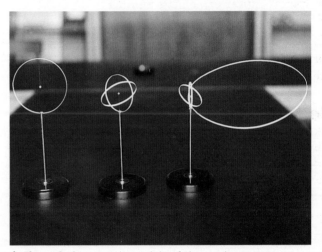
↑ **Figure 3:** Some early models of the nuclear atom.

Questions

1 Why was the idea of atoms rejected for over 200 years?

2 Why was Dalton's theory that matter is made up of atoms accepted relatively easily?

3 When people accepted Dalton's theory that all matter is made up of atoms they began to try and build up a model of what an atom looks like. Describe three different models of the atom which have been accepted at various times.

4 How have scientists built up a model of atoms without being able to see them?

H 5 Investigate the evidence built up by J J Thompson for his model of the atom and also the evidence on which Ernest Rutherford built up his model of atomic structure.

Key Ideas

⊙ John Dalton's atomic theory was accepted because it helped to explain what many other scientists were observing at the time.

Atomic structure

Atomic number

The number of protons in the nucleus of an atom is known as its **atomic number** or **proton number**. As all the atoms of a particular element have the same number of protons they also have the same atomic number. So the atomic number of hydrogen is 1 and it has 1 proton in the nucleus, the atomic number of carbon is 6 and it has 6 protons in the nucleus, and the atomic number of sodium is 11 and it has 11 protons in the nucleus.

Each element has its own atomic number. If you are told that the atomic number of an element is 8, you can identify that element from tables of data or the periodic table – in this case it is oxygen.

Mass number

Almost all of the mass of an atom is found in the nucleus, because the mass of the electrons is so small it is negligible. The total number of protons and neutrons in an atom is known as the **mass number**.

When we want to show the atomic number and mass number of an atom it is done like this:

mass number   12   23

           C (carbon)   **Na** (sodium)

atomic number   6   11

The number of neutrons present in the nucleus of an atom can be worked out by subtracting the atomic number from the mass number – the difference is the number of neutrons:

    mass number – atomic number = number of neutrons

For the two examples given, carbon has 6 protons and a mass number of 12, so the number of neutrons is $12 - 6 = 6$. Sodium, on the other hand, has an atomic number of 11 but the mass number is 23; $23 - 11 = 12$, so in this sodium atom there are 11 protons and 12 neutrons.

Isotopes

Atoms of the same element always have the same number of protons, but they do not always have the same number of neutrons. Atoms of the same element with different numbers of neutrons are known as **isotopes**. For example, carbon has two common isotopes, $^{12}_{6}C$ (carbon-12) and $^{14}_{6}C$ (carbon-14). The carbon-12 isotope has 6 protons and 6 neutrons in the nucleus, whilst the carbon-14 isotope has 6 protons and 8 neutrons.

Sometimes the extra neutrons in its nucleus make the isotope unstable, so that it is radioactive. However not all isotopes are radioactive – they are simply atoms of the same substance with a different mass. Although different isotopes of the same element may have different *physical* properties (they have a different mass and they may be radioactive), they always have the same *chemical* properties. For example, hydrogen has three isotopes: hydrogen, deuterium and tritium. They have different masses and tritium is radioactive but they can all react with oxygen to make water.

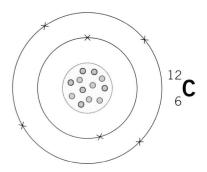

$^{12}_{6}C$

○ proton   Number of protons gives atomic number.

○ neutron   Number of protons plus number of neutrons gives mass number.

⬆ **Figure 1:** The atomic number and the mass number of an element are useful tools to the chemist in many ways.

$^{1}_{1}H$ hydrogen

$^{2}_{1}H$ deuterium

$^{3}_{1}H$ tritium

⬆ **Figure 2:** The isotopes of hydrogen – similar chemical properties, different physical properties.

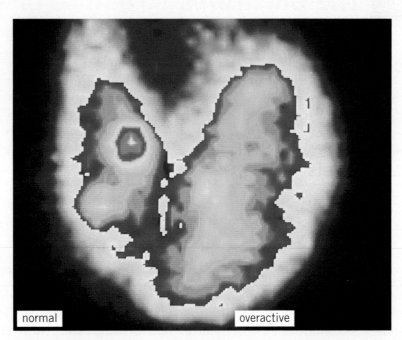

Ideas and Evidence

Isotopes in science and medicine

Radioactive isotopes can be used to find out about the chemistry of living things because they can be traced with special detectors. For example, tritium enabled scientists to work out what happens as plants make food by photosynthesis. The scientists replaced ordinary hydrogen with tritium in some water molecules. These molecules were then taken up by the plants. The tritium could be traced to show how the water was broken down in photosynthesis.

In hospitals radioactive isotopes are often used to see what is happening inside a patient's body without having to cut it open. For example, the thyroid gland is the only part of the body which takes up iodine. So if you inject a patient with radioactive iodine it can be traced to help you see how the thyroid is working.

normal | overactive

↑ **Figure 3:** The difference between normal thyroid tissue and thyroid tissue which is overactive can be seen clearly using special isotopes of iodine.

? Questions

1 What is the difference between the atomic (or proton) number and the mass number?

2 Write each of the elements below in the following way:

mass number   12

symbol for element, eg   **C**

atomic number   6

  a helium, mass number 4, atomic number 2

  b calcium, mass number 40, atomic number 20

  c oxygen, mass number 16, atomic number 8.

3 For each of the following elements give the mass number and state how many protons and neutrons would be found in the nucleus. Show your working.

  a $^{9}_{4}Be$

  b $^{24}_{12}Mg$

  c $^{80}_{35}Br$

  d $^{19}_{9}F$

  e $^{197}_{79}Au$

4 a What is an isotope?

  b How may the physical properties of isotopes of the same element vary?

5 How are radioactive isotopes used in research and medicine?

Key Ideas

- ⊙ The number of protons in the nucleus is known as the atomic number or proton number.

- ⊙ The number of protons and neutrons is known as the mass number.

- ⊙ Atoms of the same element always have the same number of protons and electrons.

- ⊙ Two atoms of the same element with different numbers of neutrons are known as isotopes.

- ⊙ The isotopes of an element may have different physical properties but they will always have the same chemical properties.

Once the nuclear model for the atom was accepted, the next puzzle for scientists to solve was the behaviour of the electrons outside the nucleus. It seemed that it was the arrangement of the electrons which affected how different atoms reacted – but a model which explained all the observed properties of the different elements was not easy to find.

Energy levels

The model of the atom which scientists now use has electrons arranged around the nucleus in **shells**, rather like the layers of an onion. Each shell is at a different **energy level**, the lowest energy level being the one which is nearest to the nucleus.

With their negative charge, electrons are attracted to the positively charged nucleus. To move an electron from a shell close to the nucleus to one further away therefore requires energy, to overcome this attractive force. This means that electrons in shells further away from the nucleus have more energy than electrons in shells closer to the nucleus. To remind us about the importance of energy levels in atoms, from now on we shall always use the term *energy level* when we talk about the arrangement of electrons in atoms.

← **Figure 1:** No one has actually seen electrons in their different energy levels around the nucleus of an atom, but with the aid of computers people have come up with some fairly spectacular models!

We could not possibly represent atoms as they are shown in Figure 1 every time we need to show the structure of an atom, so for simplicity they are usually drawn as in Figure 2.

An energy level can only hold a certain number of electrons. The first, and lowest energy level holds two electrons. The second and third levels are each filled by eight electrons. Once there are eight electrons in the third energy level, the fourth begins to fill up, and so on. Atoms where the outer energy level is full are very stable and unreactive. They are called the **noble gases** – helium, neon and argon are examples.

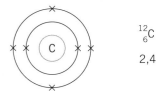

$^{12}_{6}C$

2,4

↑ **Figure 2:** A simple way of representing the electrons in an atom and the energy levels where they are found. This is sometimes called the *electronic configuration* of the atom. A carbon atom is shown here.

The most common way of showing the arrangement of electrons in an atom is to draw diagrams like those in Figure 2 and to write down the numbers of electrons in each energy level. The atomic number of an element tells us how many electrons there are in the atoms. For example, for the carbon atom in Figure 2 the atomic number is 6, giving us six electrons. We write its electronic structure as 2,4. So an atom with the atomic number 12 has an electronic structure 2,8,2, with two electrons in the inner energy level, then eight in the next energy level and two in the outer, highest energy level. The simplest way to understand these arrangements is to look at lots of examples of them.

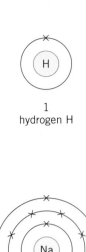

1
hydrogen H

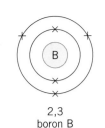

2,3
boron B

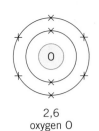

2,6
oxygen O

2,8,1
sodium Na

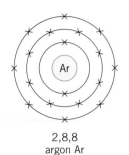

2,8,8
argon Ar

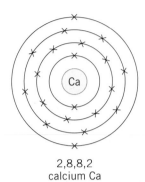

2,8,8,2
calcium Ca

↑ **Figure 3:** Once we know the pattern we can draw the energy levels of the electrons in any atom we choose.

? Questions

1 Why do the electrons in the shell closest to the nucleus have least energy?

2 Which group of elements have full outer energy shells?

3 Identify each of the elements shown below and give the atomic number and the electronic structure numerically.

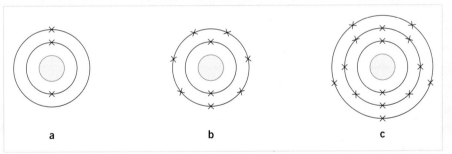

a   b   c

4 a Draw diagrams to show the energy shells and give the numerical electronic structure for the following elements.

    i helium (atomic number 2)

    ii nitrogen (atomic number 7)

    iii neon (atomic number 10)

    iv sulphur (atomic number 16)

    v potassium (atomic number 19)

    vi chlorine (atomic number 17)

    vii aluminium (atomic number 13)

    viii beryllium (atomic number 4)

    ix magnesium (atomic number 12)

  b What is special about the arrangement of helium, neon and argon?

Key Ideas

⊙ Electrons are arranged around the nucleus in shells.

⊙ Each shell is at a different energy level.

⊙ The lowest energy level is closest to the nucleus; the highest energy level is furthest away from the nucleus.

⊙ Different energy levels can hold different numbers of electrons.

1.5 The states of matter

All matter is made up of atoms, but even the same types of matter can sometimes look very different because they can exist in more than one state – as a solid, a liquid or a gas. Understanding these different states is an important part of chemistry.

Changing state

In Figure 1 the solid water in the icicle is forming drips of liquid water as it melts in the warmth of the sun – it is changing state. Changes of state involve energy changes.

The particles in all substances are vibrating (moving), even if the movement is very slight, unless they are at absolute zero (−273 °C), when all movement stops. If energy is put into a solid, for example by heating, its particles will vibrate more violently. If enough energy is supplied the particles may move further away from each other and become freer to move around. At this point the material changes state from a solid to a liquid – it melts. The temperature at which any solid substance melts is known as its **melting point**.

On the other hand, if energy is lost from a liquid then the particles slow down and move closer together again. The attractive forces which hold particles together in a solid then form again, and the liquid becomes solid – this takes place at the **freezing point** of the liquid.

If a liquid is heated the particles within it will move around faster and faster. Eventually some of the particles will have enough energy to overcome the attractive forces between them and the rest of the particles. They will escape from the liquid and become a gas. This is known as **evaporation**. As the temperature gets higher, more particles have enough energy to escape so evaporation gets faster and faster until big bubbles of gas form in the liquid and it begins to boil. The temperature at which this happens is known as the **boiling point**.

In the reverse situation, if a gas loses energy to the surroundings then the particles may move much more slowly and become closely packed again, forming a liquid – this is **condensation**.

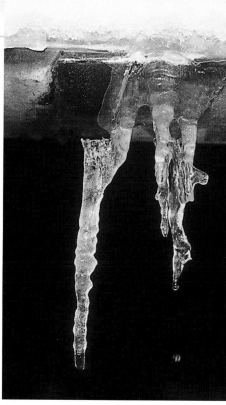

↑ **Figure 1:** Solid water (ice), with liquid water, surrounded by air containing gaseous water – the three states of matter.

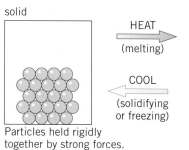 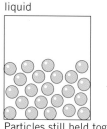 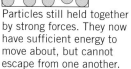 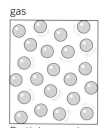

solid

HEAT (melting)

COOL (solidifying or freezing)

Particles held rigidly together by strong forces.

liquid

HEAT (evaporation or boiling)

COOL (condensing)

Particles still held together by strong forces. They now have sufficient energy to move about, but cannot escape from one another.

gas

Particles now have enough energy to move apart, overcoming attractive forces holding them together. The particles move freely throughout the container.

← **Figure 2:** Changing state involves changing amounts of energy and differences in the movements of the particles making up matter.

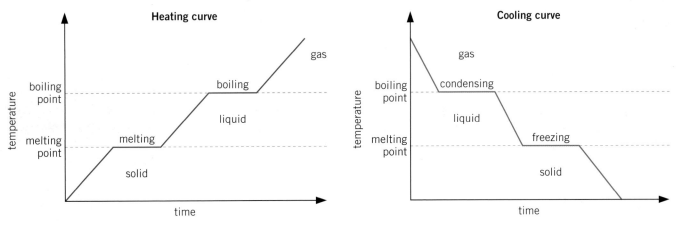

↑ **Figure 3:** As substances change state the heat energy is used to break the forces of attraction between particles instead of raising the temperature, so when things melt, boil, condense or freeze the temperature stays the same.

? Questions

1 The table shows melting and boiling points for some elements.

Element	Melting point (°C)	Boiling point (°C)
carbon	3652	4827
oxygen	−218	−183
sodium	98	883
mercury	−39	357
aluminium	660	2467

a What state will the following elements be in at a temperature of 95 °C?

  i mercury   ii oxygen   iii aluminium   iv sodium

b What state will the following elements be in at 500 °C?

  i carbon   ii mercury   iii sodium   iv aluminium

2 Some elements melt at much higher temperatures than others – for example copper melts at 1084 °C whilst iron melts at 1535 °C. Other elements are gases all the time at normal room temperature. What does this tell you about the strength of the forces between the particles in different elements? Explain your answer.

3 The data in the table were collected when a colourless liquid was being heated.

  a Make a graph of the data.

  b Explain what is happening:

   i when the temperature of the graph is increasing

   ii when the temperature of the graph becomes constant.

  c Suggest what the colourless liquid might be and explain your answer.

Time (min)	Temperature (°C)
1	20
2	35
3	50
4	65
5	80
6	95
7	100
8	100
9	100

1.6 Chemical reactions

The atoms of the chemical elements are the basis of all the chemistry in the world around us. These elements, and the symbols we use to represent them, are like the alphabet of a very specialised language. But like any other language, the alphabet alone is of little use. What really matters is the way the different letters are used together to produce words. In the same way in chemistry, what matters is the way the different elements are combined together to make new chemical compounds.

Mixing or making

Everyone knows that two substances can be mixed together without either of them changing. Sand and salt can be mixed and then separated again, and no change will have taken place. Sugar can be dissolved in tea and separated out again. But in *chemical reactions* the situation is very different. When the atoms of two (or more) elements react, they make a chemical which is different to both of them and you cannot get either of them back.

Compounds can also react together to form other compounds, but the reaction of elements is easier to understand as a starting point.

↑ Figure 1: Chemical reactions may be awe-inspiringly spectacular or relatively mundane. Whatever they are like, they involve the joining of the atoms of different elements to make another chemical.

mixing

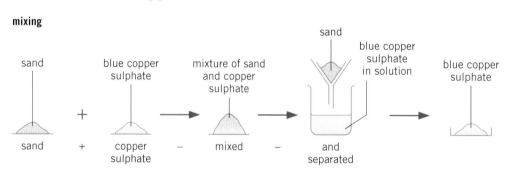

sand + copper sulphate − mixed − and separated − blue copper sulphate

reacting

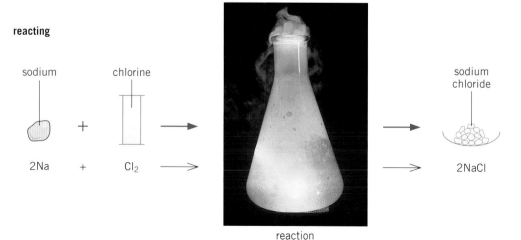

$2Na + Cl_2 \longrightarrow 2NaCl$

reaction

↖ Figure 2: The difference between mixing and reacting can be dramatic!

Classifying materials

Why do atoms react?

When an atom has a full outer shell of electrons it is stable and unreactive. However most atoms do not have a full outer shell. When atoms react they take part in changes which fill their outer shell and give them a stable arrangement of electrons. Atoms react because they 'want' a full outer shell. The more likely they are to achieve that full shell, the more 'enthusiastically' they react. This is explained in more detail on the next page.

How do reactions take place?

Chemical reactions between atoms involve the electrons in the highest occupied energy levels of the atoms – in other words, the outer layer of electrons. They join the atoms together by forming chemical **bonds**. There are two ways in which this can happen.

The atoms can gain or lose electrons from the outer energy level to form chemical bonds. When an atom has lost or gained electrons it forms an electrically charged particle called an **ion**. Atoms which lose electrons become positively charged, while atoms which gain electrons become negatively charged. Atoms with opposite charges attract one another, holding each other together strongly. This type of bonding is known as **ionic bonding**.

Other chemical reactions involve the formation of a different type of bond. In these bonds, atoms *share* electrons in their outer energy levels. This is known as **covalent bonding**.

→ **Figure 3:** Common salt (an ionic compound) and sugar (a covalent compound). It is not always possible to tell just by looking at the compounds what type of bonding they contain. But information on the electronic structure of their elements and a look at the properties of the compounds can give us the information we need.

In ionic bonding the atoms involved lose or gain electrons so that they have a complete outer shell. So, for example, if sodium (2,8,1) loses one electron it is left with the stable electronic structure of neon (2,8). However, it is also left with one more proton in the nucleus than there are electrons in orbit around the nucleus. The proton has a positive charge so the sodium atom has now become a positively charged particle known as a sodium ion. It has a single positive charge. We write the electronic structure of the sodium ion as $[2,8]^+$.

Similarly some atoms gain electrons during reactions to gain a stable noble gas structure. Chlorine, for example, has the electronic structure 2,8,7. By gaining a single electron it takes on the stable electronic structure of argon (2,8,8). In this case there is now one more electron than there are positive protons in the nucleus, so the chlorine atom becomes a negatively charged particle known as a chloride ion. It carries a single negative charge. We write the electronic structure of the chloride ion as $[2,8,8]^-$.

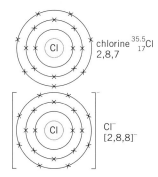

↑ **Figure 1:** A positive sodium ion (Na⁺) is formed when a sodium atom loses an electron during ionic bonding with another element.

Representing ionic bonding

When atoms react together to form ionic bonds, atoms which need to lose electrons react with atoms which need to gain electrons. So when sodium reacts with chlorine, sodium loses an electron and chlorine gains that electron so they both form stable ions. This is shown in a *dot and cross diagram*, in which the electrons of one atom are represented by dots, and the electrons of the other atom are represented by crosses.

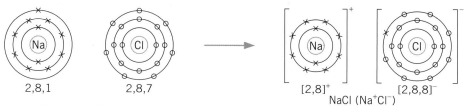

Showing all the energy levels makes these dot and cross diagrams very complex, so for simplicity sometimes only the outer energy level is shown:

↑ **Figure 3:** The formation of sodium chloride (NaCl) – an example of ionic bonding.

Sometimes the atoms reacting need to gain or lose two electrons to gain a stable noble gas structure – for example, when magnesium (2,8,2) reacts with oxygen (2,6). When these two elements react they form magnesium oxide (MgO), which is made up of magnesium ions with a double positive charge (Mg^{2+}) and oxide ions with a double negative charge (O^{2-}).

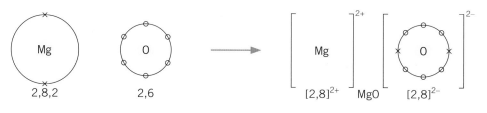

↑ **Figure 2:** A negative chloride ion (Cl⁻) is formed when a chlorine atom gains an electron during ionic bonding with another element.

↑ **Figure 4:** The formation of magnesium oxide (MgO) is a familiar reaction in the laboratory – the reacting atoms lose or gain two electrons.

In some cases one of the atoms needs to gain or lose more electrons than the other has to lose or gain. In this case two or more atoms of each element may react. For example, when calcium chloride is formed each calcium atom needs to lose two electrons but each chlorine atom needs to gain only one electron. This means that two chlorine atoms react with every one calcium atom to form calcium chloride.

Ionic compounds are usually formed when metals react with non-metals.

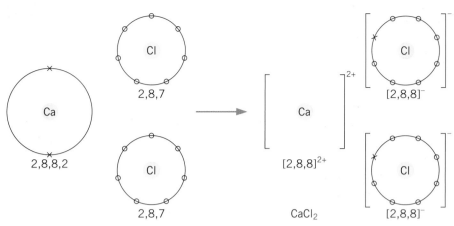

↑ **Figure 5:** The formation of calcium chloride ($CaCl_2$).

The properties of ionic compounds

The positive and negative ions formed during ionic bonding are held together by enormously strong forces of attraction between the oppositely charged ions. These ionic bonds between the charged particles result in a giant structure of ions. Because the ions are held together tightly in these giant structures it takes a lot of energy to break all the bonds. As a result ionic compounds have high melting points and boiling points.

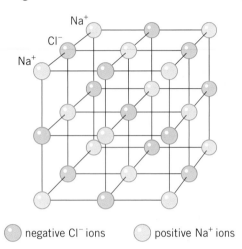

negative Cl^- ions   positive Na^+ ions

↑ **Figure 6:** The giant structure of ionic compounds results from the attraction of the positive and negative ions formed when electrons are lost or gained.

↑ **Figure 7:** Sodium chloride (NaCl or common salt) is a good example of an ionic substance. It is a crystalline solid with a high melting point (801 °C) and boiling point (1413 °C).

? Questions

1 Draw diagrams to show the ions that would be formed when the following atoms are involved in ionic bonding. For each one state whether electrons have been lost or gained.

   a aluminium (Al; 2,8,3)

   b fluorine (F; 2,7)

   c potassium (K; 2,8,8,1)

   d oxygen (O; 2,6)

2 Draw dot and cross diagrams to show the reactions you would expect in the formation of the following ionic compounds (use the data at the back of the book to get the information you need about the elements involved).

   a calcium oxide (CaO)

   b lithium chloride (LiCl)

   c aluminium chloride ($AlCl_3$)

3 Explain with the help of diagrams why ionic compounds have high melting and boiling points.

⊶ Key Ideas

- ⊙ When electrons are lost or gained in the formation of ionic bonds the atoms gain the structure of a noble gas.

- ⊙ When atoms react together to form ionic bonds, atoms which need to lose electrons react with elements which need to gain electrons.

- ⊙ Ionic compounds always form crystals with high melting points and boiling points.

Covalent bonding

Reactions between metals and non-metals usually result in ionic bonding. However, many, many compounds are formed in a very different way. When non-metals react together they *share* electrons to form molecules – this is known as **covalent bonding**.

Forming covalent bonds

Non-metals generally need to gain electrons to achieve a stable outer energy level. When they react together neither atom can give away electrons, so they achieve the electronic structure of a noble gas by sharing electrons. The atoms in the molecules are then held together because they are sharing pairs of electrons. These strong bonds between the atoms are known as **covalent bonds**.

↑ **Figure 1:** Many of the compounds which make up the living world are formed by covalent bonding between non-metals.

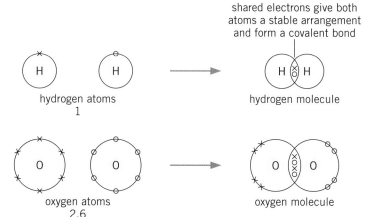

↑ **Figure 2:** Atoms of hydrogen and oxygen do not exist freely – they undergo covalent bonding to form stable molecules.

Sometimes in covalent bonding each atom brings the same number of electrons to the reaction for sharing. But this is not always the case – sometimes one element will need several electrons, whilst the other reactant only needs one more for a stable arrangement. In this case more atoms become involved in the reaction.

Representing covalent bonds

When we are representing covalent bonds in substances such as water, ammonia and methane, there are a number of ways in which we can write them down. Each way of representing them means exactly the same thing – it just depends what we want to show.

Properties of covalent compounds

Substances made up of molecules containing covalent bonds have low melting and boiling points. Some are gases at room temperature, others are liquids and some are solids. They do not conduct electricity.

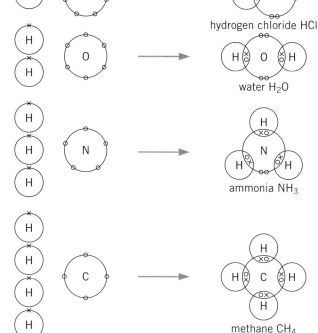

↑ **Figure 3:** The principles of covalent bonding remain the same however many atoms are involved.

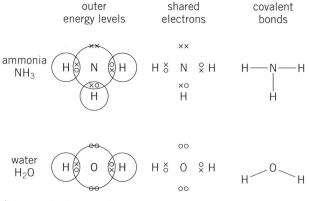

↑ **Figure 4:** By choosing how we represent a covalent compound we can show the outer energy level, the shared electrons or just the fact that there are a certain number of covalent bonds.

Explaining covalent properties

Covalent bonds are very strong – the atoms within the covalent molecules are held very tightly together. However, each molecule tends to be quite separate, and the attraction between the individual molecules in a covalent compound tends to be small. The small attractive forces between the molecules (weak intermolecular forces) and the fact that covalent molecules do not carry an overall electric charge means that it takes relatively little energy to separate them, and this results in the low melting points and boiling points of covalent compounds.

As a result, covalent compounds which consist of individual molecules are gases at room temperature and pressure – carbon dioxide and sulphur dioxide are examples – or liquids with relatively low boiling points, such as water.

Many other covalent compounds are solids with low melting points, but a small number have a very different structure. They form giant structures where huge numbers of atoms are held together because they are sharing electrons. These giant molecular structures are lattices made up of molecules, and covalent bonds hold the structure together. Because covalent bonds are very strong, these covalent compounds tend to be very hard with very high melting points – very different from the majority of covalent compounds. Good examples of these structures are carbon in the form of diamond and graphite, and silicon dioxide (silica).

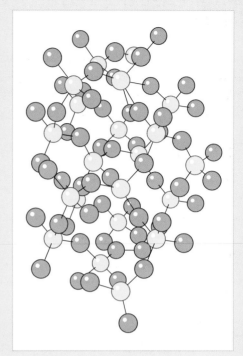

↑ **Figure 6:** A giant covalent lattice of silicon and oxygen atoms (silica).

? Questions

1 With the help of the data at the back of the book, work out the electronic structure of the following non-metals. For each one, state how many electrons it would need to share in a covalent bond.

  a nitrogen (N)

  b sulphur (S)

  c fluorine (F)

  d phosphorus (P)

2 Draw dot and cross diagrams to show the following reactions.

  a carbon + oxygen ⟶ carbon dioxide

  b sulphur + chlorine ⟶ sulphur chloride

  c hydrogen + fluorine ⟶ hydrogen fluoride

3 Represent the covalent bonds in each of the following molecules in three different ways.

  a hydrogen chloride (HCl)

  b oxygen (O_2)

  c hydrogen (H_2)

  d methane (CH_4)

H 4 The melting point of sand (silicon dioxide) is more than 1600 °C, while the melting point of ice is 0 °C. Both of these are covalent compounds. Explain the difference in their melting points.

⚿ Key Ideas

⊙ Atoms in molecules are held together by covalent bonds.

⊙ A covalent bond is formed when two atoms share electrons between them to gain the electronic structure of a noble gas.

⊙ Substances made up of molecules containing covalent bonds have low melting and boiling points.

⊙ Giant covalent structures are held together by covalent bonds.

H ⊙ The properties of giant covalent structures differ from those of molecular covalent structures.

Ionic compounds can also form **giant structures** – arrangements of atoms or ions that extend over large distances.

Ionic solids

The ions within an ionic compound are held together by forces of mutual attraction in a seemingly endless array known as a giant ionic lattice. The arrangement of ions within these lattices always forms a regular pattern.

The strong forces between the oppositely charged ions in giant ionic lattices result in high melting and boiling points for the compounds.

Another property of ionic compounds is that once they are dissolved in water or melted, they conduct electricity. The charged ions become free to move and so can carry charge through the liquid. In the solid state ionic substances do not conduct electricity because the ions are held in the rigid giant lattice structure.

More about covalent structures

As we saw in Section 1.8 a small number of covalent compounds also have giant structures. Covalent giant structures are held together by covalent bonds which give them unusually high melting points and hardness for covalent structures. Diamonds are well known for their hardness and their stability – they react with very little. These characteristics are the result of the chemical bonding within the giant molecular structure which makes up a diamond. Each carbon atom forms four covalent bonds with its neighbours in a rigid giant covalent lattice (Figure 2).

Carbon doesn't always turn up as diamonds – another form is graphite (well known as the lead in your pencils!). In graphite each carbon atom forms three covalent bonds so the carbon atoms form layers or sheets which can slide freely over each other. This is another type of giant covalent lattice.

Another important characteristic of graphite comes from the fact that there are free electrons within the structure. These free electrons, which are not directly involved in covalent bonds, allow graphite to conduct electricity, which diamond – and most other covalent compounds – cannot do.

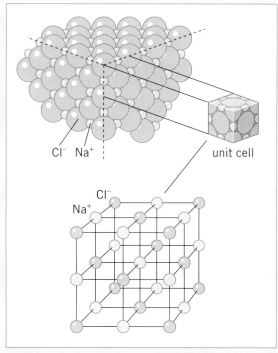

↑ **Figure 1:** The regular patterns of giant ionic lattices affect their physical properties – this is sodium chloride again.

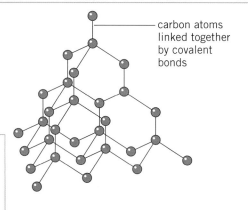

↓ **Figure 2:** Diamonds owe their hardness and long-lasting nature to the way the carbon molecules are arranged.

carbon atoms linked together by covalent bonds

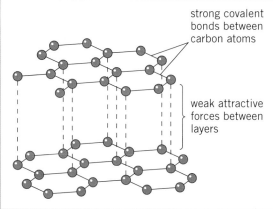

strong covalent bonds between carbon atoms

weak attractive forces between layers

↑ **Figure 3:** The giant structure of graphite. When you write with a pencil, some layers of carbon atoms slide off the 'lead' and are left on the paper.

Metals

Metals are yet other examples of giant structures. You can think of metal as a lattice of metal atoms which have each given up one or more of their outer electrons. This means that they become positively charged (remember that a charged atom is called an *ion*). The electrons they give up form a 'sea' of free electrons surrounding the positive metal ions. The negatively charged electrons attract the positively charged metal ions and hold them together just like glue.

However, unlike glue the electrons are able to move throughout the whole lattice. Because they can move and hold the metal ions together at the same time, the free electrons enable the lattice to distort so that the metal ions can move past one another. This means that it is possible to hammer metals into shape and to draw them out into wires.

Metal cooking utensils are used the world over, because metals are good conductors of heat. Wherever electricity is generated, metal wires carry the electricity to where it is needed, because metals are also good conductors of electricity. Both of these properties are a direct result of the ability of electrons to flow through the sea of free electrons surrounding the metal atoms in the giant metal lattice.

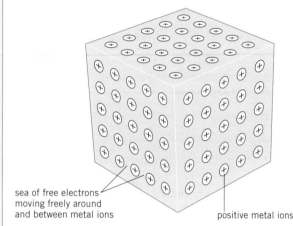

sea of free electrons moving freely around and between metal ions

positive metal ions

↖ **Figure 4:** People have shaped and used metals for thousands of years – making horseshoes is a skill that is centuries old. The ability of metals to be shaped in this way is dependent on a giant lattice structure of positive metal ions surrounded by free electrons.

? Questions

1 Explain why substances consisting of giant structures usually have high melting and boiling points.

2 Copy and complete the table.

Substance	Melting point (°C)	Boiling point (°C)	Conducts electricity at room temperature?	Conducts electricity when liquid?	Structure (giant ionic / giant covalent / giant metal / covalent molecular)
quartz (silicon dioxide)	1610	2230			
rubidium fluoride	795	1410			
manganese	1244	1962			
sulphur dioxide	−73	−10			

3 Why can ionic compounds conduct electricity when they melt or are in solution?

4 Why can graphite and metals conduct electricity?

5 Why can you write with graphite?

⊙━ Key Ideas

- ⊙ Giant structures consist of large numbers of atoms or ions arranged in a regular array.

- ⊙ Ionic compounds have giant ionic lattices in which the strong forces between oppositely charged ions hold the ions tightly together.

- ⊙ Giant covalent structures are held together by covalent bonds.

- ⊙ Giant metal structures are held together by free electrons which hold the lattice of metal atoms together.

1 a Methane and propane are two fuels. The diagrams represent a molecule of each.

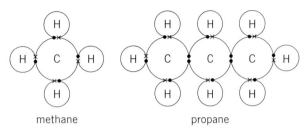

methane   propane

i Which is the correct formula for methane?

CH   CH$_2$ CH$_3$ CH$_4$ (1 mark)

ii Which is the correct formula for propane?

CH$_8$ C$_2$H$_8$ C$_3$H$_8$ C$_8$H$_8$ (1 mark)

iii Both methane and propane have covalent bonds. Copy the sentence below, choosing the correct word from the list to complete it.

exchanged   gained   lost   shared

In covalent bonds, the electrons from each atom are ....   (1 mark)

b i When coal is burnt the sulphur it contains is changed into sulphur dioxide (SO$_2$). The reaction is shown in the equation

$$S(s) + O_2(g) \longrightarrow SO_2(g)$$

Which word describes the state of the sulphur dioxide?

aqueous   gas   liquid   solid (1 mark)

ii What does the formula SO$_2$ tell you about a molecule of sulphur dioxide?   (2 marks)

(Total 6 marks)

AQA specimen question

2 a The diagram shows the atomic structure of an atom of lithium.

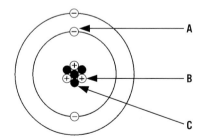

i The atom contains electrons, neutrons and protons. Which type of particle is labelled **A**, **B** and **C**?   (2 marks)

ii What is the atomic number of lithium?

(1 mark)

b The diagrams show the electron arrangement of the atoms of two elements.

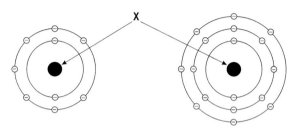

i Name the part of the atoms labelled **X**.   (1 mark)

ii What is the significance of the rings around part **X**?   (2 marks)

(Total 6 marks)

AQA specimen question

③ 3 a The structural formula of a hydrazine molecule is shown below.

Copy and complete the diagram to show how the outer energy level (shell) electrons are arranged in a hydrazine molecule. Show the electrons as dots and crosses.   (2 marks)

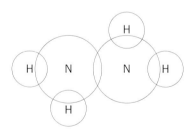

b Explain why hydrazine has a low boiling point.   (2 marks)

(Total 4 marks)

AQA specimen question

H **4** Silicon has a structure similar to diamond.

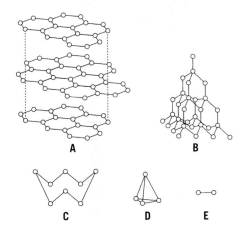

a Which of the diagrams, **A** to **E**, represents the structure of silicon? (1 mark)

b Explain why silicon has a very high melting point. (2 marks)

(Total 3 marks)

AQA specimen question

5 The diagrams labelled **A** to **D** are atoms of four different elements. The elements are oxygen ($^{16}_{8}$O), carbon ($^{12}_{6}$C), sodium ($^{23}_{11}$Na) and neon ($^{20}_{10}$Ne).

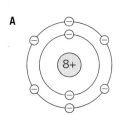
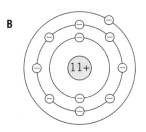

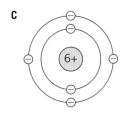
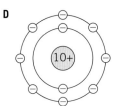

a Identify each atom, **A** to **D**, and for each one give its electronic structure. (4 marks)

b **i** What type of bonding would you expect in a reaction between elements **A** and **C**? (1 mark)

ii Draw a dot and cross diagram to show the reaction between these two elements. (2 marks)

c What type of bonding would you expect in a reaction between elements **A** and **B**? (1 mark)

ii Draw a dot and cross diagram to show the reaction between these two elements. (2 marks)

d Would you expect element **D** to react with element **A**? Explain your answer. (2 marks)

(Total 12 marks)

6 Explain in your own words, using good English, the difference between the following:

a elements and compounds (2 marks)

b mixtures and compounds (2 marks)

c atomic number and atomic mass. (2 marks)

(Total 6 marks)

7 The diagram represents the structure of a metal.

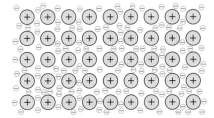

a Copy the sentence below, choosing the correct word from the list to complete it.

molecular   ionic   giant   strong

The arrangement of positive ions and a sea of electrons in a metal is an example of a .... structure. (1 mark)

b How does this structure explain:

i the high melting point of most metals (1 mark)

ii the fact that solid metals conduct electricity? (1 mark)

c How does the structure of an ionic substance like sodium chloride differ from the metallic structure shown here? (2 marks)

d How does the structure of a covalent substance like graphite differ from the metallic structure shown here? (2 marks)

(Total 7 marks)

Representing chemicals

When a chemical reaction takes place we can observe what happens and describe it, but to enable someone else to carry out the same reaction, that is simply not enough. 'Add 3 g of a white powder to 10 cm³ of a colourless liquid' could have any number of outcomes, from nothing happening at all to a violent explosion.

Whether a chemical reaction takes place in a laboratory or a chemical factory, chemists need to be able to represent what happens on paper. What is more, they need to do this in a way which gives as much information as possible about what is going on.

Representing elements

The simplest way to describe chemical elements and compounds is to use their full names – water, copper sulphate, hydrochloric acid. But the names are different in different languages. Much scientific work is international so we use symbols for the elements which are understood and used across the whole world.

11 **B** boron 5	12 **C** carbon 6	14 **N** nitrogen 7	16 **O** oxygen 8	19 **F** fluorine 9	20 **Ne** neon 10
27 **Al** aluminium 13	28 **Si** silicon 14	31 **P** phosphorus 15	32 **S** sulphur 16	35 **Cl** chlorine 17	40 **Ar** argon 18
70 **Ga** gallium 31	73 **Ge** germanium 32	75 **As** arsenic 33	79 **Se** selenium 34	80 **Br** bromine 35	84 **Kr** krypton 36

↑ **Figure 1:** It is very important that once a chemical experiment has been carried out, other chemists can understand what has been done and try it for themselves.

← **Figure 2:** The periodic table gives you the international symbols for all of the commonly known elements and many others besides! (Only a part of it is shown here – the full version is given on page 88 and at the back of the book.)

Representing compounds

It is not only important for a chemist to know what elements make up a compound. A chemist also wants to know how many atoms of the different elements have combined together to form the compound. This is where chemical formulae are vital.

Appearance of compound	Name of compound	Chemical formula	What the formula means
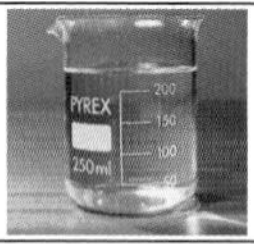	water	H_2O	2 atoms of hydrogen are combined with 1 atom of oxygen
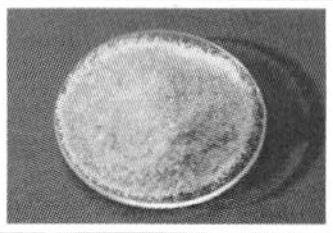	copper sulphate	$CuSO_4$	1 atom of copper, 1 atom of sulphur and 4 oxygen atoms are combined
	sodium chloride	$NaCl$	1 atom of sodium is combined with 1 atom of chlorine
	nitric acid	HNO_3	1 atom of hydrogen, 1 atom of nitrogen and 3 atoms of oxygen are combined

Word equations

Similarly chemical reactions can be represented using word equations:

$$\text{reactants} \longrightarrow \text{products}$$

$$\text{sodium} + \text{chlorine} \longrightarrow \text{sodium chloride}$$

$$\text{zinc} + \text{sulphuric acid} \longrightarrow \text{zinc sulphate} + \text{hydrogen}$$

$$\text{hydrogen} + \text{oxygen} \longrightarrow \text{water}$$

These word equations are useful – they can tell us what is going on in a reaction. But they have their limitations.

Firstly they are only useful when working with other people who speak the same language.

Secondly, they give us no idea of the amounts of substances involved in the reaction. For example, hydrogen peroxide is a clear liquid which looks just like water and which can be used to bleach hair. Over a long period of time hydrogen peroxide decomposes, producing water and oxygen:

$$\text{hydrogen peroxide} \longrightarrow \text{water} + \text{oxygen}$$

But how much water and oxygen are produced for a given amount of hydrogen peroxide? We need to know – because if hydrogen peroxide produces a large volume of oxygen when it decomposes this could lead to a dangerous build-up of pressure in the container in which it is stored.

A third problem with word equations is that they can become very long-winded. The ones above are all relatively simple. However, when reactions involve a large number of chemicals, some of which themselves have long and complex names such as 2,4-diphenylamine, then the use of word equations becomes much less practical!

? Questions

1 **a** Write a word equation for reactions which form:

    i water

    ii sodium chloride

    iii magnesium oxide.

  b What are the limitations of word equations like these?

2 Use the periodic table or other data at the back of the book to give the chemical symbols for the following elements: sodium, lead, nitrogen, bromine, potassium.

3 For each of the following, give the name of the compound and state how many atoms of each element have combined to form the compound. (Use the data at the back of the book to help you identify the elements from their symbols.)

  a CO_2

  b $FeSO_4$

  c $CaCl_2$

  d NH_3

  e $MgCO_3$

Key Ideas

- Chemical compounds and chemical reactions can be represented by word equations.
- Chemical elements are represented by symbols which are internationally recognised.
- Chemical compounds can be represented by formulae which show the ratios of atoms which are combined together to form the compound. The formulae use chemical symbols.

Instead of using word equations we can use the chemical symbols for elements and compounds to represent chemical reactions.

For example, when carbon burns in a plentiful supply of oxygen, an atom of carbon reacts with a molecule of oxygen to form a colourless gas, carbon dioxide.

$$C + O_2 \longrightarrow CO_2$$

This shows that one atom of carbon joins with a molecule made up of two atoms of oxygen to make carbon dioxide. The gas elements, like hydrogen, oxygen and chlorine always float around in two-atom molecules (diatomic gases), not single atoms. Only the noble gases like argon exist as single atoms.

Balancing equations

Not all chemical reactions are as simple as the one above.

When magnesium burns in air, one atom of magnesium reacts with one atom of oxygen to form the white powder magnesium oxide. A bright white light is given off in the process (Figure 1). In theory this reaction can be represented by a simple chemical equation:

$$Mg + O \longrightarrow MgO \qquad ✗$$

But oxygen does not exist as individual atoms, so this equation does not really represent what happens. This means that the equation should read:

$$Mg + O_2 \longrightarrow MgO + O \qquad ✗$$

But this doesn't work either, because we can't have a free oxygen atom left over! We need to produce a *balanced* equation, in which the number of atoms of each element involved is the same on both sides of the equation. This is because the products of a chemical reaction are always made up of exactly the same atoms as the reactants – they have just been arranged in a different way. Just as the mass of the products is the same as the mass of the reactants, the number and type of atoms in the products are the same as those in the reactants.

The balanced equation for the reaction between magnesium and oxygen is:

$$2Mg + O_2 \longrightarrow 2MgO \qquad ✓$$

2Mg means two times the Mg atoms, 2MgO means two times the atoms in MgO.

Another example is the reaction between sodium and chlorine. Once again single metal atoms are reacting with an element which has two atoms in each molecule. So in the same way:

$$2Na + Cl_2 \longrightarrow 2NaCl \qquad ✓$$

This kind of balancing act is needed in every chemical equation. It shows just how much you really need of each reactant to make the product.

The way to check if an equation is balanced is to count the number of each type of atom on both sides of the equation. If the numbers are equal, and all the molecules shown are complete, then the equation is balanced.

↑ **Figure 1:** The reaction between magnesium and oxygen produces a white flash – so distinctive that most people can remember it easily!

↓ **Figure 2:** Chemical equations must be perfectly balanced.

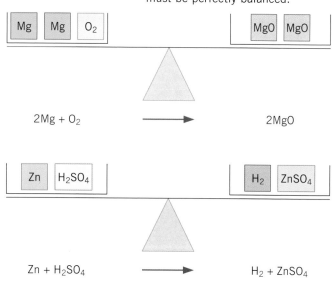

Examples of balancing equations

Sometimes, as in the case of the reactions of sodium and chlorine, or zinc and sulphuric acid, it is relatively easy to balance the equations. In other cases it is not so easy. Here are some examples of reactions and the way they must be written to produce balanced equations.

When magnesium reacts with hydrochloric acid, hydrogen gas is given off. Magnesium chloride is left behind. Magnesium chloride has the formula $MgCl_2$ and hydrogen gas is H_2 so the equation starts off as:

$$Mg + HCl \longrightarrow MgCl_2 + H_2 \qquad ✗$$

But this means that there are not enough H and Cl atoms on the left-hand side. By adding another HCl molecule we can balance the equation, which now reads:

$$Mg + 2HCl \longrightarrow MgCl_2 + H_2 \qquad ✓$$

When nitrogen gas reacts with hydrogen gas the very pungent gas ammonia is produced. So we might write:

$$N + H \longrightarrow NH_3 \qquad ✗$$

Nitrogen gas and hydrogen gas only exist as N_2 and H_2. But we need more than one hydrogen molecule to get the 'H_3' part of the ammonia. We need one and a half hydrogen molecules:

$$N_2 + 1\tfrac{1}{2} H_2 \longrightarrow NH_3 + N \qquad ✗$$

This gives us two problems – we can't have half molecules and we are left with a single nitrogen atom! So to balance this equation we must use three molecules of hydrogen, which allows us to make two ammonia molecules:

$$N_2 + 3H_2 \longrightarrow 2NH_3 \qquad ✓$$

To check that this equation is balanced correctly, simply add up the different atoms. There are two nitrogen atoms and six hydrogen atoms on both sides of the equation, all arranged in complete molecules – so it is balanced.

State symbols

When we are planning an experiment it is important to know what state the reacting chemicals are in. The apparatus needed if the reactants or products are gases is very different from the equipment needed to react two solids together.

This sort of information can be included in equations by indicating whether each chemical is a solid (shown by an **s**), a liquid (**l**), a gas (**g**), or in solution in water (aqueous solution, **aq**). These are called **state symbols**.

For example, an experiment where solid zinc is reacted with a solution of sulphuric acid to make a solution of zinc sulphate plus hydrogen gas is shown like this:

$$Zn(s) + H_2SO_4 (aq) \longrightarrow ZnSO_4(aq) + H_2(g)$$

Key Ideas

- Chemical reactions can be represented by chemical equations.
- Chemical equations must be balanced, with the same numbers of atoms of each type on both sides of the equation.

Questions

1 Copy out and balance each of these chemical equations.

   a $\quad K + Cl \longrightarrow KCl$

   b $\quad Mg + HCl \longrightarrow MgCl + H$

   c $NaOH + HCl \longrightarrow NaCl + H_2O$

2 Write out balanced equations for the following word equations. Use the data at the back of the book to help you.

   a iron + oxygen $\longrightarrow$ iron oxide

   b potassium + water $\longrightarrow$ hydrogen + potassium hydroxide

   c calcium carbonate $\longrightarrow$ calcium oxide + carbon dioxide

Chemical symbols and chemical formulae seem very neat, clean and mathematical. However, many of the chemicals and reactions they represent can be risky, and sometimes downright dangerous! In the real world, chemical formulae are not enough.

In any laboratory there are chemicals which can cause considerable damage to anyone who accidentally comes into contact with them. Clothing can be destroyed, skin horribly burnt, and eyesight lost. If certain chemicals are drunk or inhaled, they can kill. Other compounds burn easily, and spilling them in a laboratory full of lighted Bunsen burners could be very dangerous indeed.

Similarly, dangerous chemicals are transported all over the country in tankers from the various chemical plants where they are produced to the industries which need to use them.

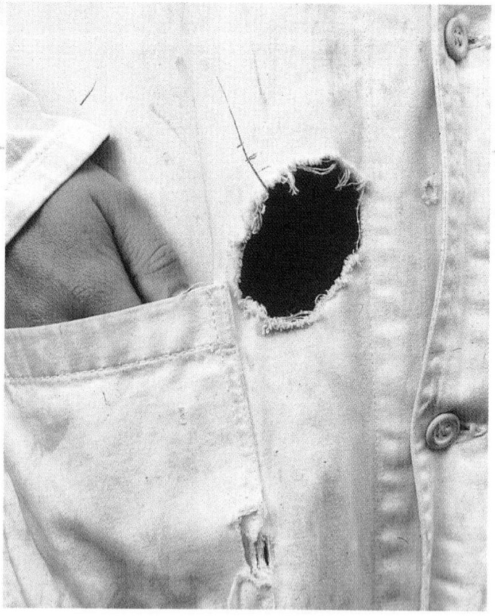

↑ **Figure 1:** Chemistry, even in a school lab, involves the use of some very dangerous chemicals.

Hazard symbols

Although most of the people using a lab – whether in a school, a university or in industry – understand the chemical formulae on bottles of chemicals, they can still make mistakes. People are careless, or sometimes plain silly, and accidents can happen anywhere. So simply using chemical formulae to inform people of the contents of potentially dangerous chemicals is not enough. If a road tanker has a spillage or is involved in an accident, there is no guarantee at all that any members of the public involved, or even the emergency services, would understand a chemical formula printed on the side of the tank.

When it is really important that certain properties are recognised and remembered anywhere and everywhere, graphic information is needed. A series of six hazard symbols for various chemicals has been developed. The symbols are found on the labels on bottles of chemicals, on tankers and anywhere else that those chemicals are stored. If you see one of these symbols on a chemical you are using, take care!

↑ **Figure 2:** In situations like this, anywhere in the world, chemical hazard warning signs can save lives. These firefighters wear special clothing and breathing apparatus to protect them from toxic chemicals which may have been spilled.

OXIDISING

These substances provide oxygen which allows other materials to burn more fiercely. *Examples:* potassium manganate(VII) ($KMnO_4$), hydrogen peroxide (H_2O_2).

potassium manganate(VII)

TOXIC

These substances can cause death. They may have their effects when swallowed or breathed in or absorbed through the skin. *Examples:* mercury (Hg) and many of its compounds, lead (Pb) and many of its compounds.

mercury

HARMFUL

These substances are similar to toxic substances – they are poisonous – but they are less dangerous. *Examples:* lead(II) nitrate ($PbNO_3$), copper(II) chloride ($CuCl_2$).

copper(II) chloride

HIGHLY FLAMMABLE

These substances catch fire easily. *Examples:* methanol (CH_3OH), ethanol (C_2H_5OH), petrol.

ethanol

CORROSIVE

These substances attack and destroy living tissues, including eyes and skin. *Examples:* hydrochloric acid (HCl), sodium hydroxide (NaOH).

concentrated hydrochloric acid

IRRITANT

These substances are not corrosive but can cause reddening or blistering of the skin. *Example:* copper(II) oxide (CuO).

copper(II) oxide

↑ **Figure 3:** The six hazard symbols are recognised throughout the world.

Hazards in the home

The lab and industrial sites and vehicles are not the only places where chemical hazard symbols are used. In our homes we use a wide variety of chemicals which may be irritants, toxic, oxidising agents or have other potential risks. Hazardous substances are labelled with hazard symbols to warn us of the dangers. For example, household bleach carries the irritant symbol and methylated spirits are shown as highly flammable, while poisons designed to kill rats and mice have the toxic symbol on their packets. So for work in the lab and life outside the school or college gates, these symbols are worth remembering!

↑ **Figure 4:** Weedkillers containing chemicals like sodium chlorate are shown as harmful and oxidising agents.

 Questions

1 Either design a poster for the laboratory walls, showing the hazard symbols and explaining what they mean and why they are important,

or design a leaflet which could be given to each individual child when they start science lessons in year 7. Make sure that the leaflet is informative in a way they will understand but not so frightening that they refuse to enter the science labs.

Key Ideas

⊙ Some chemicals are particularly dangerous. They are labelled with special hazard symbols which are recognised internationally.

⊙ The six types of hazardous chemicals are oxidising, toxic, harmful, highly flammable, corrosive and irritant.

Chemical equations show you how many atoms you need of the reactants to make the products of a reaction. But when you are actually carrying out a chemical reaction you need to know what amounts to use in grams or cm^3. You might think that a chemical equation would also tell you this. For example, does the equation

$$Mg + 2HCl \longrightarrow MgCl_2 + H_2$$

mean that you need twice as much hydrochloric acid as magnesium to make magnesium chloride?

Unfortunately it isn't that simple, because the atoms of different elements have different masses. So, you need twice as many hydrogen and chlorine atoms as magnesium atoms, but this doesn't mean that the mass of hydrochloric acid will be twice the mass of magnesium. Atoms of different elements have different masses because each element contains a different number of protons and neutrons in the nucleus of its atoms.

To translate equations into something we can actually do in the lab or factory we have to know a bit more about the mass of atoms.

Relative atomic masses

The mass of a single atom is so tiny (a single hydrogen atom has a mass of less than $0.000\,000\,000\,000\,000\,000\,000\,002$ grams) that it would be incredibly awkward to use in calculations. To make the whole thing manageable scientists use a much simpler way of looking at the masses of atoms. Instead of working with the real masses of atoms, we focus on how the masses of atoms of different elements compare with each other.

How did this method come about? The first step was to choose a **standard atom**. The original choice was hydrogen, but it was finally decided that an atom of carbon ($^{12}_{6}C$) would be used as the standard. It was given a 'mass' of 12 units, because it has six protons and six neutrons. The masses of the atoms of all the other elements were then compared to the standard carbon atom, using a mass spectrometer. The mass of an atom found by comparing it to the $^{12}_{6}C$ atom is known as its **relative atomic mass (A_r)**.

The relative atomic mass of an element is usually the same as, or very similar to, the mass number of that element. The A_r takes into account any isotopes of the element – it is the average mass of the isotopes of the element in the proportions they are usually found, compared to the standard carbon atom.

When atoms change into ions they either lose or gain electrons. However, for all practical purposes the mass of electrons isn't worth bothering about, so the **relative ionic mass** of an ion is exactly the same as the relative atomic mass of that element.

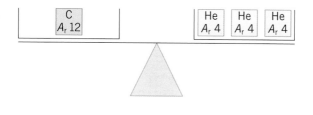

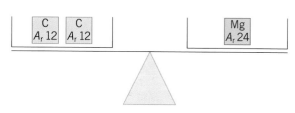

↑ **Figure 1:** The A_r for carbon is 12. Compared to this, the A_r for helium is 4, and for magnesium, 24.

Relative atomic mass		Relative ionic mass	
Na	23	Na^+	23
O	16	O^{2-}	16
Mg	24	Mg^{2+}	24

Mass spectrometer

Much of our chemical calculation would not be possible without relative atomic masses. They were only worked out with the help of a mass spectrometer. These amazing machines make it possible to measure the mass of individual isotopes. They were invented by **Francis Aston**, a British scientist, in 1919.

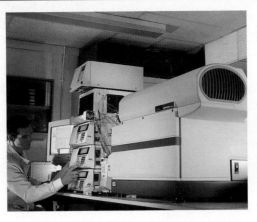

← **Figure 2:** Mass spectrometers have many uses – they are even sent up into space to analyse the gases in the atmospheres of other planets by identifying the relative atomic masses!

Relative formula masses

We can use the A_r of the various elements to work out the **relative formula mass** (M_r) of chemical compounds, whether they are made up of molecules or collections of ions.

A simple example is a substance like sodium chloride. We know that the A_r of sodium is 23 and of chlorine is 35.5. The formula mass of sodium chloride (NaCl) is:

$$23 + 35.5 = 58.5$$

A_r Na A_r Cl M_r NaCl

Another example is water. Water is made up of hydrogen and oxygen. The A_r of hydrogen is 1, and of oxygen is 16. Water has the formula H_2O, containing two hydrogen atoms for every one oxygen, so the M_r is:

$$(1 \times 2) + 16 = 18$$

A_r H × 2 A_r O M_r H_2O

The same approach works even with relatively complicated molecules like sulphuric acid, H_2SO_4. Hydrogen has an A_r of 1, sulphur of 32 and oxygen 16. This means that the M_r of sulphuric acid is:

$$(1 \times 2) + 32 + (16 \times 4) = 2 + 32 + 64 = 98$$

? Questions

1 Using the data at the back of the book, find the relative atomic masses of the following elements and ions.

   a Li   **b** S   **c** Ca^{2+} **d** Al   **e** F^- **f** N

2 There are two isotopes of chlorine. Three out of every four chlorine atoms have a mass of 35. One out of every four has a mass of 37. Use this information to work out the relative atomic mass of chlorine (the average mass of all the isotopes). Use the data at the back of the book to check your answer.

3 Use the data at the back of the book to help you work out the relative formula mass of the following compounds.

   a MgO   **b** NH_3 **c** $ZnSO_4$ **d** Cl_2 **e** CH_4 **f** $Mg(NO_3)_2$

Key Ideas

⊙ The relative atomic mass A_r of an element is the average mass of its isotopes compared with an atom of $^{12}_{6}C$.

⊙ The relative formula mass M_r of a compound is the sum of the relative atomic masses of all the atoms or ions which make up the chemical compound.

← **Figure 1:** Spectacular patterns in the Earth's surface – but how can we find out if these rocks contain minerals that can be extracted and used?

We can use the formula mass of a compound to calculate the percentage mass of each element in it. Calculations like this are not just done in GCSE chemistry exams! In life outside the school laboratory, geologists and mining companies base their decisions about whether to exploit mineral finds on calculations like those shown here.

Working out the amount of an element in a compound

We can use the relative atomic mass (A_r) of elements and the relative formula mass (M_r) of compounds to help us work out the percentage of an element in a compound. For example, what percentage by mass of white magnesium oxide is actually magnesium, and how much is oxygen?

The first thing we need is the formula of magnesium oxide, MgO. The A_r of magnesium is 24 g, whilst the A_r of oxygen is 16 g. Adding these together gives us an M_r of 40 g. We know that 24 g out of that 40 g is actually magnesium:

$$\frac{\text{mass of magnesium}}{\text{total mass of compound}} = \frac{24}{40}$$

So the percentage of magnesium in the compound is:

$$\frac{24}{40} \times 100 = 60\%$$

To calculate the percentage of an element in a compound

⊙ Write down the formula of the compound.

⊙ Using the relative atomic masses from the data at the back of the book, work out the relative formula mass M_r of the compound. Write down the mass of each element making up the compound as you work it out.

⊙ Write the mass of the element you are investigating as a fraction of the total M_r.

⊙ Find the percentage by multiplying your fraction by 100.

These sorts of calculations can be very important. For example, the decision about whether to mine an ore and extract the metal from it will depend at least in part on the actual percentage of the metal in the ore. Haematite (Fe_2O_3) and magnetite (Fe_3O_4) are both ores of iron used in the blast furnace, but one is a richer source of the metal than the other. Which one?

Iron (Fe) has an A_r of 56 g and oxygen has an A_r of 16 g.

Fe_2O_3 has a formula mass of $(56 \times 2) + (16 \times 3) = 112 + 48 = 160$ g.

Of that 160 g, 112 g is iron, so the percentage of iron in haematite is:

$$\frac{112}{160} \times 100 = 70\%$$

Fe_3O_4 has a formula mass of $(56 \times 3) + (16 \times 4) = 168 + 64 = 232$ g.

Of that 232 g, 168 g is iron, so the percentage of iron in magnetite is:

$$\frac{168}{232} \times 100 = 72.4\%$$

↑ **Figure 2:** Iron ore is obtained from huge open cast mines like this. A difference of 2.4% in the amount of iron in the ore many not seem very much, but when millions of tonnes of iron ore are extracted and processed each year, it all adds up!

So given a choice, magnetite is the better ore to use to extract iron from, because the amount of iron it contains is higher.

Strychnine is a deadly poison. It has the formula $C_{21}H_{22}N_2O_2$. A sample of white powder found at the scene of a murder is analysed by a chemist, who says that its mass is 78% carbon. Could the powder be strychnine?

To use the evidence we have to work out whether the white powder is strychnine. We need to calculate the percentage mass of carbon in strychnine and compare it with the percentage mass of carbon in the sample found at the scene of the murder.

The formula mass of strychnine is:

$(12 \times 21) + (1 \times 22) + (14 \times 2) + (16 \times 2)$
$= 252 + 22 + 28 + 32 = 334$

The percentage mass of carbon in strychnine is therefore:

$$\frac{252}{334} \times 100 = 75.4\%$$

↑ **Figure 3:** Chemical analysis of substances found at the scene of a crime may help to bring a murderer to justice – or to free an innocent suspect.

This is not the same as the percentage mass of carbon in the white powder (78%). This suggests that the powder is not strychnine.

? Questions

1 NH_4NO_3 is a commonly used nitrate fertiliser. What is the percentage of nitrogen in the fertiliser?

2 Ammonia (NH_3) and urea (CON_2H_4) can both be used as fertilisers. Which has the greater percentage mass of nitrogen in it?

3 Aluminium is found in two different ores, cryolite (Na_3AlF_6) and bauxite (Al_2O_3). What is the percentage of aluminium in each of these ores? Explain which ore you would expect to be used to extract aluminium, giving reasons based on your calculations.

Key Ideas

⊙ The percentage of an element found in a compound can be worked out using A_r and M_r.

Using relative atomic mass (II)

How much reactant and product to use?

We can use the relative atomic mass of elements and the relative molecular mass of compounds to work out the actual masses of reactants and products in a reaction. The relative atomic mass in grams of any element will contain the same number of atoms as the relative atomic mass in grams of any other element. For example, the A_r of sodium is 23, and the A_r of sulphur is 32. This means that 23 g of sodium contains exactly the same number of atoms as 32 g of sulphur.

The same thing is true for compounds, except here we use the relative formula mass. So, the M_r for water (H_2O) is $(1 \times 2) + 16 = 18$, while the M_r for carbon dioxide (CO_2) is $12 + (16 \times 2) = 44$. This tells us that 18 g of water contains as many molecules as 44 g of carbon dioxide.

While sodium has an A_r of 23, chlorine has an A_r of 35.5. This means that if 23 g of sodium react with 35.5 g of chlorine, each element has the same number of atoms in the reaction. Putting this into a balanced equation:

$$2Na \quad + \quad Cl_2 \quad \longrightarrow \quad 2NaCl$$
$$2 \times 23\,g \quad + \quad 2 \times 35.5\,g \quad \longrightarrow \quad 2 \times 58.5\,g$$
$$46\,g \quad + \quad 71\,g \quad \longrightarrow \quad 117\,g$$

So 46 g of sodium added to 71 g of chlorine will give you 117 g of sodium chloride.

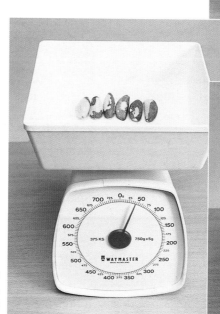

→ **Figure 1:** We would not expect six tomatoes, six brazil nuts and six oranges to weigh the same, because they are different sizes. The same is true for atoms of different elements.

sulphur   lithium   sodium chloride

↑ **Figure 2:** 32 g of sulphur, 7 g of lithium and 58.5 g of sodium chloride – each of these contains the same number of atoms or molecules as the others.

The relative formula mass of a compound is important when we want to calculate what mass of chemicals we need to react together to make a substance. For example, a chemical called sodium hydroxide reacts with chlorine gas to make bleach, as the following chemical equation shows:

$$2NaOH + Cl_2 \longrightarrow NaClO + NaCl + H_2O$$

sodium   chlorine   bleach   salt   water
hydroxide

↓ **Figure 3:** Bleach is used in some swimming pools to control and kill harmful bacteria. Getting the quantities right here also involves some careful calculation!

The reaction takes place when chlorine gas is bubbled through a solution of sodium hydroxide dissolved in water. If a chemical manufacturer has a solution containing 100 kg of sodium hydroxide it will be important to know what mass of chlorine gas to pass through the solution – too much, and some chlorine will be wasted, too little and not all of the sodium hydroxide will react.

The M_r of sodium hydroxide is 40. If we had 100 g of sodium hydroxide we should therefore have $100/40 = 2.5$ times the relative formula mass of sodium hydroxide in grams.

The chemical equation for the reaction tells us that for every two relative formula masses of sodium hydroxide, we need one relative formula mass of chlorine gas.

The M_r of chlorine gas is $35.5 \times 2 = 71$. Therefore we need $(2.5/2) \times 71\,g = 88.75\,g$ of chlorine to react with 100 g of sodium hydroxide.

If we had 100 kg of sodium hydroxide, we should therefore need 88.75 kg of chlorine.

Key Ideas

- The percentage of an element found in a compound can be worked out using A_r and M_r.
- The quantities of reactants and products in a reaction can be calculated using their A_r and M_r together with the balanced equation of the reaction.

? Questions

1 Use the data at the back of the book to help you find the relative atomic or formula mass in grams of:

  a calcium atoms

  b nitrogen molecules

  c copper sulphate ($CuSO_4$)

  d ethanol molecules (C_2H_5OH)

  e CO_3^{2-} ions.

2 Magnesium fluoride has the formula MgF_2. How much magnesium is needed to react exactly with 38 g of fluorine?

3 Calcium reacts with oxygen in the following way:

$$2Ca + O_2 \longrightarrow 2CaO$$

What mass of oxygen will react exactly with 40 g of calcium?

4 Nitrogen and oxygen react together in the following way:

$$N_2 + 2O_2 \longrightarrow 2NO_2$$

What mass of nitrogen and oxygen must be reacted together to make 46 g of NO_2?

2.7 Finding the mole (H)

We already know that the relative atomic mass in grams of any element contains the same number of atoms. In the same way, the relative formula mass in grams of any compound contains the same number of particles as any other compound.

Talking about relative atomic mass in grams or relative formula mass in grams all the time gets clumsy so chemists have a shorthand word for it – the **mole**. One mole is simply the relative atomic or formula mass of any substance in grams. A mole of any substance contains the same number of particles as a mole of any other substance.

The relative formula mass in grams of a gas will give you a mole of that gas in exactly the same way as it would for a solid or a liquid. However, when working with gases, it can be useful to know that 1 mole of any gas at room temperature and pressure occupies a volume of $24\,dm^3$. This can be used in calculations in just the same way as the masses of substances.

Using moles

In the laboratory we often work with larger or smaller quantities than complete moles. It helps to express these quantities as moles to help us see what we are doing.

To find the mass of a given number of moles we find the mass of 1 mole of the substance and then multiply it by the number of moles we want:

mass = mass of 1 mole × the number of moles wanted

Examples

3 moles of sodium chloride

The mass of 1 mole of NaCl is 58.5 g (23 + 35.5).

The mass of 3 moles is 58.5 × 3 = **175.5 g**.

0.5 moles of copper sulphate

The mass of 1 mole of $CuSO_4$ is 160 g (64 + 32 + (16 × 4))

The mass of 0.5 moles is 160 × 0.5 = **80 g**.

0.1 moles of hydrogen chloride

The mass of 1 mole of HCl is 36.5 g (1 + 35.5).

The mass of 0.1 mole is 36.5 × 0.1 = **3.65 g**.

0.5 moles of sulphur dioxide

The volume of 1 mole of any gas is $24\,dm^3$ (at standard temperature and pressure).

The volume of 0.5 moles of SO_2 (or any other gas) is therefore 0.5 × 24 = $12\,dm^3$.

This lets you calculate the *mass* of gas you have in a certain volume, which is otherwise very difficult to measure. You can work out the mass using M_r.

The M_r for SO_2 is 64 g, so $12\,dm^3$ (0.5 moles) of SO_2 contain 0.5 × 64 g = 32 g.

↑ **Figure 2:** 'How much of the mole do you want, Sir?'

Calculating formulae from experiments

The same idea can also be used in reverse. If we are given the masses of some of the substances involved in a reaction, we can work out the ratio of the number of atoms in the compound. This is known as the **empirical formula**. Sometimes it is the same as the actual number of atoms in one molecule (the *molecular formula*), but not always. For example the empirical formula of water is H_2O, which is also its molecular formula. However, hydrogen peroxide has the empirical formula HO, but its molecular formula is H_2O_2.

For example, if 12 g of carbon combine with 4 g of hydrogen, what does this tell us about the product?

For carbon (A_r 12):

$$\frac{12\,g}{12} = 1,$$ so 1 mole of carbon atoms is present in the product of the reaction.

For hydrogen (A_r 1):

$$\frac{4\,g}{1} = 4,$$ so 4 moles of hydrogen atoms are present in the product.

This tells us that 4 moles of hydrogen atoms combine with 1 mole of carbon atoms. In turn this means that 4 hydrogen atoms combine with each carbon atom so the product of the reaction has the empirical formula $\mathbf{CH_4}$.

↑ **Figure 3:** When magnesium is reacted in air for a quantitative experiment, the reaction takes place in a closed crucible so none of the magnesium oxide can escape.

How to work out the formula from reacting masses

- ⊙ Begin with the number of grams of the substances that combine.
- ⊙ Change the number of grams to moles of atoms by dividing the number of grams by the A_r or the M_r. This tells you how many moles of the different substances combine.
- ⊙ Use this to tell you how many atoms of the different substances combine.
- ⊙ This gives you the empirical formula of the product.

Key Ideas

- ⊙ From the masses of substances involved in reactions it is possible to work out the empirical formula of the product(s).

Example

In a reaction, 2.4 g of magnesium were reacted with oxygen in the air (see Figure 3). After the reaction, 4.0 g of the product, magnesium oxide, had been produced. This tells us that $4.0 - 2.4\,g = 1.6\,g$ of oxygen was used up in the reaction.

This tells us 2.4 g of magnesium reacted with 1.6 g of oxygen.

The A_r of magnesium is 24, so the number of moles of magnesium atoms reacting is $2.4/24 = 0.1$.

The A_r of oxygen is 16, so the number of moles of oxygen atoms reacting is $1.6/16 = 0.1$.

So 0.1 moles of magnesium atoms combine with 0.1 moles of oxygen atoms. This tells us that 1 atom of magnesium reacts with 1 atom of oxygen – so the empirical formula of the product, magnesium oxide, is $\mathbf{MgO}$.

? Questions

1 Sodium chloride has the formula NaCl. How many moles of sodium atoms must be reacted with 1 mole of chlorine atoms to form 1 mole of sodium chloride?

2 When nitrogen and hydrogen react together to form ammonia, 14 g of nitrogen react with 3 g of hydrogen. What is the empirical formula of ammonia?

3 Phosphorus reacts with chlorine to produce two different compounds, A and B. A is formed when 1.55 g of phosphorus reacts with 5.25 g of chlorine. B is formed when 1.55 g of phosphorus reacts with 8.75 g of chlorine. Calculate the empirical formulae of A and B.

1 The diagram shows an experiment using concentrated ammonia solution and concentrated hydrochloric acid.

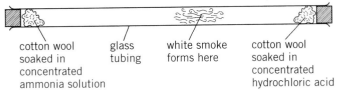

cotton wool soaked in concentrated ammonia solution

glass tubing

white smoke forms here

cotton wool soaked in concentrated hydrochloric acid

Concentrated ammonia solution is an irritant.
Concentrated hydrochloric acid is corrosive.

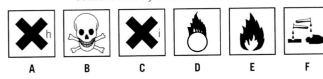

A   B   C   D   E   F

a Which of the hazard warning labels, **A** to **F**, should be placed on:

  i the bottle containing concentrated ammonia solution

  ii the bottle containing concentrated hydrochloric acid? (2 marks)

b Suggest two precautions which should be taken when putting the cotton wool soaked in concentrated hydrochloric acid into the tube. (2 marks)
(Total 4 marks)
AQA specimen question

2 The diagram shows the structures of five simple chemical compounds, **A** to **E**.

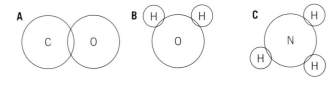

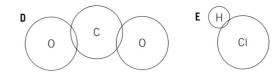

The names and chemical formulae of compounds **A** to **E** are given below.

hydrogen chloride   carbon monoxide   water
ammonia   carbon dioxide
CO   HCl   CO$_2$ H$_2$O   NH$_3$

Copy and complete the table, matching the correct name and formula for each compound.

Compound	Formula	Name
A		
B		
C		
D		
E		

(8 marks)
(Total 8 marks)

3 The relative atomic mass of an element can be weighed out in grams.

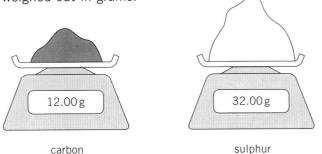

carbon   sulphur

a The relative atomic mass of an atom is the mass of that atom compared to the mass of a particular type of atom. Which atom is used as the standard atom for the measurement of relative atomic mass? (1 mark)

b Work out the relative formula masses of the following compounds.

You must show your working to get full marks.

  i potassium chloride (KCl) (2 marks)

  ii water (H$_2$O) (2 marks)

  iii magnesium sulphate (MgSO$_4$) (2 marks)

  iv ethane (C$_2$H$_6$) (2 marks)

(Relative atomic masses: H = 1, C = 12, O = 16, Mg = 24, S = 32, Cl = 35.5, K = 39)
(Total 9 marks)

4 We rely on modern technology like computers, and one of the most important components of this technology is the silicon chip.

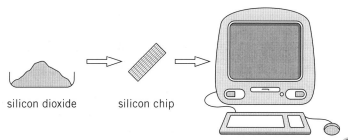

silicon dioxide   silicon chip

Pure silicon is extracted from silicon dioxide.

a If the silicon is extracted from 120 g of silicon dioxide, what mass of silicon would you expect?

Show all your working.   (3 marks)

b In a commercial setting, if 360 tonnes of silicon dioxide are processed, what mass of silicon would you expect?   (2 marks)

(Total 5 marks)

5 When magnesium reacts with the oxygen in the air the reaction is quite spectacular.

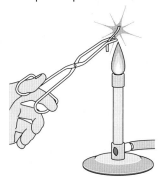

a Give a word equation for the reaction.   (1 mark)

b Give a balanced chemical equation for the reaction.   (2 marks)

c If 12 g of magnesium are burned in air, what mass of oxygen will react with it and what will the final mass of the product be?

Show all your working.   (3 marks)

(Total 6 marks)

H 6 Uranium is the heaviest naturally occurring element. It reacts with fluorine to form uranium fluoride, which is a gas at room temperature.

A sample of uranium fluoride was found to contain 0.65 g of uranium and 0.31 g of fluorine.

Calculate the formula of uranium fluoride.

To gain full marks you must show all your working.

(Relative atomic masses: F = 19, U = 238.)

(4 marks)

(Total 4 marks)

H 7 Hydrazine is produced from ammonia. The equation which represents this reaction is

$$2NH_3 + NaOCl \longrightarrow N_2H_4 + NaCl + H_2O$$

What mass of ammonia, NH_3, is needed to make 32 g of hydrazine, N_2H_4?

(Relative atomic masses: H = 1, N = 14)   (2 marks)

(Total 2 marks)

AQA specimen question

3.1 What is oil?

Some of the most important chemistry which goes on in the 21st century involves chemicals which come from oil. Chemicals from oil are enormously important. They play a major part in the lives of people in the developed world – and increasingly in the developing world – both as fuels and as part of chemicals such as plastics and pharmaceuticals. They also have a massive impact on society. Countries which produce oil have an economic hold over countries which do not, and they can affect the whole world economy by the price they charge for this vital commodity.

← **Figure 1:** Our economy depends heavily on fuel made from oil – when oil prices change it has an effect on the price of nearly everything we buy, not just those things made directly from it. The cost of transporting goods affects the price we pay for them in the shops.

Where does oil come from?

Oil, like coal and natural gas, is a fossil fuel. It is formed from the bodies of minute sea animals and plants, as the result of millions of years of heat and pressure acting on them in the absence of air.

Millions of years ago, far more of the surface of the Earth was covered in sea than today. As untold millions of minute marine creatures died and sank to the bottom, they formed a rich, decomposing sludge that in time became trapped in rock. This is what eventually formed crude oil (see Figure 2).

Like all fossil fuels, oil is a finite resource – there is a limited amount of it in the crust of the Earth and no more is being formed so eventually it will all be used up.

The composition of oil

Crude oil is a thick, black, smelly liquid, made up of a mixture of a large number of different compounds, most of which are useful to us in one form or another. These compounds are used as fuels for vehicles, for heating and cooking and to make other materials like plastics.

Almost all of the compounds in crude oil are made up of atoms from just two chemical elements – hydrogen and carbon. They are known as **hydrocarbons**. In the form crude oil is pumped out of the ground or from under the sea it is of little use to us. The different hydrocarbons need to be separated from the mixture before we can use them.

Separating mixtures

A mixture contains two or more elements or compounds which are not chemically combined together. The chemical properties of each substance are completely unchanged by being mixed. As a result it is possible to separate the components of a mixture by physical methods, such as filtration and distillation.

1 Filtration

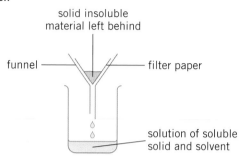

2 Evaporation

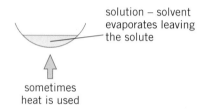

3 Distillation

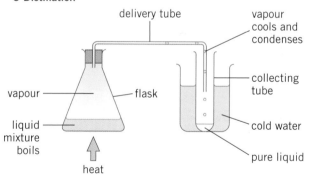

↑ **Figure 3:** There are lots of ways of separating mixtures, but for a complex mixture like crude oil a more complicated form of distillation (described in Section 3.2) is the only realistic option.

↘ **Figure 2:** It takes millions of years to turn tiny marine organisms into the smelly black liquid which is the basis of much of 21st century civilisation. Not for nothing is crude oil sometimes referred to as 'black gold'.

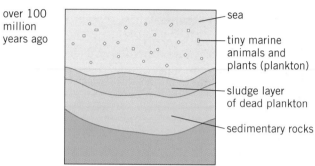

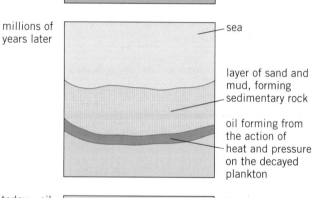

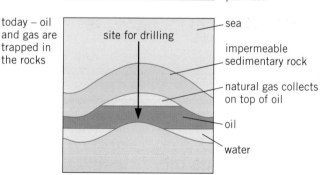

Questions

1 Why is oil a 'fossil fuel'?

2 How is crude oil formed?

3 Why is oil so important in our society?

4 **a** Crude oil is a mixture of chemical compounds. Explain the difference between a *mixture* and a *compound*.

   b What sort of chemicals make up crude oil?

Key Ideas

⊙ Oil is a fossil fuel.

⊙ Oil was formed by the action of heat and pressure over millions of years in the absence of air on the bodies of tiny marine animals and plants.

⊙ A mixture contains two or more substances which are not chemically combined. Crude oil is a mixture of many different hydrocarbon compounds.

⊙ Mixtures can be separated by physical methods which include filtration, evaporation and distillation.

Hydrocarbons in crude oil

Before we can understand how crude oil is separated into the various chemical compounds it contains we need to understand the compounds which are in the crude oil mixture.

Hydrocarbon molecules vary a great deal. Some are quite small, with relatively few carbon atoms and short chains – the most useful hydrocarbons tend to be these short chain molecules. Others contain very large numbers of carbon atoms which may have branches or side chains. The size of the molecule affects both the chemical and the physical properties of the compound. This in turn affects the way in which the compounds can be separated.

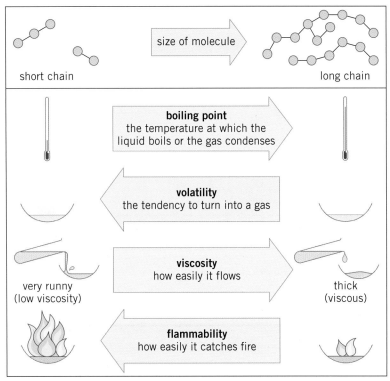

Figure 1: The different hydrocarbons making up crude oil have very different physical and chemical properties. Some of these differences make it possible to separate out the different compounds.

Refining crude oil

The hydrocarbons in crude oil are separated (refined) into **fractions** by a process known as **fractional distillation**. Each fraction contains hydrocarbons with similar numbers of carbon atoms in the molecule. The crude oil is fed into the bottom of a tall tower (a fractionating column) and heated. Compounds begin to boil off and evaporate. The tower is kept very hot at the bottom and much cooler at the top. The gases produced condense at different temperatures and the different fractions are collected. The smallest molecules have the lowest boiling points and so they are collected at the cool top of the tower. At the bottom of the tower the fractions are very thick liquids, with high boiling points, or solids. Once they have been collected the fractions need more refining before they can be used.

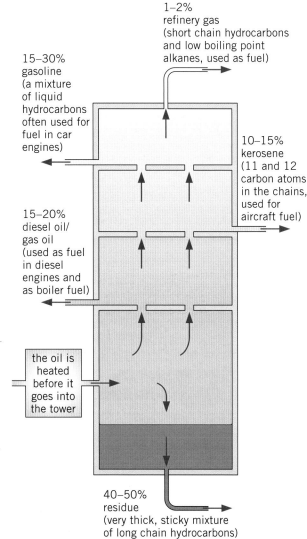

↑ **Figure 2:** Fractional distillation turns thick smelly crude oil into a wide range of useful compounds.

The proportion of the different fractions obtained after fractional distillation will depend on the type of crude oil which is fed into the process. There are many different types of crude oil. For example, crude oil from Venezuela contains many long chain hydrocarbons. It is very dark and thick and is known as 'heavy' crude. Other countries such as Nigeria and Saudi Arabia produce crude oil which is much paler in colour and more runny – this is 'light' crude.

Light crude oil contains many more of the smaller molecules which are particularly useful as fuels and for making other chemicals, so it costs more to buy than the heavier crude oils which contain a higher percentage of the bigger hydrocarbons.

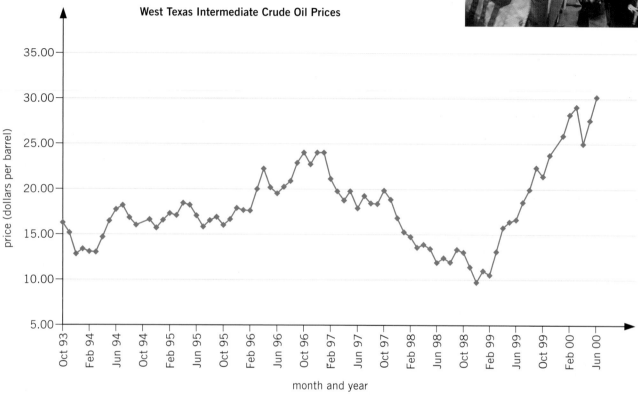

↗ **Figure 3:** The price of crude oil – one of the major factors which affect the economy of the whole world – is negotiated in oil trading rooms like the one in the photograph. The type of crude for sale has a big effect on the price.

? Questions

1 Crude oil is a mixture which has to be separated or refined before it can be used. How is this refining carried out?

2 Many different fractions are collected during the refining of crude oil. For each of the following fractions, describe what you would expect the properties to be:

   a a very short carbon chain

   b a medium length carbon chain

   c a very long carbon chain.

3 **a** Which property of the hydrocarbons in crude oil allows them to be separated by fractional distillation?

   b How is this related to the size of the hydrocarbon molecules?

0━ Key Ideas

⊙ There are different types of crude oil which contain different mixtures of hydrocarbons.

⊙ The size of the molecule affects the boiling point, volatility, viscosity and flammability of a hydrocarbon.

⊙ Crude oil is separated into different fractions by fractional distillation.

Using oil products

Fractional distillation separates crude oil into fractions made up of similar sized molecules. However, the fractions cannot be used as they are – they all need further treatment. There are several different ways in which the crude oil fractions may be further refined – one of these is *cracking*.

Cracking

Many of the heavier fractions are of only limited use in the form they leave the fractionating column. Some of them contain very large hydrocarbon molecules, and some contain quite short molecules which are not as much in demand as the even smaller molecules used for fuel. The largest hydrocarbons are thick liquids or solids with very high boiling points. They are difficult to vaporise and don't burn easily, so they are of very limited usefulness as fuels. Yet the main demand from crude oil is for fuels.

Luckily these larger hydrocarbon molecules can be broken down in a process known as **cracking**. The most successful way of doing this involves the use of heat and a catalyst, so it is known as **catalytic cracking** which takes place in a **cat cracker**. The crude oil fraction is heated to vaporise the hydrocarbons, which are then passed over a hot catalyst. (A catalyst makes a reaction go faster but does not get used up in the reaction.) Thermal decomposition reactions take place – the large molecules break down to form smaller, more useful ones.

↑ **Figure 1:** Massive crackers like this one are used to split up hydrocarbon fractions from crude oil to produce more useful molecules.

Example 1

Decane (a medium sized molecule) is broken down at a temperature of 800 °C in the presence of a catalyst to give pentane, which is used in petrol, along with propene and ethene, both of which are important in the production of other chemicals.

$$C_{10}H_{22} \xrightarrow{\text{800 °C, catalyst}} C_5H_{12} + C_3H_6 + C_2H_4$$
$$\text{decane} \qquad\qquad \text{pentane} \quad \text{propene} \quad \text{ethene}$$

Catalytic cracking is not only used for breaking up the largest molecules from fractional distillation. It can also be used to convert one small molecule to another, more reactive molecule which will be more useful in other reactions.

Example 2

When ethane (C_2H_6) is mixed with steam at high temperatures ethene and hydrogen are formed as the molecule undergoes thermal decomposition. Ethene is much more reactive than ethane and is very useful in many other chemical reactions.

$$C_2H_6 \xrightarrow{\text{> 800 °C, steam}} C_2H_4 + H_2$$

↑ **Figure 2:** 'I don't like the sound of this cat cracker…'

Useful products from oil

The downside of fossil fuels

Many of the products of the refining of oil are used as fuels (see Section 3.5). When these fossil fuels are burnt to drive our vehicles and provide heating or power, they produce waste gases, some of which cause considerable damage to the environment. Carbon dioxide and water vapour are produced by the hydrocarbons when they burn. Impurities in the fuels form gases such as sulphur dioxide, which contribute to air pollution and form acid rain.

Perhaps most worrying is the build-up of carbon dioxide from burning fossil fuels. It builds up in the atmosphere and traps the radiation from the sun. This seems to be having a long-term effect on temperatures at the surface of the planet. The climate is warming up all over the world. What the effect of this will be we don't yet know. Patterns of weather around the world will certainly change, and if the polar icecaps melt the sea levels will rise. This in turn could mean that low-lying countries disappear. It may be a race against time to see if the fossil fuels run out before the damage we inflict on the planet becomes irreparable!

↑ **Figure 3:** Fossil fuels have become vital to our lifestyles, but the results of burning them pollute our atmosphere and may put the health of the planet at risk.

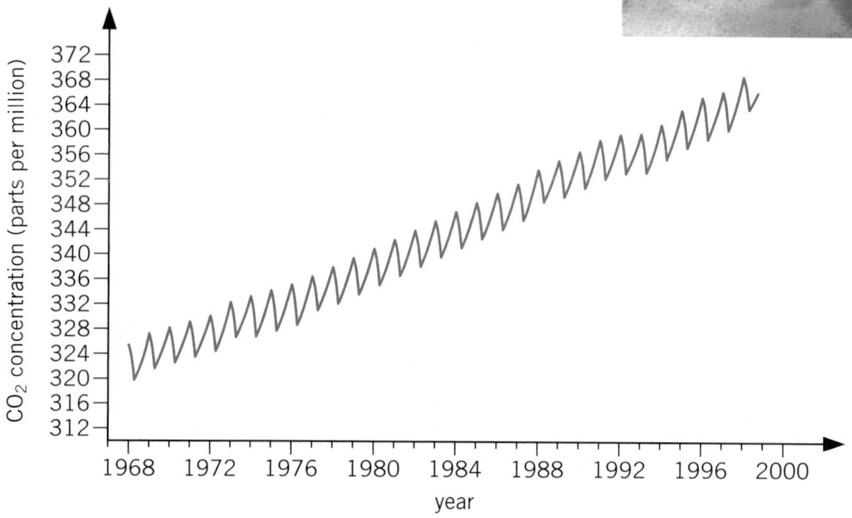

← **Figure 4:** The concentration of carbon dioxide in the atmosphere has been steadily increasing.

CO$_2$ concentration (parts per million) — *year*

(see Section 3.5)

? Questions

1 Why do the fractions of crude oil from fractional distillation need further refining?

2 **a** What happens in a catalytic cracker?

   b Why are small molecules sometimes put into a catalytic cracker?

3 The word equation for methane (CH$_4$) burning is:

   methane + oxygen $\longrightarrow$ carbon dioxide + water

   Write the chemical equation for this reaction and balance it.

4 Use the graph in Figure 4 to help you write a piece for the local newspaper encouraging people to use their cars as little as possible for the good of the environment.

0⟲ Key Ideas

⊙ After fractional distillation many products of crude oil need further refining before they can be used.

⊙ Large hydrocarbons are heated in the presence of catalysts and undergo thermal decomposition.

⊙ Burning fossil fuels can damage the environment.

The refining process of crude oil provides a range of hydrocarbon molecules which are very important to our way of life. Oil products are all around us – it is almost impossible to imagine life without them.

Using chemicals from oil

The most obvious use of oil-based chemicals is as fuels, not only in vehicles of all types but also for cooking and heating systems in homes and in providing electricity from oil-fired power stations.

Chemicals derived from oil are also in use throughout the chemical industries. They are used in the manufacture of products which range from margarines to medicines, from dyes to explosives. But one of the most important uses of oil-based chemicals is in the production of plastics.

↑ **Figure 1:** Oil-based chemicals are used as fuels throughout the world – here oil is the fuel in a power station producing electricity.

Plastics

Plastics are huge molecules made up of lots of small molecules which have joined together. The small molecules are called **monomers** and the plastics are called **polymers** ('poly' means 'many'). Different types of plastic with very different properties may be made using different monomers.

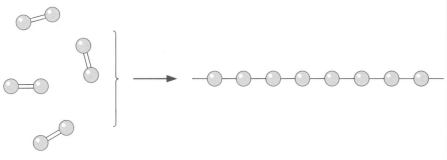

monomers   polymer

↑ **Figure 2:** Polymers are very common in the natural world, but when we learnt to make artificial polymers a whole new world of materials opened up. Polymers like these are now part of our everyday lives.

Ethene (C_2H_4) consists of small hydrocarbon molecules. These can be turned into a polymer known as poly(ethene) or polythene. Polythene is an enormously useful plastic. It is easy to shape, strong, and transparent unless coloured. 'Plastic' bags, plastic drink bottles, dustbins and clingfilm are all examples which are very familiar in everyday life.

Propene is another chemical from oil. When polymers are made with propene as the monomer, the plastic formed is called poly(propene). Poly(propene) is a very strong, tough plastic which has many uses, including crates and ropes.

The number of plastics available is growing all the time, and they have a wide range of properties. This means they can be used for functions ranging from clothing to housing, including vehicles and even replacement parts of the human body!

Getting rid of plastics

Plastics are light, cheap and often longer lasting than natural materials. This is why these artificial polymers produced from oil are so popular. However, there are some problems arising from the same properties which make plastics so useful.

Most plastics are incredibly long-lasting. They do not disintegrate naturally and they are not broken down by the microorganisms which cause all living material to decay. In other words they are not **biodegradable**. When we get rid of plastic rubbish it goes to the rubbish tips with all the rest of our household waste, but unlike everything else the plastic will still be there 10, 50 and even 100 years from now. The build-up of waste plastic will have serious consequences for the environment.

Almost all plastics will burn, so we could get rid of them by incineration. Unfortunately most plastics also produce toxic gases when they burn, which pollute the atmosphere and are a serious risk both to human health and to other living things.

At the moment there seem to be two approaches which may solve the problem of plastic disposal in the future.

⊙ **Recycling:** Some plastics can be melted down and reused. More and more people save the plastic bottles used for fizzy drinks, ketchup etc and take them to collection points for recycling. It only works for some types of plastic, but even plastic bits of cars are now recycled. As more and more plastic is collected and recycled, less and less oil has to be used to make new polymers and less plastic builds up in the environment.

⊙ **Biodegradable plastics:** More and more new polymers are being developed which can be broken down by bacteria – they are biodegradable. This means that when they are dumped they will eventually be broken down naturally. Even if they take a long time to break down, at least it holds out the hope that our grandchildren will not be living in the middle of the plastic waste we produce today.

↑ **Figure 3:** Plastic rubbish can be now found all over the world, carried by wind and water even to places where no people live – and the problem is simply not going to disappear.

The compounds making up crude oil are called hydrocarbons. As the name suggests, hydrocarbons are made up of the elements hydrogen and carbon. They all have a spine of carbon atoms, with the hydrogen atoms attached around the spine. Although they all contain the same basic elements, hydrocarbons vary enormously in their properties and reactions. They form families of compounds, and each family has similar bonds in the carbon spine. The study of these families of hydrocarbons makes up part of the study of **organic chemistry**.

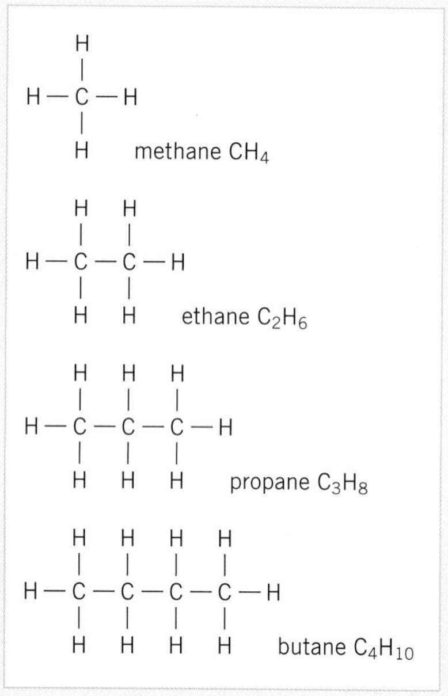

The alkanes

The simplest family of hydrocarbons is the **alkanes**. In this family the carbon atoms are joined by single covalent carbon–carbon bonds. All of the remaining bonds are carbon–hydrogen bonds. The alkanes are found in the lightest, gaseous fraction of crude oil.

When hydrocarbons are named, the final part of the name indicates which family of compounds the compound belongs to. In this case the ending **–ane** indicates an alkane. The prefix tells us how many carbon atoms there are in the molecule:

Prefix	Number of carbon atoms
Meth-	1
Eth-	2
Prop-	3
But-	4
Pent-	5

↑ Figure 1: The first four members of the alkane family.

One important reaction of the alkanes is that they burn in air to give a considerable amount of heat. For this reason they are important as fuels.

methane + oxygen ⟶ carbon dioxide + water
$$CH_4 + 2O_2 \longrightarrow CO_2 + 2H_2O$$

propane + oxygen ⟶ carbon dioxide + water
$$C_3H_8 + 5O_2 \longrightarrow 3CO_2 + 4H_2O$$

The alkenes

Another common family of hydrocarbons found in crude oil is the **alkenes**. In this family there is at least one carbon–carbon double bond. This double bond makes a big difference to the chemistry of the compounds of the family.

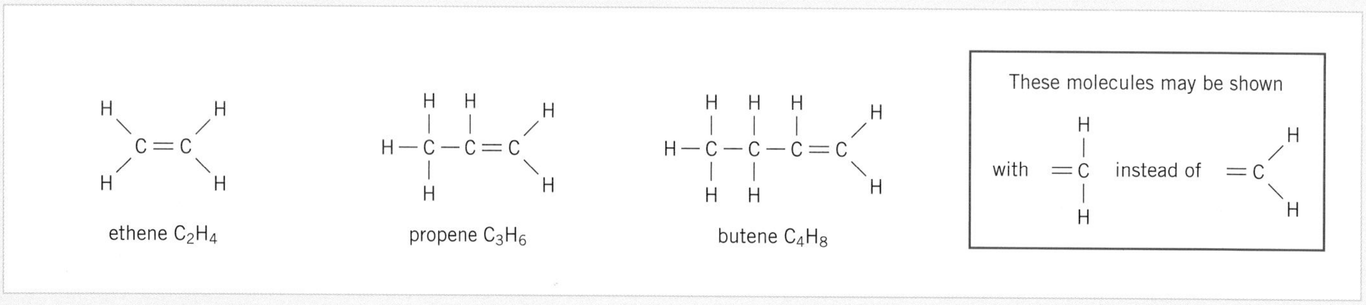

↓ Figure 2: The combustion reaction of methane with the oxygen in the air provides millions of us with heating, hot water and a way to cook our food.

↑ Figure 3: The first three members of the alkene family.

The alkenes, and particularly ethene, are tremendously important in the chemical industry. They are not found in crude oil in very large quantities but are produced by the cracking of the alkanes (see Section 3.3, Example 2).

The alkenes, like all the hydrocarbons, burn in air to form carbon dioxide and water. In oxygen, ethene reacts *explosively* so it is not much good as a fuel!

$$C_2H_4 + 3O_2 \longrightarrow 2CO_2 + 2H_2O$$

The alkenes are also too useful in the chemical industry (for the manufacture of plastics and many other chemicals) to be used as fuels.

Saturated and unsaturated hydrocarbons

Hydrocarbon molecules which have no double bonds in them are called **saturated**. This simply means that there are as many hydrogen atoms as possible in the molecule, and no more can be added. Hydrocarbon molecules with at least one double bond are called **unsaturated** – meaning that more hydrogen atoms *can* be added to these molecules. Unsaturated molecules are much more reactive than saturated ones. This is because the double bond is less than twice as strong as a single bond, making it easier to break one part of the double bond apart than it would be to break a single bond. The result of this is that the alkenes are much more reactive than the alkanes, as the bromine water test shows.

The bromine water test

When bromine is dissolved in water a yellowy-brown liquid known as bromine water results. This is a convenient way to use bromine in the lab.

If the colourless gas ethane, a saturated hydrocarbon, is bubbled through yellow-brown bromine water nothing happens. However, if the colourless gas ethene, an unsaturated hydrocarbon, is bubbled through bromine water the liquid becomes colourless as the bromine reacts with the unsaturated hydrocarbon.

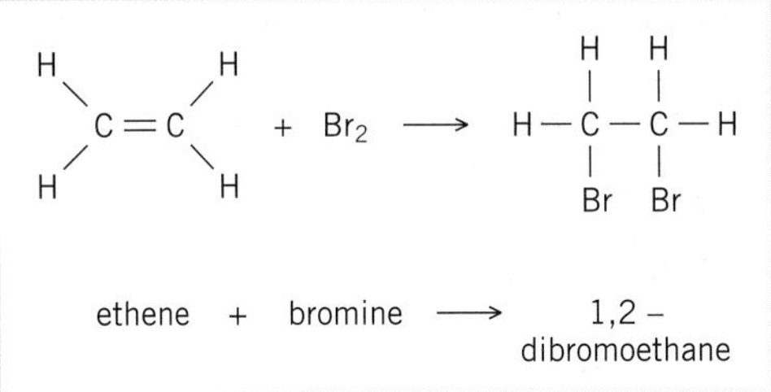

↑ **Figure 4:** The bromine molecule is added to the hydrocarbon across the double bond, forming a saturated compound and removing the bromine (and so the colour) from the bromine water.

? Questions

1 a What is an alkane?

  b Draw the structure of a molecule of pentane.

  c How do alkanes react with oxygen in the air?

  d Give two uses of members of the alkane family.

  e Write a balanced equation showing how butane burns in air.

2 a What is an alkene?

  b Draw the structures of a molecule of pentene.

  c How are the alkenes formed from the alkanes?

  d Give two reasons why the alkenes are not used as fuels.

  e Write a balanced equation showing how butene burns in air.

3 Why is an unsaturated hydrocarbon more reactive than a saturated one?

4 Explain why an alkene but not an alkane turns bromine water colourless.

Key Ideas

⊙ Carbon atoms form the spine of hydrocarbon molecules.

⊙ Hydrocarbons with only single carbon–carbon bonds are known as alkanes.

⊙ Hydrocarbons with at least one carbon–carbon double bond are known as alkenes.

⊙ Alkenes react with bromine water and decolourise it; alkanes do not react.

A polymer is a very large molecule which is made up of long chains of repeating smaller monomer units joined together. A molecule is regarded as a polymer, rather than just a big molecule, when there are at least 50 repeating monomer units in the chain. In some polymers the monomer units are all the same, in others there are a number of different alternating monomer units. The world is full of natural polymers including the proteins, carbohydrates and fats which make up the cells of most living things.

Over the last 50 years or so, we have rapidly developed the ability to make all sorts of synthetic polymers. We can design polymers to have just the properties which make them useful for a particular job. The alkenes and related compounds, with their reactive double bonds, are very important in the manufacture of polymers.

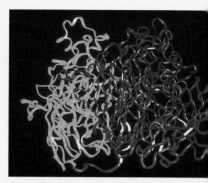

↑ **Figure 1:** Proteins are long chains of monomers known as amino acids. Computer models like this one of Factor VIII (a blood clotting protein) help us imagine what they look like.

Forming polymers

When many small monomer units join together to form a very large polymer, the reaction is known as **polymerisation**. Sometimes the monomers join together and form molecules of water as well, as they join. Often, however, unsaturated monomers join together and no other substance is produced in the reaction. This process is known as **addition polymerisation**.

Unsaturated hydrocarbons contain at least one double bond. This makes them reactive. They are particularly likely to be involved in addition reactions where the double bond opens up and single bonds are formed in its place. This is the type of reaction which takes place when alkenes join together to form a polymer:

monomer + monomer + monomer + ... ⟶ polymer

Making plastics

Plastics are well known artificial polymers. One of the most common and best known plastics is polythene. This is more correctly known as poly(ethene), and it is made by the polymerisation of the simplest alkene, ethene. In the polymerisation reaction the double covalent bonds of the ethene molecules are broken and replaced by single covalent bonds, as hundreds of ethene molecules join together in an addition reaction:

↓ **Figure 2:** Poly(propene) is one important addition polymer. It can be woven into very strong ropes like these, which will not rot or decay, unlike natural alternatives.

ethene monomers ⟶ poly(ethene)

This addition polymerisation can be shown in a simpler form:

many single ethene monomers ⟶ long chain of poly(ethene)   where n is a large number

Another example of the process of addition polymerisation is in the formation of poly(propene):

propene monomers ⟶ poly(propene)

← Figure 5: One of the first artificial polymers to be made and used in the mass market was nylon, which owes its existence to Wallace Hume Carothers.

↑ Figure 6: Wallace Hume Carothers – an American chemist – played an important role in the development of many synthetic polymers.

Carothers was born an only child in Iowa in 1896. When he was 18 he began studying accounting, but later switched to science. While he was still an undergraduate student, Carothers was made head of the chemistry department in which he was studying! Partly this was a reflection of his enormous talent, but the real reason behind this strange appointment was staff shortage due to the First World War. Aged 28, Carothers became a professor at Harvard University, where he started research into polymers. Four years later he left Harvard to become head of a research team at a large American chemical company called DuPont.

At DuPont, Carothers turned his brilliant mind to the task of making synthetic polymers. A quiet, shy man, he inspired his team to work hard, and by 1931 DuPont were manufacturing neoprene, a synthetic rubber that was to have an enormous impact in World War 2 when rubber supplies from the Far East were cut off.

Carothers and his team now turned their minds to producing an artificial version of silk, spurred on by worsening relations between the US and Japan, the main source of silk at that time. By 1934 they had cracked the problem, and DuPont were able to patent the new fibre, nylon, the following year. Nylon fabric was introduced to the world in 1938, when Fortune magazine wrote: 'It flouts Solomon. It is an entirely new arrangement of matter under the sun, and the first completely new synthetic fiber made by man. In over four thousand years, textiles have seen only three basic developments aside from mechanical mass production: mercerized cotton, synthetic dyes and rayon. Nylon is a fourth.'

In producing synthetic polymers, Carothers and his team advanced chemistry and may even have saved lives as a result, through the creation of synthetic rubber. Tragically Carothers' personal life was not so successful, and he suffered fits of severe depression. In April 1937 he committed suicide. He would not see the success of nylon – and neither would he see his daughter, Jane, born seven months later.

? Questions

1 a Why are some large molecules simply very big molecules when others are described as polymers?

b Why are alkenes often involved in the formation of polymers?

2 a What is meant by the term 'addition polymerisation'?

b How does addition polymerisation differ from other types of polymerisation?

c How does ethene react to form the polymer poly(ethene)?

3 Poly(butene) is formed from monomer butene units. Draw a diagram and give the equation for this reaction.

⊙━ Key Ideas

- ⊙ The joining of many small monomer units to form a polymer is known as polymerisation.

- ⊙ Unsaturated hydrocarbons undergo addition polymerisation with the breaking of the reactive double bond.

1 Crude oil contains a number of compounds. These compounds are **not** joined together chemically.

  a Which of the following is the best description of crude oil?

    compound   **element**   **fraction**   **mixture**

    (1 mark)

  b Crude oil is separated into fractions by fractional distillation. The table below shows the percentage of each fraction in North Sea crude oil.

Fraction	Percentage (%) in North Sea crude oil
gas	3
petrol	7
naphtha	10
kerosine	15
gas oil	20
fuel oil	45

The bar chart shows the percentage of each fraction an oil company uses.

Using the data in the table, copy and complete the bar chart with the percentage of each fraction in North Sea crude oil.

The bars for gas and petrol have been done for you.

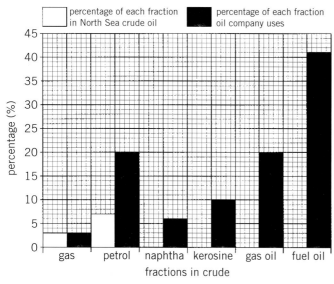

(2 marks)

  c **i** Use information from the bar chart to help you answer this question.

    The oil company uses more of one of the fractions than they can obtain by distillation of North Sea crude oil. Name this fraction. (1 mark)

    ii Copy the sentence below, choosing a word from the list to complete it.

      condensing   **cracking**   **distilling** **evaporating**

      Large hydrocarbons are broken down into smaller molecules by a process called ...... (1 mark)

    iii Use information from the bar chart to help you answer this question.
    Name **three** fractions that the oil company might want to break down into smaller molecules. (3 marks)

(Total 8 marks)

AQA specimen question

H 2 **a** Propene and propane can be produced from crude oil.

    i A propene molecule (C_3H_6) can be represented by the structure shown below.

$$\begin{array}{c} H \\ {\Large\diagdown} \\ C = C - C - H \\ {\Large\diagup} \\ H \end{array}$$

    Draw a similar diagram to show the structure of a propane molecule (C_3H_8). (1 mark)

    ii Which molecule, propene or propane, is unsaturated?

    Give a reason for your answer. (1 mark)

  b The equation below represents the polymerisation of propene.

    i Name the polymer produced by this reaction. (1 mark)

$$n\begin{bmatrix} H & H \\ | & | \\ C = C \\ | & | \\ H & CH_3 \end{bmatrix} \longrightarrow \begin{bmatrix} H & H \\ | & | \\ C = C \\ | & | \\ H & CH_3 \end{bmatrix}_n$$

    ii Explain the meaning of the term **polymerisation**. (2 marks)

    iii Describe the problems caused by the everyday use of this polymer. (3 marks)

(Total 8 marks)

AQA specimen question

3 Oil is what is known as a fossil fuel. Use the diagrams below to help you explain in your own words how oil is formed and why it is known as a fossil fuel.

In order to gain full marks you should write down your ideas in good English. Put them into a sensible order and use the correct scientific words.

over 100 million years ago

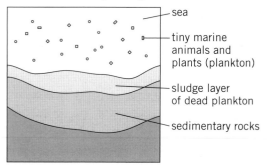

millions of years later

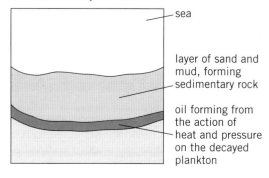

today – oil and gas are trapped in the rocks

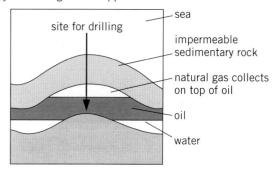

(6 marks)

(Total 6 marks)

4 The graph shows the levels of carbon dioxide in the atmosphere since 1968.

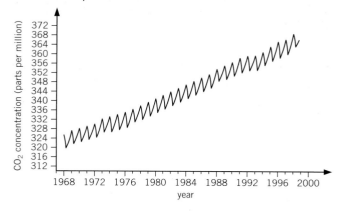

a Produce a bar chart to show the levels of carbon dioxide in the atmosphere in 1968, 1978, 1988 and 1998. (4 marks)

b What is the link between the data in this graph and fossil fuels such as oil? (2 marks)

c Many people think that the rise in carbon dioxide levels is having an effect on life on Earth. Explain how. (3 marks)

(Total 9 marks)

5 Ethene is used to make the polymer poly(ethene).

$$\begin{array}{cc} H & H \\ & \diagdown\;\;\diagup \\ & C = C \\ & \diagup\;\;\diagdown \\ H & H \end{array}$$

ethene

$$-C-C-C-C-C-C-$$

poly(ethene)

a **i** What is a polymer? (1 mark)

ii What is the more common name of poly(ethene)? (1 mark)

b Plastics like poly(ethene) are very widely used.

i Give two common uses of poly(ethene). (2 marks)

ii There are disadvantages to using plastics like poly(ethene). Explain what they are and how people are trying to overcome these problems. (4 marks)

(Total 8 marks)

Metals have been important to human beings for a very long time. We chart our movement through history by the materials we used at different periods – from the Stone Age to the Bronze Age and then on to the Iron Age. Metals have many properties which are different from stone, wood and bone, the main materials available to the earliest humans. They are strong and not brittle, they shine, they can be worked and stretched, they can be hammered to a point, they make a pleasant sound when struck, and they conduct heat.

Where do metals come from?

Metals come from the Earth's crust. A few metals, such as gold and silver, are so unreactive that they are found in the Earth uncombined with other elements, in their **native** state. These are called **noble metals**. Sometimes a nugget of gold is so large it can simply be picked up. At other times tiny flakes have to be physically separated from sand and rocks by panning.

↑ **Figure 1:** Metals are still of crucial importance in human lives. They are used in the development of all sorts of new technologies, like this amazing aircraft. At the same time they form an important part of our homes, our transport systems, our power supply and communication systems, our economic systems and our medical technology.

However, most metals are found in the Earth combined with other chemical elements, very often with oxygen to give a metal oxide. This means that the metal must be chemically separated from its compounds. If a metal or metal compound is concentrated enough in a rock to make it economic to extract the metal, the rock is known as a **metal ore.** Whether or not a mineral is an economic source of a particular metal will depend on how easy it is to extract the pure metal and how much metal it contains.

↖ **Figure 2:** Gold is a beautiful, shiny metal found uncombined with other elements. It has always been highly valued, and the chance of finding some caused the famous 'gold rush' in the early days of the US.

Getting metals from stone

Metal objects from many thousands of years ago can give us an insight into how the story of people and metals developed. Small jewels and tools carved from gold, silver and copper – all metals which can be found in their native state – have been dated to around 7000 years ago. At some point people discovered that metals became softer when they were heated, and could then be shaped, forged and cast. Once this was discovered, metal objects began to look different, whereas the earliest finds were carved like bits of bone or wood.

In the same area as native copper is found there will often be ores like malachite (copper combined with carbon and oxygen). If these are heated in a charcoal fire, pure copper is produced. Once this was discovered the Ancient Egyptians quickly exploited it. They produced thousands of tons of copper from ores before 3200 BC. Once it was realised that one metal could be extracted from rocks by fire, people soon discovered other metals and then began mixing them. Bronze, a mixture of 90% copper and 10% tin, can easily be cast into different shapes and its use resulted in harder edged tools and weapons.

The extraction of iron on a regular basis did not come about until about 1000 BC. It needs higher temperatures than many other metals and so needed the fire to be heated using bellows. We think it was the Hittites in Anatolia (modern-day Turkey) who first mastered this technology. Before that time the occasional bit of iron that was achieved was highly prized – Homer, the great Greek poet of the 9th century BC, mentions iron as a precious metal of similar value and rarity to gold.

Quench-hardening iron – thrusting it into water whilst it is still red hot – was the next development in the Iron Age. This new technology again had a massive impact, because the tools and weapons made in this way were so much superior to bronze ones – the ores were readily available, no alloying was needed and iron allowed razor sharp cutting edges to be achieved. Maintaining temperatures hot enough to cast iron rather than forge it only became possible in Europe in the 14th century AD – but in China the technology was available from around the 3rd century BC (Europeans just didn't know about it!).

→ **Figure 3:** The increasing use of metals didn't just mean that tools and weapons got better – it also made possible the crafting of much beautiful jewellery, like this piece of bronze made around 1700 BC, and also the first regular use of coins as money.

1 What is the difference between the way a noble metal is collected compared to any other metal element such as iron?

2 **a** Why were metals so important to people in our early history?
   b Why are metals so important in modern life?

3 Why were metals such as gold, silver and copper the first to be used by early peoples?

4 Draw a timeline showing the approximate dates for the developing use of metal technology by early peoples.

⊙ The Earth's crust contains metals and metal compounds mixed with other substances.

⊙ In a metal ore the metal or metal compound is concentrated enough to make it economic to extract the metal.

⊙ Gold and the other noble metals are found in their native state.

⊙ Many ores contain metal oxides.

The crust of the Earth is made up of many very different compounds as well as the uncombined native elements like gold, silver, copper and sulphur. However, most elements are only found in very small amounts. The main elements in the crust are actually non-metals – oxygen and silicon. These combine to give silicon dioxide or sand, as well as making up many other rocks. Oxygen is also part of all the metal oxides found in the crust.

The rest of the crust is mainly made up of six metals, all of which are found combined with other elements like oxygen and carbon to form metal ores. The six are aluminium, iron, calcium, magnesium, sodium and potassium. All the other metals and non-metals make up a tiny proportion of the Earth's resources. These scarce metals include gold, silver, copper, zinc, lead, tin, platinum and mercury.

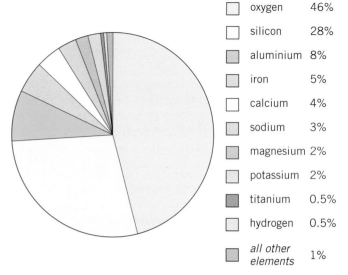

□	oxygen	46%
□	silicon	28%
□	aluminium	8%
□	iron	5%
□	calcium	4%
□	sodium	3%
□	magnesium	2%
□	potassium	2%
▨	titanium	0.5%
□	hydrogen	0.5%
▨	all other elements	1%

↑ **Figure 1:** The crust of the Earth is made up of a wide variety of elements – and some of them are very useful to us.

The reactivity series

Metal ore is no use to us as it stands – it is simply a pile of rocks. To get the metal out of the ore we need to decompose the compound in the ore to release the pure metal. There are a number of different ways in which the metal may be extracted from its ore. The method used will depend on how reactive the metal is – in other words, on its place in the reactivity series.

Reactivity series of metals

potassium	most reactive
sodium	
calcium	
magnesium	
aluminium	
carbon	
zinc	
iron	
tin	
lead	
hydrogen	
copper	
silver	
gold	
platinum	least reactive

← **Figure 2:** The reactivity series is drawn up by observing how vigorously metals react:

⊙ with air, to produce metal oxides →

⊙ with water (cold, hot or as steam) to produce metal hydroxides or oxides and hydrogen →

⊙ with dilute acids to produce metal salts and hydrogen. →

Carbon and hydrogen are non-metals which have been included in the series for comparison.

The reactivity series lists the metals in order of their reactivity, with the most reactive at the top and the least reactive at the bottom. A more reactive metal will displace a less reactive metal from its compounds. Also, the two non-metals carbon and hydrogen will also displace less reactive metals from their oxides. This is very useful to us in the commercial extraction of metals from their ores.

Extracting metals from their ores

The most reactive metals are the most difficult to extract from their ores. The less reactive metals are extracted more easily and the very unreactive metals like gold are not found in ores at all.

Using reduction reactions

Many of the less reactive metals such as copper, lead, iron and zinc occur in their ores as oxides. Because carbon is more reactive than all of these metals, it can be used to extract them from their ores. When the metal oxide is heated with carbon or carbon monoxide, the carbon removes the oxygen from the metal oxide to form carbon dioxide, leaving the pure metal behind:

metal oxide + carbon ⟶ metal + carbon dioxide

Reactions which involve the removal of oxygen in this way are known as **reduction reactions**.

H Redox reactions

The extraction of the less reactive metals from their ores involves a reduction reaction, as the oxygen is removed from the metal oxide. However, at the same time as the metal oxide loses oxygen, the carbon or carbon monoxide gains it. When a chemical gains oxygen it is said to be **oxidised**. The reduction of one chemical in a reaction is normally accompanied by the oxidation of another chemical in the same reaction, and vice versa. This linking of these two processes is the reason that such reactions are often known as **redox reactions**, taking part of the name from each – **red**uction and **ox**idation.

? Questions

1 Taking the data from the pie chart in Figure 1, display the data in a different form to show the proportions of the different metal components of the Earth's crust.

2 Describe two experiments by which you might investigate the reactivity of three different metals compared to each other.

3 Explain how a reactivity series is drawn up by seeing how different elements react with air, water and acid.

4 Look at the reactivity series (Figure 2). Which metals can be extracted from their ores using carbon? Explain your answer.

5 Which of the following reactions are reduction reactions?

$CuO + H_2 \longrightarrow Cu + H_2O$

$Fe_2O_3 + 3CO \longrightarrow 2Fe + 3CO_2$

$NaOH + HCl \longrightarrow NaCl + H_2O$

$SnO_2 + 2C \longrightarrow Sn + 2CO$

 6 Explain what a 'redox' reaction is.

Key Ideas

⊙ The reactivity series of metals lists metals in order of their reactivity with the most reactive at the top.

⊙ The reactivity series is useful in deciding the best way to extract a metal from its ore.

⊙ Metals below carbon in the reactivity series can be extracted using reduction reactions with carbon.

The extraction of iron from its ore worldwide is a massive industry. Iron is the second most common metal found in the Earth's crust. Iron is less reactive than carbon, and so we can extract it by removing the oxygen from the iron oxide using carbon in a reduction reaction.

The blast furnace

The extraction of iron takes place in a **blast furnace**. This is made of steel lined with fireproof bricks to withstand the high temperatures inside. There are three solid raw materials which are used in the blast furnace, as well as lots of air. They are:

⊙ iron ore – the most common ore is haematite, which contains mainly iron oxide (Fe_2O_3) and sand

⊙ coke – which is made from coal and is almost pure carbon – to provide the reducing power

⊙ limestone – mainly calcium carbonate ($CaCO_3$) – to remove impurities.

Hot air is blown into the blast furnace and this makes the coke burn, which heats the furnace and forms carbon dioxide.

$$C + O_2 \longrightarrow CO_2$$

At the high temperatures in the blast furnace this carbon dioxide reacts again with the coke to form carbon monoxide.

$$CO_2 + C \longrightarrow 2CO$$

The carbon monoxide reacts with the iron oxide, removing the oxygen and reducing it to molten iron which then flows to the bottom of the blast furnace.

$$Fe_2O_3 + 3CO \longrightarrow 2Fe + 3CO_2$$

The limestone reacts with the acidic impurities in the ore. This forms a molten slag which floats on top of the molten iron and can be removed. Some of the molten iron is left to solidify in moulds – this is known as cast iron – whilst the rest is kept molten to be turned into steel. Steel is made by removing some of the impurities from iron and then mixing it with other elements to change its properties.

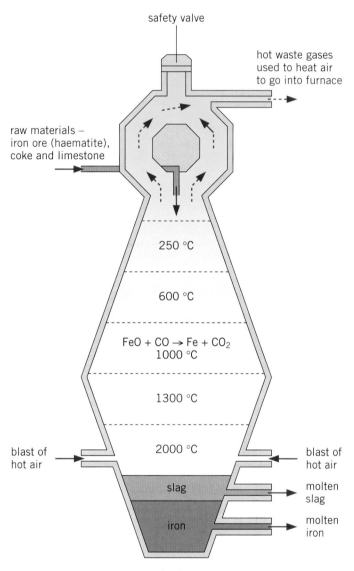

↑ **Figure 1:** The blast furnace in action produces tonnes of molten iron to be used as pure iron or to be made into steel.

The rust problem

Iron and steel are tremendously useful but they have a major drawback. They corrode far more rapidly than many other metals, due to the reaction of iron with oxygen and water in the air. The product of the reaction is reddish brown iron oxide – better known as rust. Rusting can eat away and destroy anything made of iron and basic steel (iron and carbon mixed) but there are several ways of protecting iron from rusting.

The iron can be connected to a more reactive metal which will react with oxygen leaving the iron or steel untouched. This is called **sacrificial protection**, because the more reactive metal is 'sacrificed' to protect the iron. The metals most commonly used are zinc and magnesium. A large lump of zinc is often attached to the hulls of steel ships where it is corroded away, needing to be replaced at regular intervals. The iron can also be completely covered by a protective layer of zinc, or **galvanised**. Even if the coating is scratched or damaged, the iron will not corrode because of the sacrificial effect of the zinc.

Another way of preventing iron from corroding is to mix it with other substances to form an alloy which does not corrode. For example, if iron is mixed with chromium it forms a metal known as stainless steel – 'stainless' because it does not rust or corrode. Alloy steels like this are enormously useful. Not only are they immune to corrosion, but the strength and other properties of the metal can be modified to fit them for a wide variety of jobs.

↑ **Figure 3:** Making steel is a hot, noisy business – and can be quite spectacular!

Composition	Steel 1	Steel 2
max % carbon	0.20	0.22
max % sulphur	0.035	0.035

Property	Steel 1	Steel 2
breaking strength (N/mm^2)	410–560	490–630

↑ **Figure 2:** The addition of other elements to iron can change its properties.

4.4 Electrolysis

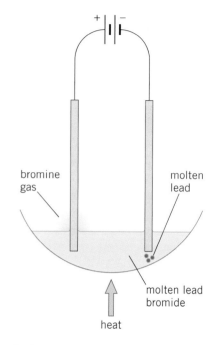

↑ **Figure 2:** Molten lead and brown bromine gas are formed when electricity is passed through molten lead bromide.

The basis of electrolysis is that substances made up of ions can be broken down (decomposed) into simpler substances by passing an electric current through them. The substance being broken down by electrolysis is known as the **electrolyte**.

An electrical circuit is set up with two **electrodes** dipping into the electrolyte. The electrodes are conducting rods, one positive and one negative. They are usually made out of a very inert substance like graphite or platinum so they do not react with either the electrolyte or the products of the reaction. (The positive electrode is sometimes called the *anode* and the negative electrode the *cathode*.)

During electrolysis, positively charged ions move to the negative electrode, and negative ions move to the positive electrode. When the ions reach the electrodes they can lose their charge and be deposited as elements. Depending on the compound being electrolysed gases may be given off or metals deposited at the electrodes.

In the example in Figure 2 the electrical energy has brought about a chemical change – the breakdown of lead bromide into lead and bromine.

$$\text{lead bromide} \longrightarrow \text{lead} + \text{bromine}$$
$$PbBr(l) \longrightarrow Pb(l) + Br_2(g)$$

Lead bromide is an ionic substance. When it is melted the ions are free to move towards the oppositely charged electrode.

Many ionic substances have very high melting points, which makes electrolysis difficult if not impossible. However some dissolve in water – when this happens the ions are once again free to move. The only complication when substances are in solution is that water also forms ions, and so the products at the electrodes are not always easy to predict.

Covalent compounds cannot be split by electrolysis.

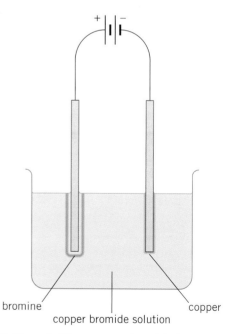

↑ **Figure 3:** When copper bromide is dissolved in water it can be decomposed by electrolysis. The positive copper ions move to the negative electrode and copper metal appears. At the same time the negative bromide ions move to the positive electrode and brown bromine appears:

$$\text{copper bromide} \longrightarrow \text{copper} + \text{bromine}$$
$$CuBr_2(aq) \longrightarrow Cu(s) + Br_2(aq)$$

H **What happens at the electrodes?**

During electrolysis, ions gain or lose electrons at the electrodes. Electrically neutral atoms or molecules are released. The reactions which take place at the electrodes can be shown by **half equations**. This term is used because what happens at one electrode is only half of the story – you need to know what is happening at both the electrodes to understand the whole reaction.

Example 1: Electrolysis of molten lead bromide

When the positive lead ions move to the negative electrode, they gain electrons in a reduction reaction:

$$Pb^{2+} + 2e^- \longrightarrow Pb$$

Similarly when the negative bromide ions move to the positive electrode they lose electrons in an oxidation reaction:

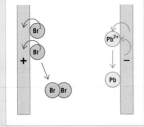

$$2Br^- - 2e^- \longrightarrow Br_2$$

Sometimes oxidation reactions are written with '$+2e^-$' on the right of the arrow instead of '$-2e^-$' on the left.

In this case the alternative half equation is:

$$2Br^- \longrightarrow Br_2 + 2e^-$$

Example 2: Electrolysis of copper bromide solution

At the negative electrode there is a reduction reaction:

$$Cu^{2+} + 2e^- \longrightarrow Cu$$

At the positive electrode there is an oxidation reaction:

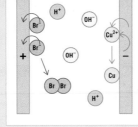

$$2Br^- - 2e^- \longrightarrow Br_2$$

Notice that a reaction in which electrons are gained is called reduction and one in which electrons are lost is called oxidation, even though oxygen itself may not be involved.

As you can see from these equations, the decomposition of ionic substances during electrolysis involves **redox** reactions, with reduction and oxidation taking place at the same time.

? Questions

1 What is meant by the following terms?

   a electrolysis   **b** electrolyte   **c** electrode

2 Solid ionic substances do not conduct electricity. Why do they conduct electricity if melted or dissolved in water?

3 What happens to ionic compounds as an electric current passes through them?

4 Make a table to show which of these ions would move towards the positive electrode and which towards the negative electrode during electrolysis:

   sodium, iodide, zinc, iron, oxide, aluminium, chloride, fluoride, silver.

   (Use the data at the back of the book to help you.)

5 Draw and label a diagram to show what you would expect to happen if molten sodium chloride was electrolysed.

H 6 Complete and balance the following half equations for reactions at electrodes during electrolysis:

   a $Cl^- - e^- \longrightarrow Cl_2$

   b $Mg^{2+} + ... \longrightarrow Mg$

   c $O^{2-} - e^- \longrightarrow O_2$

Key Ideas

⊙ Ionic substances which are dissolved in water or melted can be decomposed into simpler substances by passing an electric current through them. This process is called electrolysis.

⊙ Positively charged ions move to the negative electrode and negatively charged electrons move to the positive electrode.

⊙ At the negative electrode positively charged ions gain electrons (reduction). At the positive electrode negatively charged ions lose electrons (oxidation).

⊙ Neutral atoms or molecules are produced by electrolysis.

⊙ The reactions which take place at the electrodes can be represented by balanced half equations.

4.5 Using electrolysis

It is impossible to extract reactive metals such as aluminium from their ores using reduction reactions (unless highly reactive metals like sodium are used). Since aluminium oxide is insoluble in water and does not melt below 2000 °C, for years extracting aluminium using electrolysis was also almost impossible. Then in 1886 a 21-year-old American student, Charles Hall, found that if he dissolved aluminium oxide in a substance called cryolite (another aluminium compound) the melting point dropped to 850 °C. This much lower temperature made aluminium extraction by electrolysis a realistic possibility.

The extraction of aluminium

There is more aluminium in the Earth's crust than any other metal, and most of it is in the form of bauxite – aluminium oxide mixed with impurities like sand. The first step in the extraction after the ore has been mined is to purify it, to give white aluminium oxide. This is then dissolved in molten cryolite in special steel tanks lined with carbon (graphite), which acts as the negative electrode. Large positive electrodes, also made of graphite, dip into the tank and an electric current is passed through the mixture. Molten aluminium forms at the negative electrode and is run off and collected. Oxygen forms at the positive electrodes. It immediately reacts with the carbon electrodes to form carbon dioxide, burning them away – so they need frequent replacement.

↑ **Figure 1:** Today, using gold and silver tableware like this is the height of luxury. For many years the extraction of reactive metals like aluminium was terribly difficult, so aluminium was very expensive. In the 19th century only the very rich and privileged could afford to use aluminium plates and cutlery – a far cry from our everyday aluminium drinks cans!

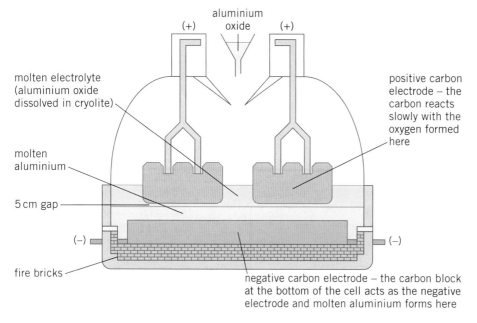

molten electrolyte (aluminium oxide dissolved in cryolite)

molten aluminium

5 cm gap

fire bricks

aluminium oxide

(+)   (+)

positive carbon electrode – the carbon reacts slowly with the oxygen formed here

(−)   (−)

negative carbon electrode – the carbon block at the bottom of the cell acts as the negative electrode and molten aluminium forms here

← **Figure 2:** The extraction of aluminium by electrolysis is still not cheap, as it uses a lot of electricity both for the electrolysis itself and to keep the electrolyte molten.

Why is the extraction of aluminium so important?

Aluminium is a silvery, shiny metal which is surprisingly light – it has a relatively low density for a metal. It is an excellent conductor of heat and electricity and it can be shaped and drawn into wires easily. In addition, although aluminium is a relatively reactive metal, it does not corrode easily. This is because, when aluminium is exposed to air, it immediately reacts with the oxygen in the air to form a thin layer of aluminium oxide (Al_2O_3). This then prevents any further corrosion from taking place, making aluminium more useful than ever.

$$4Al + 3O_2 \longrightarrow 2Al_2O_3$$

Aluminium is not a particularly strong metal when it is pure, but it forms alloys which make it harder, stiffer and stronger so that it makes a good structural material. As a result of all these properties aluminium is an extremely useful metal. It is used for a whole range of goods, from cans, cooking foil and saucepans through to electricity cables, planes and space vehicles.

Purifying metals

Another important use of electrolysis is in purifying metals. For example, when copper is first obtained from its ore it is about 99% pure. The impurities, which include gold, silver and platinum, are enough to affect the ability of copper to conduct electricity, so before it can be used in electric wires it must be purified. A bar of impure copper is used as the positive electrode, and a thin sheet of pure copper is used as the negative electrode. The electrolysis must take place in a solution containing copper ions – usually copper sulphate solution. Copper is lost from the positive electrode – it dissolves – and pure copper is deposited on the negative electrode.

↑ **Figure 3:** Aluminium is present in large amounts in the Earth's crust, and has many different uses. Here it is used in the form of aluminium cladding, covering a sewage treatment plant in Germany.

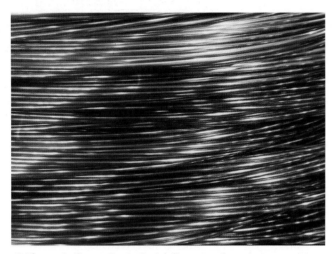

↗ **Figure 4:** To conduct electricity around our homes, copper wires like these are used – so the purification of copper by electrolysis is very important to our everyday lives.

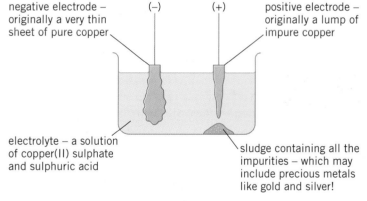

negative electrode – originally a very thin sheet of pure copper

(−)   (+)

positive electrode – originally a lump of impure copper

electrolyte – a solution of copper(II) sulphate and sulphuric acid

sludge containing all the impurities – which may include precious metals like gold and silver!

? Questions

1. Make a flow chart to show the extraction of aluminium from its bauxite ore.

2. Why do the positive carbon electrodes used to extract aluminium need regular replacement, whilst the negative carbon electrode does not?

3. Give five different uses of aluminium and for each use suggest which properties of the metal are important.

4. Once tin has been extracted from its ore it is still contaminated by trace elements and needs to be purified further before it can be used to plate steel cans to make 'tin' cans. Suggest how this could be done.

0ᴛᴛ Key Ideas

- ⊙ Aluminium is extracted from the ore bauxite by electrolysis.
- ⊙ Aluminium oxide is dissolved in molten cryolite in a tank with carbon electrodes.
- ⊙ Molten aluminium is collected at the negative electrode. Oxygen gas is produced which reacts with the positive carbon electrode.
- ⊙ Copper can be purified by electrolysis with an impure copper positive electrode and a pure copper negative electrode.

Using electrolysis

The situation when electrolysis is used on a large industrial scale to extract aluminium from its ore or to purify metals like copper can be represented using half equations, as we saw in Section 4.4.

The reactions at the electrodes in the extraction of aluminium from aluminium oxide (Al_2O_3) are represented by the following half equations.

At the negative electrode, positive ions gain electrons:

$$Al^{3+}(l) + 3e^- \longrightarrow Al(l)$$

At the positive electrode, negative ions lose electrons:

$$2O^{2-}(l) - 4e^- \longrightarrow O_2(g)$$

Similarly the events at the electrodes during the purification of copper are as follows.

At the positive electrode impure copper forms copper ions:

$$Cu(s) - 2e^- \longrightarrow Cu^{2+}(aq)$$

At the negative electrode copper ions form copper metal:

$$Cu^{2+}(aq) + 2e^- \longrightarrow Cu(s)$$

Using half equations

Half equations are very important when we want to calculate the amount of substances formed during electrolysis. For example, in the electrolysis of copper bromide solution, the two half equations for the reactions at the electrodes are:

negative electrode: $Cu^{2+}(aq) + 2e^- \longrightarrow Cu(s)$

positive electrode: $2Br^-(aq) - 2e^- \longrightarrow Br_2(aq)$

Notice how the number of electrons produced (lost) by the bromide ions at the positive electrode is the same as the number of electrons needed by the copper ion at the negative electrode – so these half equations are balanced. We can now use the two half equations in calculations involving the amounts of each substance produced at the electrodes. Suppose that 16 g of bromine are produced at the positive electrode when a solution of copper bromide is being electrolysed. We can calculate how much copper is produced at the negative electrode like this:

The A_r of bromine is 80. Bromine molecules have the formula Br_2, so the M_r of bromine is 2 × 80 = 160.

The number of moles of bromine molecules produced is 16 / 160 = 0.1 moles.

The balanced half equations tell us that for every mole of bromine molecules produced, 1 mole of copper atoms is produced, so if 0.1 moles of bromine molecules are produced, 0.1 moles of copper atoms are also produced.

The A_r of copper is 63, so the mass of copper produced is 0.1 × 63 = 6.3 g.

↑ Figure 1: Thousands of tonnes of aluminium are extracted from bauxite each year – all by the process represented by the half equations shown on the left. The aluminium is often made into sheets and wound onto huge rolls like these.

Sometimes the calculation is a little more difficult. For example, during the production of aluminium, the two half equations involved are:

negative electrode: $Al^{3+}(l) + 3e^- \longrightarrow Al(l)$

positive electrode: $2O^{2-}(l) - 4e^- \longrightarrow O_2(g)$

As it stands these two half equations do not balance – aluminium ions are combining with 3 electrons, while oxygen ions are giving up 4 electrons. For the half equations to balance we must have the same number of electrons in each. To get them to balance in this case we need to multiply the half equation for the negative electrode by 4 and the half equation for the positive electrode by 3:

negative electrode: $4Al^{3+}(l) + 12e^- \longrightarrow 4Al(l)$

positive electrode: $6O^{2-}(l) - 12e^- \longrightarrow 3O_2(g)$

Now the number of electrons produced by the oxide ions at the positive electrode is the same as the number of electrons needed by the aluminium ions at the negative electrode, so we can do the calculation in the same way as before. For example, this is how we calculate the mass of oxygen formed when 5.4 kg of aluminium is produced:

The A_r of aluminium is 27. The mass of aluminium produced is 5.4 kg, which is 5400 g. So the number of moles of aluminium atoms produced is 5400/27 = 200 moles.

The balanced half equations tell us that for every 4 moles of aluminium atoms produced, 3 moles of oxygen molecules are produced, so if 200 moles of aluminium atoms are produced, this will produce $\frac{3}{4} \times 200 = 150$ moles of oxygen molecules.

The A_r of oxygen is 16. Oxygen molecules have the formula O_2, so the M_r of oxygen is 32. This means that the mass of oxygen produced is $150 \times 32 = 4800$ g or 4.8 kg.

Key Ideas

- If we know the mass/volume of a substance produced at one electrode it is possible to predict the mass/volume of substance which will be produced at the other electrode.

? Questions

1 Complete and balance the following half equations for reactions at electrodes during electrolysis:

   a $Br^- - e^- \longrightarrow Br_2$

   b $Cu^{2+} + ... \longrightarrow Cu$

   c $O^{2-} - e^- \longrightarrow O_2$

2 a Write the half equations for the electrolysis of aluminium oxide.

   b During the electrolysis of aluminium oxide 54 g of molten aluminium is collected at the negative electrode. What volume of oxygen would you expect to be given off at the positive electrode?

3 Electrolysis can be used to coat one metal with another. For example, if a fork is used as the negative electrode with a pure silver positive electrode and the electrolyte contains silver ions (eg silver nitrate solution), silver is plated onto the fork.

   a Produce a diagram to show what is happening during the silver plating of a fork.

   b Give half equations for the events at the electrodes when an object is silver plated.

Metals and their ores are not the only useful substances which can be extracted from the rocks of the Earth. Many other minerals come from the Earth's crust and are used in various ways by people. One of the most important is **limestone**.

What is limestone?

What is the link between the food in your local supermarket, cement and blast furnaces? The answer is limestone! Limestone is a white rock made mainly of calcium carbonate ($CaCO_3$) which has been formed over millions of years from the remains of sea organisms such as corals.

↑ **Figure 1:** These white cliffs are made of chalk – one type of limestone, formed from the shells of tiny creatures which secreted calcium carbonate.

Limestone is quarried around the world on an enormous scale, for use in the chemical industry, in agriculture and in the building industry. Sometimes it is used as it is. Often it is treated and undergoes chemical reactions before it is used.

Uses of limestone

One major use of limestone is as a building material. Throughout Europe many large and famous buildings are made of limestone, although sadly some of them are now showing signs of damage by acid rain – the acid reacts with the calcium carbonate and erodes it away.

When limestone is broken into lumps it is used in the blast furnace in the extraction of iron from its ore, reacting with the impurities in the iron to form slag (see Section 4.3).

Finally, when limestone is powdered it has a number of uses. It can be added to lakes and soils to neutralise acidity. It is often added to lakes where the pH has been lowered due to acid rain.

↑ **Figure 2:** St Paul's cathedral is a famous example of a building made out of limestone blocks.

← **Figure 3:** Glass – made using processed limestone – plays an important role in our lives in many ways. It has many practical uses but it can also be used to create objects of great beauty, as shown here.

Processed limestone

Not only is limestone useful in its pure form, it can also be processed in a number of ways to provide a whole range of valuable products.

Powdered limestone can be heated to high temperatures with a mixture of sand and sodium carbonate (soda) to make glass. It has been used in this industry for hundreds of years.

In another, very different use, powdered limestone is roasted with powdered clay in a rotary kiln to produce cement, widely used in the building industry. When this cement powder is mixed with water, sand and crushed rock – which may well be limestone too – a slow chemical reaction takes place which produces a hard, stone-like building material called concrete.

When limestone is heated in a furnace (known as a lime kiln), it breaks down to form **quicklime** (calcium oxide) and carbon dioxide in a type of reaction known as **thermal decomposition**.

$$CaCO_3(s) \longrightarrow CaO(s) + CO_2(g)$$

Many other carbonates behave in the same way.

If water is added to quicklime it produces another calcium compound (calcium hydroxide) known as **slaked lime** or **hydrated lime**.

$$CaO(s) + H_2O(l) \longrightarrow Ca(OH)_2(s)$$

Slaked lime is used in agriculture – farmers 'lime' their land, adding slaked lime to improve the fertility and structure of the soil and to balance the pH if the soil is acidic.

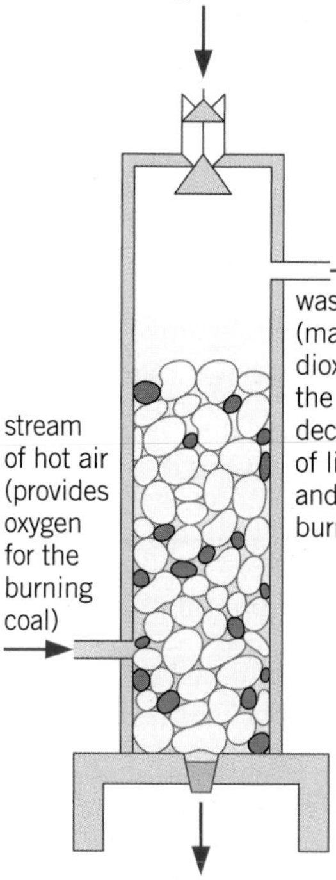

← **Figure 4:** This concrete building (The National Theatre) looks very different to St Paul's cathedral – but both are made largely of limestone!

limestone and coal
(the coal burns to provide the heat, forming carbon dioxide)

waste gases (mainly carbon dioxide from the thermal decomposition of limestone and from the burning coal)

stream of hot air (provides oxygen for the burning coal)

quicklime

↑ **Figure 5:** Quicklime is produced in a lime kiln. A rotary kiln works in the same way, except that the chemicals are heated in a rotating drum to ensure that they are thoroughly mixed with the stream of hot air.

Plants are vital for life on Earth. To grow successfully plants need nitrogen to form proteins, yet they cannot use nitrogen from the air. Although nitrogen gas makes up around 80% of the air around us it is very unreactive and inert, so plants cannot use it. Instead, plants take in soluble nitrates through their roots. These nitrates are then returned to the soil when the plants rot and die.

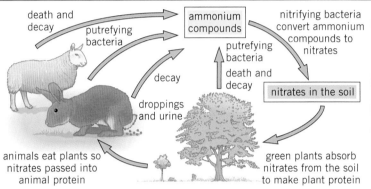

Figure 1: Plants grow surrounded by nitrogen in the air. They need it and yet they cannot use it – they have to rely on nitrates from the soil to supply their needs.

When people harvest plants for food, the nitrates in those plants are not returned to the soil and need to be replaced in some other way to keep the soil fertile. Today this is usually done by using fertilisers which contain nitrates. These were made possible by a process developed by a young German chemist called Fritz Haber at the beginning of the 20th century.

What is the Haber process?

The Haber process provides us with a way of turning the nitrogen in the air into ammonia, a compound with a number of uses. The raw materials are nitrogen from the air and hydrogen obtained from natural gas (methane). The purified gases are passed over an iron catalyst at high temperatures (about 450 °C) and pressures (about 200 atmospheres). The product of the reaction is ammonia. However, this reaction is reversible, which means that the ammonia breaks down again into hydrogen and nitrogen. To reduce this, the ammonia is cooled, liquefied and removed as soon as it is formed. Any hydrogen and nitrogen left is recycled and reacted again.

nitrogen + hydrogen $\rightleftharpoons$ ammonia

$$N_2(g) \ + \ 3H_2(g) \ \underset{\text{iron catalyst}}{\overset{450\,°C,\,200\,atm}{\rightleftharpoons}} \ 2NH_3(g)$$

The reaction conditions for the Haber process are chosen to give a reasonable yield of ammonia as quickly as possible.

H The economics of the Haber process

The industrial version of the Haber process is a compromise designed to make ammonia as rapidly and cheaply as possible. In any manufacturing process the costs must be kept as low as possible to maximise profit when the product is sold. For example, the catalyst which Haber used when he first worked on his process in the laboratory was too expensive, so a cheaper iron catalyst was used for the industrial process.

There are two different factors to consider – the yield of ammonia and the rate of reaction – both of which depend on the reaction conditions. If the reacting temperature is lower, more ammonia is formed in the reacting mixture, but very slowly. Increasing the temperature means that the reaction happens more quickly, but the yield of ammonia is reduced. If the pressure is higher more ammonia is formed in the mixture, but it would be incredibly expensive to build a factory to withstand such very high pressures. The practical solution is to use moderate temperatures and pressures.

Section 9.6 includes more detail on the factors affecting the production of ammonia.

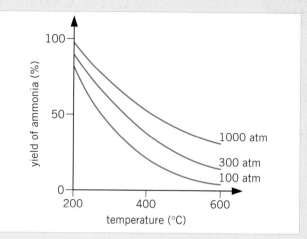

↑ **Figure 2:** The graph shows the effect of different temperatures and pressures on the yield of ammonia in the Haber process.

? Questions

1 a Why is nitrogen so important?

   b Explain why plants and animals cannot simply make use of nitrogen from the air.

   c Explain how nitrogen is moved around in a natural cycle through living organisms.

2 a Draw a flow diagram to show the events of the Haber process.

   b Why is the Haber process so important to us?

 3 a What is the effect on the yield of ammonia if the Haber process operates at:

   i   200 atm and 350 °C

   ii 400 atm and 450 °C

   iii 200atm and 450 °C?

   b Explain how these different conditions affect the rate of the reaction in the Haber process and suggest why the operating conditions were chosen.

0— Key Ideas

⊙ Air is almost 80% nitrogen.

⊙ Ammonia is manufactured in the Haber process from nitrogen in the air and hydrogen from methane gas.

⊙ The conditions of the Haber process are designed to get a reasonable yield of ammonia as rapidly and cheaply as possible.

Much of the ammonia formed from nitrogen by the Haber process is used in further chemical reactions. The main one is the oxidation of ammonia to form nitric acid.

Using ammonia

First, ammonia gas reacts with oxygen in the air in the presence of a hot platinum catalyst. This forms nitrogen monoxide, a colourless gas:

ammonia + oxygen $\longrightarrow$ nitrogen monoxide + water

$$4NH_3(g) + 5O_2(g) \longrightarrow 4NO(g) + 6H_2O(g)$$

The nitrogen monoxide gas is cooled and then reacted with more oxygen and water to form nitric acid solution:

$$6NO(g) + 3O_2(g) + 2H_2O(l) \longrightarrow 4HNO_3(aq) + 2NO(g)$$

The nitric acid produced can then be used in a variety of ways. About 75% is used to make nitrate fertilisers, where the nitric acid is often reacted with more ammonia in a neutralisation reaction to form ammonium nitrate. Another 15% of the nitric acid produced is used to make explosives and the remaining 10% is used in a variety of other manufacturing processes.

Science people

The story of Fritz Haber

Fritz Haber was born in the German town of Breslau in 1868. He became a research chemist and lecturer at the technical college in Karlsruhe. As part of his work in 1908 he discovered a way of combining hydrogen and nitrogen to form ammonia.

By this time Germany was already preparing for the war which would become the First World War. The military leaders realised that once war was declared Germany would be blockaded. This in turn meant that they would need to be self-sufficient in many things, including food and weapons. To grow enough food meant lots of fertiliser, and weapons need explosives.

To make nitrate fertiliser and explosives requires nitric acid, easily made from ammonia. Fritz Haber's simple process was the answer, and he sold it to a major German chemical company. Carl Bosch, a brilliant chemical engineer, then designed a chemical plant which could manufacture ammonia using Haber's process.

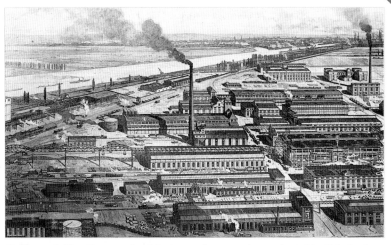

↑ **Figure 1** The thousands of tonnes of ammonia produced in this factory allowed the Germans to feed themselves and make new weapons throughout the First World War.

Haber's process may have prolonged the war, resulting in the loss of hundreds of thousands of lives on all sides. However, since the end of the war, the Haber process has been responsible for the manufacture of millions of tonnes of nitrate fertiliser which improves crop yields and feeds hungry people. Although manufacture of explosives has also continued, far more fertiliser has been made than explosives.

Using nitrogen-based fertilisers

Adding relatively cheap nitrogen-based fertilisers to the soil has been a great advantage to the human race in many ways. In the developed world it has made possible cheap and readily available food for everyone, while in the developing world it is helping to supply more food where it is desperately needed.

↑ **Figure 2:** Nitrogen-based fertilisers have brought us great benefits – but everything has a price… .

However, there are some problems which go with the use of these fertilisers, particularly in the developed world where they are very heavily used. The nitrates from the fertilisers get carried by rainwater into streams, rivers, lakes and groundwater. Once in the waterways they can have two damaging effects. They can cause excess plant growth in the water. When this dies and decays it uses up all the oxygen so that fish and other animals can no longer survive. This is called **eutrophication**.

The nitrate ions also get into the drinking water supply, causing problems for babies and young children. The pollution affects the blood so it does not carry oxygen properly. Small babies can turn blue and even die as a result.

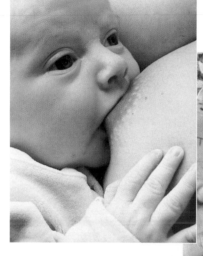

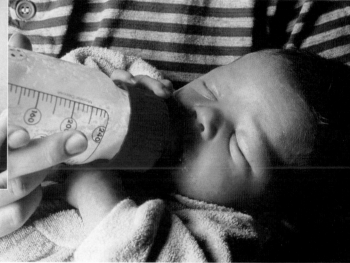

→ **Figure 3:** Bottle-fed babies are most at risk from nitrate pollution as the ions are in the water they are drinking. But even breast-fed babies are not completely safe, as the effects of nitrate ion pollution can reach them through their mother's milk.

? Questions

1 **a** How is nitrogen-based fertiliser made from ammonia?

(H) **b** Give a balanced equation for the reaction between ammonia and nitric acid.

2 **a** The First World War accelerated the industrial application of the Haber process. How?

b Do you think Fritz Haber should have kept his discovery to himself? Give your arguments one way or the other.

3 Imagine that some people are trying to ban the use of nitrate fertilisers on farms in your area. Farmers and others are angry. People are getting very heated on both sides. Produce a leaflet which gives a balanced view of the issues, explaining the benefits and the risks of nitrate fertilisers. Try to devise a solution to the problem which would be acceptable to both sides.

🔑 Key Ideas

- Nitrogen can be used to manufacture several important chemicals, including nitrogen-based fertilisers.
- Ammonia can be oxidised to form nitric acid which is used to make nitrogen-based fertilisers and explosives.
- Nitrates can cause problems if they find their way into streams, rivers or groundwater and contaminate drinking water.

1 Limestone is an important raw material.

a Limestone has many uses. Choose from the list **two** important materials made from limestone.

cement   diesel oil   glass
poly(ethene)   sodium hydroxide
sulphuric acid   (2 marks)

b The diagram shows a lime kiln. The limestone is heated by the burning coal.

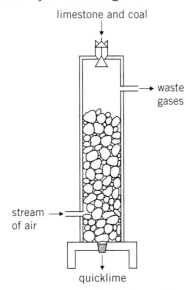

limestone and coal

waste gases

stream of air

quicklime

i Suggest why hot air is blown into the lime kiln.   (1 mark)

ii Give two reactions which produce carbon dioxide in the lime kiln.   (2 marks)

c **i** Quicklime (calcium oxide) can be converted to slaked lime (calcium hydroxide) by adding water.

Write a word equation to represent this reaction.

...... + ... $\longrightarrow$ ......   (1 mark)

ii Why do farmers sometimes add slaked lime to acidic soil?   (1 mark)

(Total 7 marks)
AQA specimen question

2 Ammonium nitrate is used as a fertiliser.

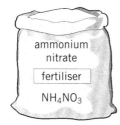

ammonium nitrate

fertiliser

NH_4NO_3

a **i** How many different elements are there in ammonium nitrate?   (1 mark)

ii For its use as a fertiliser, which is the most important element in ammonium nitrate?   (1 mark)

iii Give **one** reason why fertilisers are added to soil.   (1 mark)

b Ammonia, NH_3, is also used as a fertiliser. Ammonia is made from the raw materials air, natural gas and water.

i Which raw material contains nitrogen?   (1 mark)

ii Copy and complete the word equation for the formation of ammonia from its elements:

nitrogen + ... $\rightleftharpoons$ ammonia   (1 mark)

iii What is meant by $\rightleftharpoons$ in the word equation?   (1 mark)

(Total 6 marks)
AQA specimen question

3 **a** Iron can be extracted from iron oxide in a blast furnace.

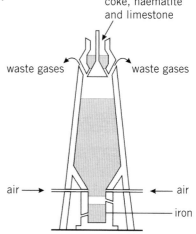

coke, haematite and limestone

waste gases   waste gases

air $\rightarrow$ $\leftarrow$ air

iron

i Which **one** of the substances added to the furnace contains the iron oxide?   (1 mark)

ii Inside the furnace the coke (carbon) burns in air to release heat. Name the type of reaction that transfers heat to the surroundings.   (1 mark)

b Carbon monoxide is formed in the furnace. The carbon monoxide reacts with iron oxide to make iron.

Balance the chemical equation for this reaction:

Fe_2O_3 + ... CO $\longrightarrow$ ... Fe + ... CO_2 (1 mark)

c *To gain full marks you should write down your ideas in good English. Put them into a sensible order and use the correct scientific words.*

Aluminium can be extracted from a mineral called bauxite.

  i Bauxite contains aluminium oxide. Describe how aluminium is extracted from aluminium oxide. (3 marks)

  ii About five thousand years passed between the first extraction of iron and that of aluminium. Explain why. (2 marks)

(Total 8 marks)

AQA specimen question

4 Electrolysis is an important process. During electrolysis, substances made of ions (the electrolyte) can be broken down onto simpler substances by passing an electric current through them. Electrolysis is sometimes used to extract metals from their ores.

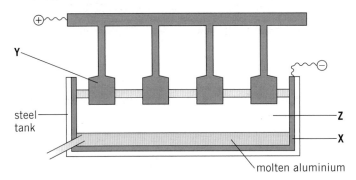

a The diagram shows the apparatus used to extract aluminium metal from its ore, aluminium oxide.

  i What are the parts labelled **X**, **Y** and **Z**? (3 marks)

  ii What is happening at part **X**? (1 mark)

  iii Why does part **Y** have to be replaced regularly? (2 marks)

b Although aluminium is one of the most common metals in the Earth's crust, it has only been extracted easily in useful quantities for a hundred years or so. Why did it take so long before aluminium could be extracted successfully? (3 marks)

c Electrolysis can only be used with ionic substances, and then only when they are either molten or in solution in water. Why is this? (2 marks)

d Give **one** other use of electrolysis in addition to the extraction of metals. (1 mark)

(Total 12 marks)

H 5 Electrolysis can be used in purifying copper, as seen in the diagram.

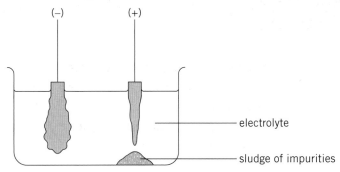

a What is the most commonly used electrolyte in this reaction? (1 mark)

b Explain in words what is happening at the positive electrode. (2 marks)

c Explain in words what is happening at the negative electrode. (2 marks)

d Give half equations for the reactions at:

  i the positive electrode (2 marks)

  ii the negative electrode. (2 marks)

(Total 9 marks)

5.1 The history of the atmosphere

Scientists think that the Earth was formed about 4.5 billion years ago. To begin with it was a molten ball of rock and minerals and for its first billion years it was a very violent place.

The Earth's surface was covered with volcanoes belching fire and smoke into the atmosphere.

The volcanoes released nitrogen and carbon dioxide gas, which formed the early atmosphere, along with water vapour, which condensed as it rose into cooler air and fell as rain to form the first oceans. Comets also brought water to the Earth – as icy comets rained down on the surface of the Earth they melted, adding to the water supplies. Even today many thousands of tonnes of water fall onto the surface of the Earth from space every year.

So as the Earth began to stabilise, the early atmosphere was probably mainly carbon dioxide, with some nitrogen and water vapour and traces of methane and ammonia – in other words, very like the atmospheres which we know exist today on the planets Mars and Venus.

↑ **Figure 1:** Volcanoes moved chemicals from within the Earth to the surface and into the newly forming atmosphere.

← **Figure 2:** The surface of one of Jupiter's moons called Io, with its small atmosphere and active volcanoes. This photograph probably gives us a reasonable glimpse of what our own Earth was like billions of years ago.

🔍 Ideas and Evidence

How do we know what the atmosphere of the early Earth was like? Of course we cannot know for sure! However chemists have reconstructed what they think the atmosphere must have been like, based on evidence from gas bubbles trapped in rocks and from the atmospheres of other planets in the solar system.

The effect of life

After the initial violent years of the history of the Earth the atmosphere remained relatively stable – until life first appeared on Earth. The scientific view is that life on Earth began some 3.4 billion years ago, in the form of simple bacteria-like organisms which could make food for themselves using the breakdown of other chemicals as a source of energy. Later, bacteria and other simple organisms such as algae evolved which could use the energy of the sun to make their own food in the process of photosynthesis with oxygen as a waste product.

By 2 billion years ago the levels of oxygen were rising steadily as algae and bacteria filled the seas, all photosynthesising. More and more plants of increasing complexity evolved, all of them also carrying out photosynthesis and making oxygen:

carbon dioxide + water + [energy from the sun] $\longrightarrow$ sugar + oxygen

When plants had evolved and successfully colonised most of the surface of the Earth, the atmosphere became increasingly rich in oxygen. Conditions were now favourable for the evolution of animals – organisms which could not make their own food and needed oxygen to respire. On the other hand, many of the earliest living microorganisms could not tolerate oxygen (because they had evolved without it) and they largely died out as there were fewer and fewer places where they could live.

↑ **Figure 3:** Some of the first photosynthesising bacteria probably lived in colonies, like these stromatolites. They grew in water and released oxygen into the early atmosphere.

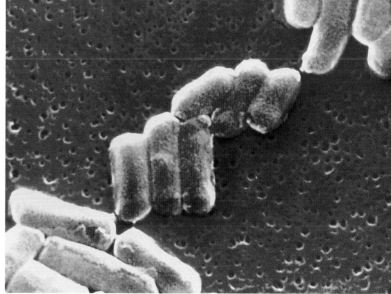

→ **Figure 4:** Bacteria such as these *Clostridium perfringens* not only *do not need* oxygen – they *die* if they are exposed to it. But in decaying tissue and in marshy rotting soil they still survive and breed.

? Questions

1 a How was the atmosphere of the early Earth formed?

  b What were the main gases it contained?

2 Why was there no life on Earth for several billion years?

3 How have we developed our current picture of the early development of the Earth and its atmosphere?

0— Key Ideas

⊙ The first billion years of the Earth's existence was marked by intense volcanic activity.

⊙ This released the gases which formed the early atmosphere and water vapour which condensed to form the oceans.

⊙ As plants colonised the Earth there was more oxygen – and fewer microorganisms which could not tolerate oxygen.

What happened to the atmosphere?

We think that the early atmosphere of the Earth contained a great deal of carbon dioxide, yet the modern atmosphere of the Earth has only around 0.04% of this gas. Where has it all gone? The answer is mostly into living organisms and into the materials which are derived from living organisms.

Carbon dioxide is taken up by plants and turned into new plant material during photosynthesis. Then animals eat the plants and the carbon is transferred to the animal tissues, including bones, teeth and shells. Over millions of years ago the dead bodies of huge numbers of these living organisms accumulated at the bottom of vast oceans where they formed sedimentary carbonate rocks like limestone. Some were crushed by movements of the Earth and heated within the crust and they formed fossil fuels such as coal and oil. In this way much of the carbon dioxide from the ancient atmosphere became locked up within the Earth's crust.

Carbon dioxide also dissolved in the oceans, forming insoluble carbonate compounds which fell to the bottom and helped to form carbonate rocks.

At the same time, the small amounts of ammonia and methane remaining in the atmosphere reacted with the oxygen formed by the plants. The oxygen removed these poisonous gases and the levels of nitrogen and carbon dioxide increased.

$$CH_4 + 2O_2 \longrightarrow CO_2 + 2H_2O$$

$$4NH_3 + 3O_2 \longrightarrow 2N_2 + 6H_2O$$

By 200 million years ago the proportions of the different gases in the atmosphere of the Earth were very much the same as they are now (see Figure 3).

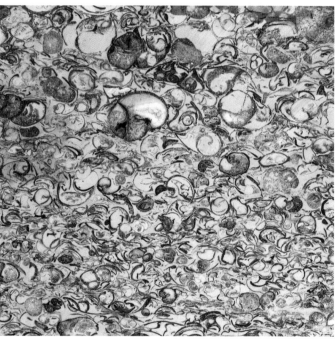

↑ **Figure 1:** Carbonate rocks contain clear evidence of organisms which lived millions of years ago. This piece of Bethersden Marble contains specimens of *Viviparus elongatus* that lived in the Cretaceous period. Along with the dinosaurs, they are now preserved with their ancient carbon in the structure of our rocks.

H The nitrogen gas in the atmosphere came partly from the reaction between ammonia and oxygen (above). But the main source of nitrogen in the air was the action of bacteria on the cells of dead and decaying plants and animals. The nitrogen-containing compounds (mainly proteins) in the bodies of plants and animals are broken down and nitrogen is released into the air. The bacteria bringing about this release of nitrogen are known as **denitrifying bacteria**.

The oxygen released into the atmosphere by plants was vital for the development of animal life. It also resulted in the formation of an ozone layer in the upper atmosphere (ozone is three oxygen atoms joined together, O_3). This was another important step in the evolution of life on Earth, because the ozone layer filters out some of the harmful ultraviolet radiation from the sun. The presence of the ozone layer made it possible for a much wider variety of new living organisms to evolve, because they did not need to be able to withstand so much ultraviolet radiation. ↓

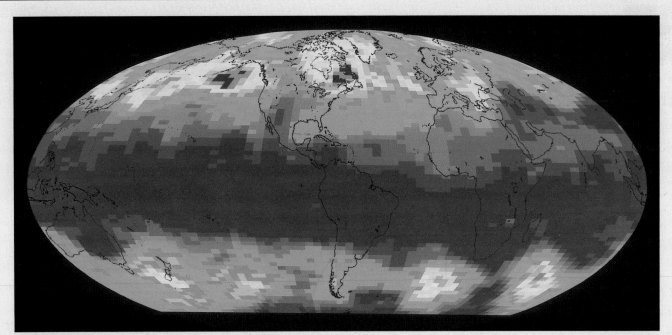

↑ **Figure 2:** This computer-enhanced image shows how the thickness of the ozone layer varies around the Earth. The ozone layer still protects the Earth from harmful ultraviolet radiation, although human activities are damaging it and reducing the protection it gives.

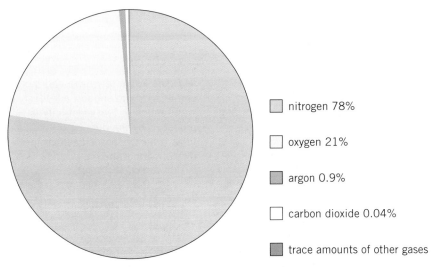

- nitrogen 78%
- oxygen 21%
- argon 0.9%
- carbon dioxide 0.04%
- trace amounts of other gases

↑ **Figure 3:** The relative proportions of nitrogen, oxygen and other gases in the atmosphere.

? Questions

1 What are the main gases which make up the atmosphere of the Earth?

2 How has the carbon dioxide which we think made up a large proportion of the early atmosphere of the Earth become a substantial part of the modern Earth's crust?

H 3 Explain the role of living organisms in determining the proportions of nitrogen, oxygen and ozone in the modern atmosphere.

⊙ᴛᴛ Key Ideas

- Most of the carbon from the carbon dioxide in the air became locked up in fossil fuels and sedimentary rocks like carbonates.

- Methane and ammonia in the air reacted with the oxygen.

- For 200 million years the proportions of the different gases in the atmosphere have stayed stable.

- Nitrogen gas was also released into the air by the action of denitrifying bacteria.

- The ozone layer formed from oxygen and protects against ultraviolet radiation.

The carbon cycle

Over thousands of years, the levels of carbon dioxide in the atmosphere have probably remained fairly stable due to the natural carbon cycle, in which carbon moves between oceans, rocks and atmosphere.

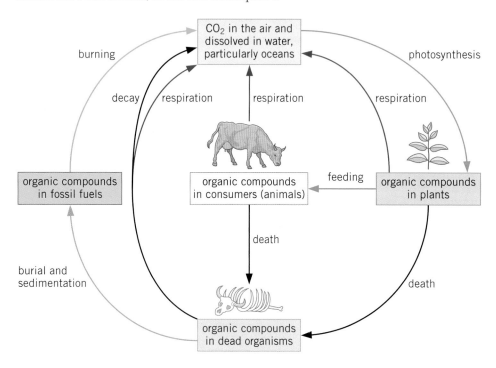

← **Figure 1:** The carbon cycle in nature has maintained the atmospheric level of carbon dioxide for 200 million years.

Left to itself, the carbon cycle is self-regulating. The oceans act as massive reservoirs of carbon dioxide, absorbing excess when it is produced and releasing it when it is in short supply. Plants also soak up excess carbon dioxide from the atmosphere. The plants and oceans are often called carbon dioxide **sinks**.

Carbon dioxide moves back into the atmosphere from the respiration of living things and also from volcanoes. Carbonate rocks are sometimes moved deep into the Earth by geological activity – the movements of the Earth's crust. If that rock then becomes involved in volcanic activity, the heat causes the breakdown of the carbonates and the release of carbon dioxide gas as the volcano erupts.

↓ **Figure 2:** We rely more and more on electricity to support our lifestyles – and much of that electricity is produced by the burning of fossil fuels, which releases carbon dioxide into the atmosphere.

The changing balance

Over the last 50 or so years people have increased the amount of carbon dioxide released into the atmosphere tremendously. Burning fossil fuels to produce electricity, heat homes and power cars has enormously increased carbon dioxide production.

There is no doubt that the levels of carbon dioxide in the atmosphere are increasing. The data shown in Figure 3 were collected from a mountain top in Hawaii. The annual fluctuations in the levels of carbon dioxide are due to seasonal differences in plants and show how important plants are for 'fixing' carbon dioxide and removing it from the atmosphere. The overall trend for the 30 years has been relentlessly upwards.

The balance between the carbon dioxide produced and the carbon dioxide which can be absorbed by carbon dioxide sinks is a very important one to maintain. When fossil fuels are burned, carbon which was locked up hundreds of millions of years ago in the bodies of living animals is released as carbon dioxide into the atmosphere. For example:

propane + oxygen $\longrightarrow$ carbon dioxide + water

$$C_3H_8 + 5O_2 \longrightarrow 3CO_2 + 4H_2O$$

As the carbon dioxide levels go up, so the reaction between carbon dioxide and sea water increases, resulting in the formation of insoluble carbonates (mainly calcium carbonate) which are deposited as sediment on the bottom of the ocean and soluble hydrogencarbonates (mainly calcium and magnesium) which simply remain in solution in the sea water. In this way the seas and oceans act as a buffer, absorbing excess carbon dioxide but releasing it if necessary. However, this buffering system cannot cope quickly enough to deal with all the additional carbon dioxide currently being poured out into the atmosphere.

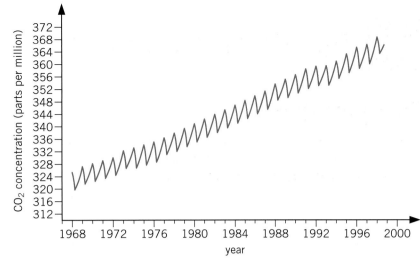

↑ **Figure 3:** The carbon dioxide levels in the atmosphere have been steadily climbing for many years.

? Questions

1 a How does carbon dioxide move into and out of the atmosphere?

b What has caused the current increase in the levels of carbon dioxide in the atmosphere?

2 Use the data in Figure 3 to answer these questions.

a What was the approximate concentration of carbon dioxide in the atmosphere in 1984?

b By how much did the level of carbon dioxide in the atmosphere increase between 1968 and the year 2000?

c Express your answer to part b as a percentage of the carbon dioxide concentration in the year 1968.

d Produce a bar chart to show the carbon dioxide levels in the years 1970, 1980, 1990 and 2000.

3 a Explain how the seas and oceans normally act as a buffer when extra carbon dioxide is produced.

b What has happened in the last 50 years or so which means that the ocean carbon dioxide sinks can no longer cope?

0—π Key Ideas

⊙ Levels of gases such as carbon dioxide have been largely self-regulating.

⊙ In recent years levels of carbon dioxide have increased as a result of the excess burning of fossil fuels.

⊙ Carbonate rocks may release carbon dioxide through volcanic activity.

⊙ The burning of fossil fuels is increasing the level of carbon dioxide in the atmosphere beyond the ability of the oceans to absorb the excess.

The record of the rocks

The rocks which make up the Earth's crust hold many clues to the history of the Earth. They have fossils which help us build up a picture of the evolution of life on Earth, they contain radioactive elements which enable us to estimate the age of the Earth itself, and within the patterns of the rocks and the gases contained in them is the story of the way the Earth has formed and changed over the millennia.

The three main types of rock are:

⊙ **igneous** – formed from molten magma (eg *quartz*, *granite*, and *basalt*)

⊙ **metamorphic** – formed from other rocks by the extremely high temperatures and pressures under the surface of the Earth (eg *marble* from limestone, *slate* from shale)

⊙ **sedimentary** – formed when fossils and the weathered fragments of other rocks are deposited in layers, usually under the sea (eg *limestone*, *sandstone* and *shale*).

These three different types of rock continually change from one type to another in a slow cycle lasting millions of years – a process known as the *rock cycle*.

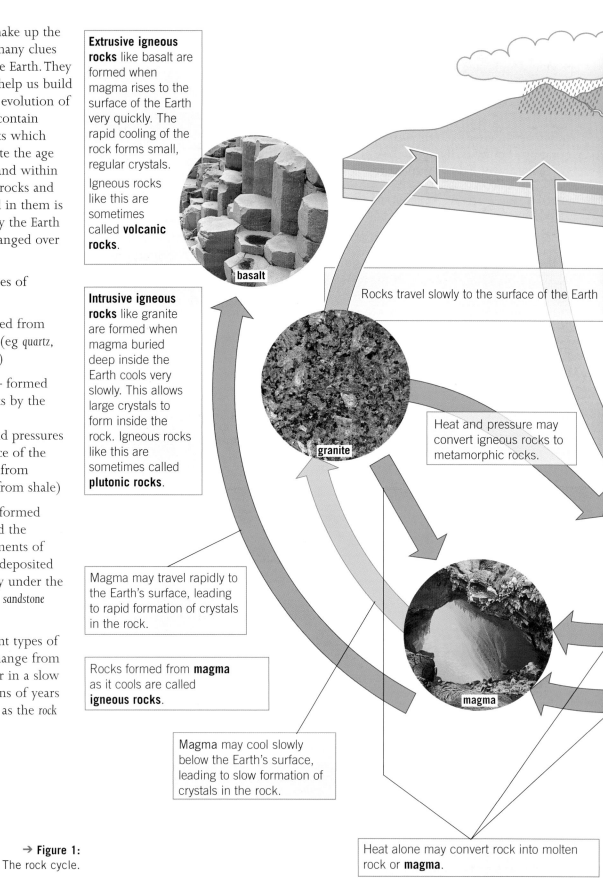

Extrusive igneous rocks like basalt are formed when magma rises to the surface of the Earth very quickly. The rapid cooling of the rock forms small, regular crystals.

Igneous rocks like this are sometimes called **volcanic rocks**.

basalt

Intrusive igneous rocks like granite are formed when magma buried deep inside the Earth cools very slowly. This allows large crystals to form inside the rock. Igneous rocks like this are sometimes called **plutonic rocks**.

granite

magma

Rocks travel slowly to the surface of the Earth

Heat and pressure may convert igneous rocks to metamorphic rocks.

Magma may travel rapidly to the Earth's surface, leading to rapid formation of crystals in the rock.

Rocks formed from **magma** as it cools are called **igneous rocks**.

Magma may cool slowly below the Earth's surface, leading to slow formation of crystals in the rock.

Heat alone may convert rock into molten rock or **magma**.

→ **Figure 1:**
The rock cycle.

Rocks are subject to **weathering** and **erosion** at the Earth's surface. These processes break the rock up into tiny pieces which are transported as sediments by rivers. Eventually the sediments end up in the Earth's oceans and lakes.

As layers of sediment are submerged beneath more and more layers above them, they become compacted due to the weight of material above them. Water carrying dissolved minerals may seep into the spaces between the layers. The minerals crystallise between the layers, holding them together. This is called **cementation**.

As a result of burial and cementation, the layers of sediment become converted into **sedimentary rock** – a process called **lithification**.

in a process called **uplift**.

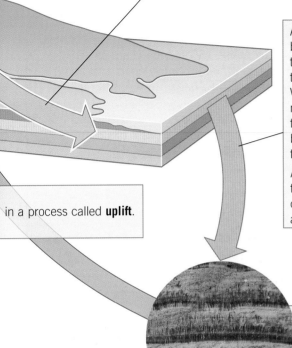

sandstone

marble

Sedimentary rocks include shale, sandstone, mudstone and limestone. Often the sediment is tiny bits of broken rocks, such as the silica which makes up sandstone. In other cases it is the shells of millions upon millions of living creatures from early seas which make up limestone. Clearly defined layers in a sedimentary rock show that the deposition was discontinuous – there was a break in the laying down of the material. Some sedimentary deposits even show ripple marks or wave patterns in the rock, showing how the original sediments were deposited by water.

When **sedimentary rocks** are subjected to high temperatures and pressures they are turned into **metamorphic rocks**. Different temperatures and pressures cause different changes in the crystal structures inside the rock. For example, at relatively low temperatures shale becomes slate, while at higher temperatures it may become schist or gneiss.

Marble is a very common metamorphic rock, produced from limestone. It is used in many buildings, and for statues.

Key Ideas

- There are three main types of rock – igneous, metamorphic and sedimentary.

- These three types of rock slowly change from one type to another in a process called the rock cycle.

- Sedimentary rocks contain evidence of how they were deposited.

Questions

1 Produce a table to show the main types of rocks, how they are formed, and examples of each type.

2 a What is the difference between extrusive and intrusive igneous rock?

   b What conditions are needed to form metamorphic rocks?

   c What is magma?

3 Summarise the rock cycle in a flow chart, starting with the weathering of rocks at the Earth's surface and finishing with the formation of two types of igneous rock.

It may seem that the crust of the Earth is solid and unmoving, but below its surface the Earth teems with restless activity causing great areas of the crust, known as **tectonic plates**, to constantly move across the surface.

Q Ideas and Evidence

According to the theory of plate tectonics, the continents of the Earth were once joined together as one land mass. Figure 1 shows the vast 'supercontinent' of Pangaea which is believed to have existed up until about 200 million years ago. Slowly Pangaea split in two, forming the northern continent of Laurasia and the southern continent of

Gondwanaland by about 160 million years ago. The land masses continued to move apart and about 100 million years ago they began to resemble the map of the world we know today. Evidence for these ideas comes from the similarity of the fossils and rock structures found on the east coast of South America and the west coast of Africa.

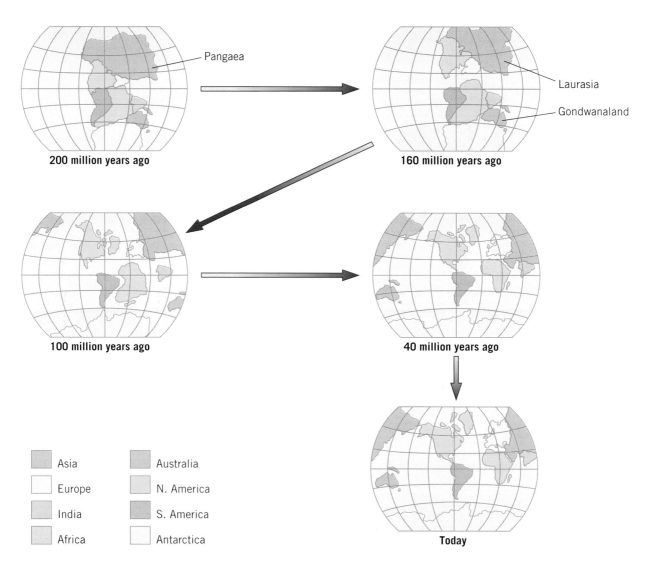

200 million years ago — Pangaea

160 million years ago — Laurasia, Gondwanaland

100 million years ago

40 million years ago

Today

Legend:
- Asia
- Europe
- India
- Africa
- Australia
- N. America
- S. America
- Antarctica

↑ **Figure 1:** The break-up of Pangaea into Laurasia and Gondwanaland led eventually to the formation of the land masses we recognise today. Notice how, 100 million years ago, India was still moving rapidly northwards to take up the position it occupies today. The collision between India and the continent of Asia produced the mountain range we call the Himalayas.

Movements of the tectonic plates are very slow – only a few centimetres a year – but they are unbelievably powerful. They are caused by radioactive decay deep within the Earth which produces vast amounts of energy. This energy heats up magma (molten rock) which expands, becomes less dense and rises towards the surface, being replaced by cooler material. It is these *convection currents* which push the tectonic plates over the surface of the Earth. The slow but large-scale movements of the tectonic plates have caused mountain ranges to be formed over millions of years and ancient mountain belts to disappear – we only know they existed because of the tell-tale record left behind in the rocks.

When tectonic plates collide they buckle at the edges as one plate is forced under the other. Where they buckle at the edges under the force of the collision they form mountain ranges, as great folds are formed which sink and rise again. The Alps were formed when Africa collided with Europe, while the Himalayas, which formed when India crashed into Asia 45 million years ago, are still rising as the two plates continue to push together – although only by about 5 mm each year. Depending on the type of rocks present in the Earth's crust in any one place, sometimes the crust does not fold – it simply shears to give a fault and a block mountain which is pushed up as a whole single block.

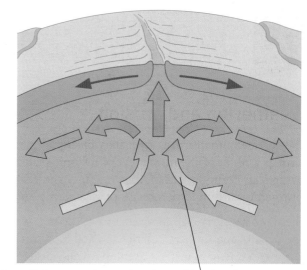

Hot magma rises and cools, pushing the plates apart.

↑ **Figure 2:** Radioactive decay deep within the Earth provides the energy which drives the tectonic plates over the Earth's surface.

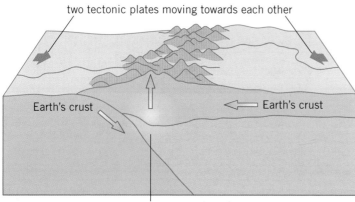

two tectonic plates moving towards each other

Earth's crust

Earth's crust

As the two plates push against each other, powerful forces produce high temperatures and enormous pressures. These melt the rock, and produce magma, which forces its way upwards, producing mountain ranges.

← **Figure 3:** The enormous temperatures and pressures which result from the formation of mountain ranges cause fundamental changes in the rocks making up the crust.

When mountain ranges are forming in this way, conditions of enormous heat and pressure build up within the rocks – up to 400 °C and 100 times atmospheric pressure. In these conditions the texture and mineral structure of both igneous rocks and sedimentary rocks may be changed *without* the rock ever becoming molten. Rocks which are changed in this way are known as metamorphic rocks, and the presence of such rocks is seen as evidence of mountain-building activity during the history of the Earth.

? Questions

1 The tectonic plates continue to move, even today. Sketch a diagram to show how you think the continents might be arranged on the surface of the Earth in 60 million years time. Label your sketch clearly to explain your ideas.

2 The presence of metamorphic rock is taken to show the presence of mountain-forming activity at some time in the history of the Earth. Why is this?

0━ᴍ Key Ideas

⊙ Large scale movements of the Earth's crust cause mountain ranges to form very slowly over millions of years. These replace older mountain ranges worn down by weathering and erosion.

⊙ Metamorphic rocks are associated with Earth movements which created present-day and ancient mountain belts. They are formed as a result of the very high temperatures and pressures produced when tectonic plates push against each other.

Weathering and erosion

The surface of the Earth is constantly changing as new mountains and valleys form as a result of the movement of tectonic plates. At the same time as new features are forming, old mountain ranges and rocks are worn away and returned to dust in the processes of weathering and erosion.

These processes happen in several ways. The rain washes material away, ice forces open cracks and the wind carries soil and loose rock particles away. Acid rain dissolves some rock material, setting up chemical erosion. Sand particles carried in the wind, particularly in desert and coastal regions, wear away rocks. Water in the form of rivers and the sea wears away massive amounts of rock, forming valleys, and glaciers do even more damage. Trampling by people and animals also adds to the damage. The result of all this weathering and erosion is that rocks which we would otherwise be quite unaware of become exposed on the surface of the Earth. At the same time, much of the material removed by weathering is deposited as sediments to begin the process of formation of sedimentary rocks all over again (see the rock cycle in Section 5.4).

Figure 1: A zeugen (above) is a mushroom shaped rock which results from the blasting effect of sand blown along by the wind about a metre above the ground, or the action of sea water or melting glaciers. On Dartmoor (left), piles of granite are left exposed after wind and rain have worn away the hillside that once surrounded them. These are both clear examples of the effect weathering and erosion can have on rocks.

The moving crust

As the Earth's surface is eroded away, younger sedimentary rocks are usually found lying on top of older rocks. However sometimes sedimentary rock layers are found which are tilted, folded, fractured (faulted) and even turned upside down. When these layers are exposed as a result of weathering, they demonstrate very clearly that the Earth's crust is unstable and that it has been subjected to very large forces as it has moved and twisted. Often the movement of the sedimentary rock layers brings fossils to the surface – fossils which would otherwise remain hidden, buried deep within the crust of the Earth. By dating the rocks we can learn when the Earth movements occurred.

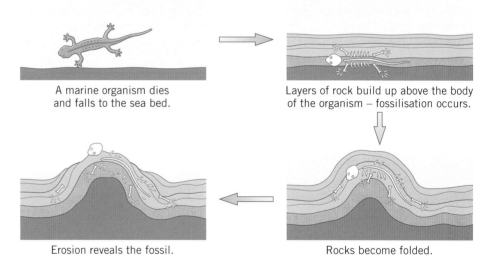

A marine organism dies and falls to the sea bed.

Layers of rock build up above the body of the organism – fossilisation occurs.

Rocks become folded.

Erosion reveals the fossil.

A fault happens when two plates in the Earth's crust move in different directions. The relative movement may be vertical or horizontal, and sometimes it is even a combination of the two. When plates move relative to each other in this way the Earth's crust breaks, causing a **fracture**. The size of this fracture can range from virtually nothing up to several hundred kilometres (see Figure 4). Usually the movement

Figure 2: The tilted and folded layers of sedimentary rock not only tell us what has been happening to the Earth's crust – they can also reveal some of the secrets of early life on Earth, like this fossil shrimp which lived on Earth about 150 million years ago.

along a fault line is imperceptible, amounting to no more than a few centimetres in a year. Despite the slow rate of movement, over millions of years motion along a fault can displace rocks over many thousands of metres, producing mountains, valleys and other large features in the landscape.

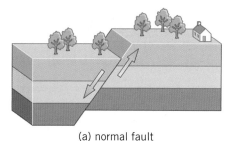 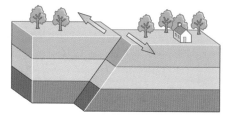

(a) normal fault   (b) strike-slip fault

↑ **Figure 3:** Different types of movement in the Earth's crust produce different types of fault.

Another common feature in the landscape is the **folding** of rocks, most easily seen where layers of sedimentary rock have been exposed. Where folding has occurred the landscape resembles a crumpled piece of cloth – the upward folds are called anticlines, while the downward folds are called synclines. Folding comes about as rocks are subjected to pressures produced as tectonic plates push together. Although rocks are brittle and will shatter if deformed quickly, if the same deformation happens over a long period of time the rocks will fold and flow as if they are made of a soft material like plasticene.

↑ **Figure 4:** The San Andreas fault extends the length of California and is responsible for major earthquakes. This photograph shows the fault 300 miles south of San Francisco, where it is at its most spectacular.

↑ **Figure 5:** These cliffs in Dorset show an anticlinal fold produced by enormous compression forces within the Earth's crust. These forces were produced in the collision between the African and European plates.

🔍 Ideas and Evidence

Earthquakes

While deformation of the Earth's crust usually happens over long periods of time, sometimes the forces produced by the relative movement of the tectonic plates are large enough to cause huge movements over periods of just a few seconds. The result of these large movements is an earthquake, where two parts of the crust move in completely different directions, setting off a series of waves which travel vast distances through the Earth and causing large amounts of damage. Earthquakes have caused human suffering on a vast scale since ancient times – an earthquake in 1556 in Shaanxi province in China killed about 800000 people, one of the largest natural disasters in the history of the world.

? Questions

1 a Describe three different ways (excluding chemical erosion) in which weathering and erosion might come about.

   b In chemical erosion, acid rain (often dilute sulphuric acid) attacks rocks such as limestone. Give a chemical equation for this reaction and use it to explain how acid rain erodes rocks.

2 Why are the processes of weathering and erosion so important:

   a in the build-up of knowledge about the history of the Earth

   b in the formation of new rocks?

3 How can scientists use information such as the presence of a particular type of rock or the angle of a particular line of sediment to help them understand the history of the Earth?

0-m Key Ideas

⊙ Weathering and erosion can wear down whole mountain ranges and often reveal evidence in the rocks of events millions of years ago.

⊙ Younger sedimentary rocks usually lie on top of older rocks but the layers can be found tilted, fractured and even turned upside down as a result of large forces in the unstable crust of the Earth.

1 The diagram shows the different rocks in a section through part of the Earth's crust.

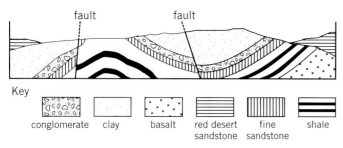

fault   fault

Key

conglomerate   clay   basalt   red desert   fine   shale
                             sandstone   sandstone

Most of the rocks are sedimentary rocks.

The deeper a sedimentary rock, the older it usually is.

a The diagram below shows the rocks in order of their ages. Using the information on the diagram above, give the correct names for the rocks **A**, **B**, **C** and **D**. (2 marks)

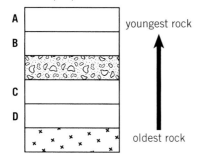

A
B   youngest rock

C

D
                      oldest rock

b The layers of rock are folded. What does this tell us about the Earth's crust in the region?
(2 marks)
(Total 4 marks)
AQA specimen question

2

The volcanoes Merapi and Mount St Helens are situated where tectonic plates push towards each other – they are called **convergent plate volcanoes**. The volcanoes Erta Ale and Surtsey are found where tectonic plates are moving apart – they are called **divergent plate volcanoes**.

a Why are volcanoes generally found at the boundaries between tectonic plates? (2 marks)

The table shows the temperatures and the relative amounts of gases given off by these four volcanoes.

	Convergent plate volcanoes		Divergent plate volcanoes	
	Merapi	Mount St Helens	Erta Ale	Surtsey
temperature (°C)	915	800	1030	1125
carbon dioxide	7.07	6.64	17.16	9.29
carbon monoxide	0.16	0.06	0.75	0.69
sulphur dioxide	1.15	0.21	9.46	4.12
sulphur	0.08	0.004	0.59	0.25

b How does the temperature of the gases produced by the convergent plate volcanoes compare to the temperature of the gases produced by the divergent plate volcanoes?
(2 marks)

c i Calculate how much carbon dioxide and carbon monoxide is produced by each volcano. (1 mark)

ii Is there a pattern in the amount of these gases produced by the two types of volcanoes? (2 marks)

d i Calculate how much sulphur dioxide and sulphur is produced by each volcano. (1 mark)

ii Is there a pattern in the amount of these gases produced by the two types of volcanoes? (2 marks)
(Total 10 marks)

3 The pie charts show the composition of the gases in the atmosphere of a planet, **A** shortly after the planet was formed and **B** many millions of years later.

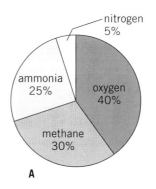

nitrogen 5%
ammonia 25%
oxygen 40%
methane 30%

A

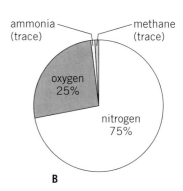

ammonia (trace)
methane (trace)
oxygen 25%
nitrogen 75%

B

a How did the atmosphere of the planet change in the period between pie chart **A** and pie chart **B**? (2 marks)

b How might the evolution of plant life on the planet have brought about this change? (4 marks)

c Copy and complete the equations showing the chemical reactions taking place in the atmosphere, making sure that the equations are balanced:

   i $CH_4 + ... \longrightarrow CO_2 + ...$ (1 mark)

   ii $NH_3 + ... \longrightarrow N_2 + ...$ (1 mark)

(Total 8 marks)

4 The **rock cycle** describes how rocks change from one type to another over millions of years.

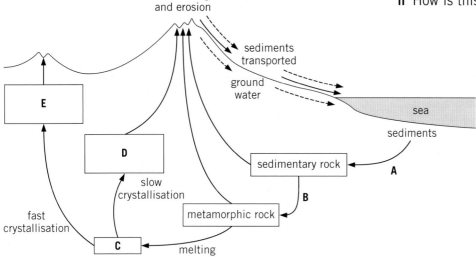

a What are the conditions needed to produce sedimentary rock at **A**? (1 mark)

b What conditions are needed to produce metamorphic rock at **B**? (1 mark)

c When metamorphic rock melts what is formed at **C**? (1 mark)

d When **C** cools slowly, what type of rock is formed at **D**? (1 mark)

e When **C** cools quickly, what type of rock is formed at **E**? (1 mark)

(Total 5 marks)

5 Two rock samples from different places on a volcanic island have the same chemical composition.

When viewed under a microscope, the two samples contain crystals of very different sizes.

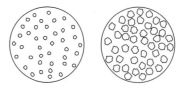

a **i** What name is given to rocks which contain very small crystals? (1 mark)

   ii How is this type of rock formed? (2 marks)

b **i** What name is given to rocks which contains large crystals? (1 mark)

   ii How is this type of rock formed? (2 marks)

(Total 6 marks)

One of the driving forces behind the work of chemists throughout the ages has been to try and find a sense of order within the vast number of chemical substances around them. This eventually led to the development of the periodic table of the elements.

The story of the periodic table

Imagine trying to understand chemistry with no knowledge of atoms, everybody using different names for the same chemical compounds and many of the elements completely unknown – not an easy task!

During the 19th century new elements were being identified almost every year. At the same time, chemists were trying harder and harder to find a pattern amongst them, which would allow them to organise and understand them better. John Dalton first suggested organising the elements in order of increasing mass, and then in 1863 John Newlands came forward with his **law of octaves** (an octave in music is eight notes). He was working on the observation that the properties of every eighth element seemed similar. He produced a table of his octaves, but he was so determined to make it hang together that he made several vital mistakes. He assumed that all the elements had been found – in spite of the fact that new ones were still turning up regularly – and filled in his octaves regardless of the fact that some of his elements were not similar at all. He even put two elements in the same place at some points, to make everything fit in. So the scientific community ridiculed him.

Earlier, in 1862, a Frenchman by the name of Alexandre-Emile Beguyer de Chancourtois had come up with a very good first version of the periodic table. He showed clear similarities between every eighth element and produced a clear diagram to demonstrate this. Unfortunately when his work was published the diagram was missed out. Without it his ideas were quite difficult to understand – so he was largely ignored and the fame of discovering the periodic table was left to others.

↑ **Figure 1:** Iodine – just one of the many elements which were being discovered in the 19th century.

→ **Figure 2:** A fellow scientist commented that an alphabetical arrangement of the elements would probably produce as many similarities as John Newlands' carefully arranged octaves!

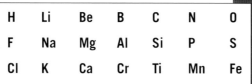

H	Li	Be	B	C	N	O
F	Na	Mg	Al	Si	P	S
Cl	K	Ca	Cr	Ti	Mn	Fe

Newlands' octaves

John Newlands

Finally, in 1869 the Russian scientist Dmitri Mendeleev cracked the problem. He arranged all of the 50 known elements of the time into a table. He placed them in the order of their atomic mass, and then arranged them so that a periodic pattern in their physical and chemical properties could be seen. His stroke of genius was to leave gaps for elements which were still to be discovered, predicting what their properties should be from his table. This was a tremendous publicity coup! A few years later, new elements were discovered with properties which matched almost exactly with Mendeleev's predictions – the case was won, and Dmitri Mendeleev went down in history as the man who first developed the periodic table.

↓ **Figure 3:** It was the gaps which Mendeleev left in his periodic table – and the excitement which arose when they were filled – which meant that his peers took notice and recognised the value of his work.

From mass to number

Using the relative atomic mass of elements was the only option available to Mendeleev – the results it gave were good enough for the patterns to be recognised and accepted, but it had limitations. Although most of the elements are placed in the appropriate group using relative atomic mass, a few of them are not. For example, argon atoms have a greater atomic mass than potassium atoms. This meant that in Mendeleev's table, argon (an unreactive gas) was grouped with extremely reactive metals such as sodium and lithium, while potassium (an extremely reactive metal) was grouped with the unreactive gases. So argon fits better in front of potassium in the periodic table in terms of its properties. Discrepancies like this meant scientists felt that Mendeleev's table was not 100% reliable.

Once the structure of the atom was better understood, the modern periodic table was developed. We arrange the elements in order of their atomic (proton) number. This puts them all in exactly the right place and their patterns of physical and chemical properties reflect this. Now we have a reliable tool which provides us with an important summary of the structure of the atoms of all the elements.

Mendeleev's periodic table

Dmitri Mendeleev

? Questions

1 **a** What did Newlands base his classification on?

  b How was this different to the basis of Mendeleev's classification?

2 The development of an accurate periodic table has depended on the growth of chemical knowledge. Explain how the development of ideas in chemistry made the development of the modern periodic table possible.

3 Why has the periodic table been regarded as a reliable source of information since it has been based on the atomic number of elements?

4 As new elements have been discovered they have taken the places already waiting for them in the periodic table. How is this useful for scientists?

0— Key Ideas

⊙ In the early periodic table developed by Dmitri Mendeleev the chemical elements were arranged in order of the relative atomic masses of their elements.

⊙ Ordering by atomic mass results in some elements being misplaced.

⊙ In the modern periodic table the elements are arranged in order of their atomic (proton) number.

Group 0

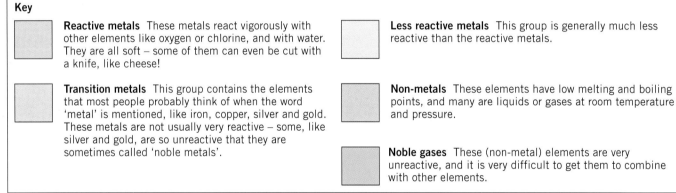

Groups

		mass number ─┐1			**Groups**					
1	**2**	atomic (proton) number ─┘1 H		**3**	**4**	**5**	**6**	**7**	He 2	

7 Li 3	9 Be 4													11 B 5	12 C 6	14 N 7	16 O 8	19 F 9	20 Ne 10
23 Na 11	24 Mg 12													27 Al 13	28 Si 14	31 P 15	32 S 16	35 Cl 17	40 Ar 18
39 K 19	40 Ca 20	45 Sc 21	48 Ti 22	51 V 23	52 Cr 24	55 Mn 25	56 Fe 26	59 Co 27	59 Ni 28	63 Cu 29	64 Zn 30	70 Ga 31	73 Ge 32	75 As 33	79 Se 34	80 Br 35	84 Kr 36
85 Rb 37	88 Sr 38	89 Y 39	91 Zr 40	93 Nb 41	96 Mo 42	Tc 43	101 Ru 44	103 Rh 45	106 Pd 46	108 Ag 47	112 Cd 48	115 In 49	119 Sn 50	122 Sb 51	128 Te 52	127 I 53	131 Xe 54
133 Cs 55	137 Ba 56	139 La 57	178 Hf 72	181 Ta 73	184 W 74	186 Re 75	190 Os 76	192 Ir 77	195 Pt 78	197 Au 79	201 Hg 80	204 Tl 81	207 Pb 82	209 Bi 83	Po 84	At 85	Rn 86
Fr 87	226 Ra 88	227 Ac 89															

Elements 58–71 and 90–103 (all metals) have been omitted.

Key

☐ **Reactive metals** These metals react vigorously with other elements like oxygen or chlorine, and with water. They are all soft – some of them can even be cut with a knife, like cheese!

☐ **Transition metals** This group contains the elements that most people probably think of when the word 'metal' is mentioned, like iron, copper, silver and gold. These metals are not usually very reactive – some, like silver and gold, are so unreactive that they are sometimes called 'noble metals'.

☐ **Less reactive metals** This group is generally much less reactive than the reactive metals.

☐ **Non-metals** These elements have low melting and boiling points, and many are liquids or gases at room temperature and pressure.

☐ **Noble gases** These (non-metal) elements are very unreactive, and it is very difficult to get them to combine with other elements.

↑ **Figure 1:** The periodic table – each element is represented by its chemical symbol, with the relative atomic mass and proton number to one side. (Notice that most of the elements are metals – in all, fewer than one-quarter of the elements are non-metals.)

The periodic table is an arrangement of elements in terms of their electronic structure and their observed properties. There are two different patterns within the periodic table, and both of them are useful to us in different ways.

Filling up the shells

The horizontal rows of the periodic table are known as **periods**. As we move across a period of the table, each successive element has one more electron in its outer shell (or energy level) than the element before it. This carries on until the elements at the far right of the table all have completely full outer energy levels, so these elements are very stable and unreactive.

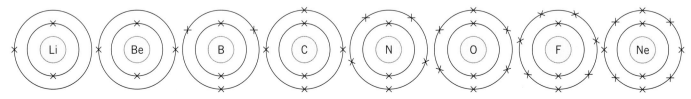

↑ **Figure 2:** As a period builds up, the number of electrons in the outer shell of each element increases by one. This example shows Period 2.

Moving down the groups

The vertical columns of the modern periodic table are called **groups** – Group 1, Group 2, etc. The elements in each group share similar properties. This is because they all have the same number of electrons in their outer energy levels.

The properties of elements are decided by how many electrons they have, and most importantly by the number of electrons in the outer energy level. The similarities and differences between elements in the same group of the periodic table can be explained by the electronic structure of their atoms. The elements in a group are similar because they have the same number of electrons in their outer energy level. They differ because each one has a different number of lower (inner) energy levels.

> **H** Elements in the same group of the periodic table have similar properties because they have the same number of electrons in the highest occupied (outer) energy level. It is the number of lower energy levels underneath which then affect the detailed properties of the elements in one group. The higher the outer energy level is (that is, the more lower energy levels there are), the further the outer electrons are from the positive nucleus. This has two effects:
> - electrons are lost more easily because they are further from the pull of the positive nucleus
> - electrons are gained less easily because they are further from the attraction of the positive nucleus.
>
> This explains many of the trends in reactivity which you will see in the following pages.

↓ **Figure 3:** All the elements in Group 1 react vigorously with water, but the reaction gets more violent moving down the group, as the number of inner energy levels changes.

lithium reacting with water

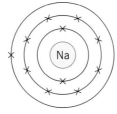

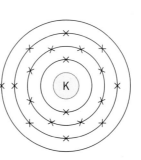

potassium reacting with water

Questions

1 What is the difference between a period and a group of the periodic table?

2 Look at Figure 2.

   a What is the main difference in the electronic structure of lithium and fluorine?

   b Why is neon so unreactive?

H 3 Explain why the elements in Group 7 get *less* reactive as they go down the group, not more reactive.

The first group of the periodic table is known as the **alkali metals**. It includes the metals **lithium**, **sodium**, **potassium**, rubidium, caesium and francium. The first three are the only ones you will usually have to deal with, as the others are frighteningly reactive – and in the case of francium, radioactive as well!

The properties of the alkali metals

All of the Group 1 metals are very reactive – they have to be stored in oil to stop them reacting with the oxygen in the air. The reactivity increases as we move down the group, so lithium is the least reactive alkali metal and francium the most reactive.

All of these metals have a very low density – lithium, sodium and potassium are less dense than water, so they all float on water. The alkali metals are also all very soft – they can be cut with a knife. They have the silvery, shiny look of typical metals when they are first cut, but they quickly go dull as they react with the air to form a white layer of oxide. The Group 1 metals also melt and boil at relatively low temperatures (for metals) and moving down the group the melting and boiling points get lower and lower.

All of the properties of this rather unusual group of metals are the result of their electronic structure. The alkali metals all have one electron in their outer energy level, which gives them similar properties. It also makes them very reactive, as they only need to lose one electron to obtain a stable outer energy level. They react with non-metals, losing their single electron and forming a metal ion carrying a +1 charge, eg Na^+, K^+. They always form ionic compounds.

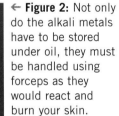

7	
Li	
lithium	
3	
23	
Na	
sodium	
11	
39	
K	
potassium	
19	
85	
Rb	
rubidium	
37	
133	
Cs	
caesium	
55	
Fr	
francium	
87	

← **Figure 1:** The alkali metals make up Group 1 of the periodic table.

← **Figure 2:** Not only do the alkali metals have to be stored under oil, they must be handled using forceps as they would react and burn your skin.

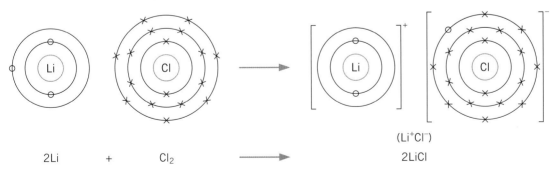

(Li⁺Cl⁻)

2Li   +   Cl₂   ⟶   2LiCl

← **Figure 3:** The reaction between lithium and chlorine shows clearly the way that the alkali metals form positive ions when they react with non-metals.

H Understanding the trends

While all of the alkali metals react in similar ways as a result of the single electron in their outer energy level, there are some definite trends in reactivity which can only be explained by looking in more detail at the structure of the atoms.

→ **Figure 4:** The trends in the properties we can observe moving down Group 1 of the periodic table are explained by the structure of the atoms themselves.

Density *increases* down the group as the atoms get bigger.

Melting points and boiling points *decrease* down the group because the metallic bonds between the electrons and the positive nuclei get less as the atoms get larger.

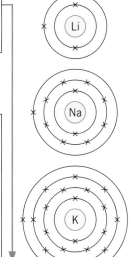

Reactivity *increases* – as the atoms get bigger, the outer electron is held less tightly by attraction to the positive nucleus because it is screened by other layers of electrons. This means the outer electron is lost more easily, so the element is more reactive.

? Questions

1 Explain the following properties of Group 1 metals:

  a they have to be stored in oil

  b they need to be handled with forceps

  c they are shiny grey when they are first cut but soon go dull.

2 Why are the elements caesium, rubidium and francium not brought out in the laboratory and reacted with water?

3 Look at Figure 5.

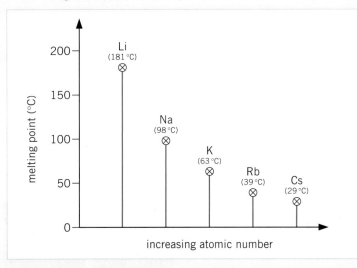

← **Figure 5:** The melting points of the Group 1 elements.

  a What is the melting point of lithium?

  b What is the melting point of rubidium?

  c What is the trend in melting points shown on the graph?

  d Sketch a graph to show the pattern you would expect in the boiling points of the Group 1 elements. The boiling point of lithium is 1342°C.

⊙ Key Ideas

- ⊙ The elements in Group 1 of the periodic table are known as the alkali metals.

- ⊙ The alkali metals are reactive, soft and have a low density.

- ⊙ The alkali metals form ions with a charge of +1 when they react with non-metals.

- ⊙ In Group 1, the further down the group an element is, the more reactive it is.

- ⊙ In Group 1, the further down the group, the lower the melting and boiling point of the element.

H ⊙ The higher the energy level of the outermost electrons, the more easily they are lost – this explains the increase in reactivity seen moving down the elements in Group 1.

Reactions of the alkali metals

Because the alkali metals all have a single electron in their outer energy level, they all react in a similar way with other elements and compounds. As they are so reactive, they are rarely used as metals. However, the compounds they make are very stable indeed and many of them are very useful.

The alkali metals react with different non-metals in very typical ways, allowing us to predict what might happen in a reaction we have never seen before. All we need to remember is that the more reactive the Group 1 metal, the more vigorous the reaction is likely to be!

Reactions with water

When a piece of lithium, sodium or potassium is added to water, the metal floats on the top, moving around and fizzing furiously. Heat is released in the reaction – sodium and potassium get so hot that they melt. The fizzing is caused because the metal reacts with the water to form hydrogen gas, which fizzes as it is given off, and a metal hydroxide. The hydroxides of the alkali metals are soluble, so they dissolve in the water and a colourless metal hydroxide solution results. These solutions are all alkalis – sodium hydroxide (NaOH) and potassium hydroxide (KOH) are examples. This is how the alkali metals get their name – they all form alkalis when they react with water!

$$2Na(s) + 2H_2O(l) \longrightarrow 2NaOH(aq) + H_2(g)$$
$$2K(s) + 2H_2O(l) \longrightarrow 2KOH(aq) + H_2(g)$$

The more reactive the metal, the more vigorously it reacts with water. The reaction with potassium, for example, gets hot enough to ignite the hydrogen which is formed.

Evidence for the reaction

Two observations show what is happening in the reaction between an alkali metal and water. All alkali metals react with water to produce hydrogen gas. When sodium and lithium react with water the hydrogen produced can be made to burn using a lighted splint. But the reaction between potassium and water is so vigorous that the heat produced by the reaction ignites the hydrogen without the need for a lighted splint.

The production of an alkaline solution can be shown by adding an indicator to the water (see Section 7.1). If universal indicator solution is used, it will turn green when added to the water before the reaction, showing that it is neutral. As the alkali metal reacts with the water the universal indicator will turn purple, showing the production of an alkaline solution due to hydroxide ions.

Reactions with oxygen

The alkali metals react with oxygen to form metal oxides. They burn in air with very attractive coloured flames. Each metal has a particular coloured flame. However, the oxides which are produced in these reactions are all white solids – not easy to tell apart just from their appearance.

$$4Li(s) + O_2(g) \longrightarrow 2Li_2O(s)$$
$$4K(s) + O_2(g) \longrightarrow 2K_2O(s)$$

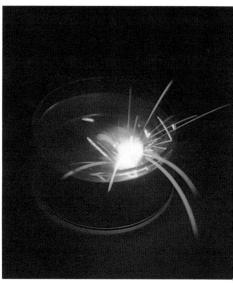

↑ **Figure 1:** The reaction between alkali metals and water is a very vigorous one, and the more reactive the metal, the more vigorous the reaction!

Safety note: The test usually used to show that a colourless gas is hydrogen is to collect some in a test tube. When the gas is lit, hydrogen burns with an explosion that is described as a 'squeaky pop'. However, it is not safe to use a test tube to collect the hydrogen in this case, since the heat of the reaction may ignite the gas as it is being collected.

↓ **Figure 2:** Bright red for lithium, bright orange for sodium and bright lilac for potassium – these are the typical colours when these alkali metals are burned in air.

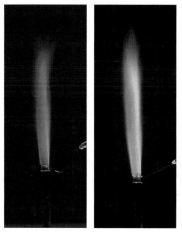

The periodic table

The oxides of the alkali metals all form alkaline solutions in water, just like the hydroxides. Both the oxides and the hydroxides react with acids to form compounds called *salts*. Examples of salts are lithium chloride (LiCl) and potassium chloride (KCl):

$$Li_2O + 2HCl \longrightarrow 2LiCl + H_2O$$
$$KOH + HCl \longrightarrow KCl + H_2O$$

Reactions with chlorine

The alkali metals also react vigorously with other non-metals such as chlorine. They produce metal chlorides – white solids which all dissolve readily in water to form colourless solutions.

The alkali metals react in a similar way with fluorine, bromine and iodine.

All of the compounds of the alkali metals are ionic, so they form crystals which dissolve easily in water.

↑ **Figure 3:** Two very reactive and dangerous substances – sodium and chlorine – react together vigorously to form a very stable ionic compound – sodium chloride, more commonly known as salt:

$$2Na + Cl_2 \longrightarrow 2NaCl$$

? **Questions**

1 Why are the Group 1 metals often known as the alkali metals?

2 An alkali metal is burned in air. The reaction produces a bright orangey yellow flame.

  a Which metal is being burnt in air?

  b Write a word equation for the reaction.

  c Write a balanced chemical equation for the reaction.

3 The reaction between sodium and chlorine is shown in Figure 3. How would you expect the reaction between the following pairs of elements to differ from this?

  a lithium and chlorine   b caesium and chlorine

4 Give balanced equations for the following reactions:

  a lithium + water   b caesium + water

  c the 'squeaky pop' reaction between hydrogen and the oxygen in the air.

5 Write balanced equations for the reaction between:

  a lithium and chlorine   b caesium and oxygen

  c rubidium and chlorine   d potassium and fluorine

  e sodium and bromine.

H

6 a Use data from Figure 4 to produce a table showing the radius of the ions of the elements in Group 1.

  b Explain the trend you observe in the ionic radius.

  c Explain the effect of this trend on the reactivity of the alkali metals.

→ **Figure 4:** The ionic radius of the elements in Group 1.

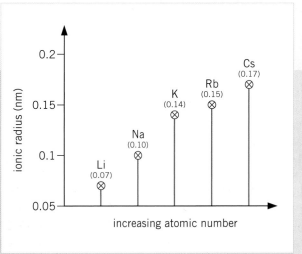

Key Ideas

⊙ The alkali metals react with water releasing hydrogen and forming soluble, alkaline metal hydroxides.

⊙ The alkali metals react readily with non-metals to form ionic compounds in which the metal ion carries a +1 charge.

⊙ The compounds are white solids which form colourless solutions in water.

← **Figure 1:** The halogens make up Group 7 of the periodic table.

The **halogens** are a group of poisonous non-metals which all have coloured vapour. They are fairly typical non-metals with low melting and boiling points and they are poor conductors of heat and electricity. The best known members of the group are **fluorine**, **chlorine**, **bromine** and **iodine**.

Getting to know the halogens

The halogens are a varied group of elements in their physical appearance. At room temperature fluorine is a very reactive, poisonous yellow gas. Chlorine is a fairly reactive, poisonous dense green gas. It is important to be able to detect chlorine if it is given off. Chlorine has a distinctive smell, but there is a far safer test. Hold damp litmus paper in the unknown gas – if the litmus paper bleaches, the gas is chlorine.

↑ **Figure 2:** Chlorine bleaches damp litmus paper – a reliable laboratory test for the presence of the gas.

Bromine is a dense, poisonous red-brown liquid which vaporises easily – it is volatile – while iodine is a poisonous dark grey crystalline solid. Iodine is used as an antiseptic because it is poisonous to bacteria, but it would poison us too if we swallowed it! The halogens take part in a wide range of reactions, many of which have to be carried out in a fume cupboard because the elements themselves are so poisonous.

As with all the groups of elements in the periodic table, there are patterns in the physical properties of the halogens.

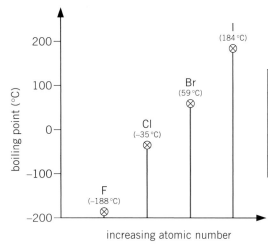

↑ **Figure 3:** Iodine appears to change straight from a solid to a gas when heated – the data in Figure 4 should help you to explain why.

← **Figure 4:** The trends in the physical properties of the halogens can be seen clearly from data like these.

Element	Melting point (°C)
fluorine	−220
chlorine	−101
bromine	−7
iodine	114

Moving down the group of the halogens, the melting and boiling points get higher – this explains the change from gas to liquid to solid at room temperature, from fluorine through chlorine and bromine to iodine.

Down to basics

The way the halogens react with other elements and compounds is a direct result of their electronic structure. They all have a relatively full outer energy level containing seven electrons, so they need one more electron to achieve a stable arrangement. Because of this arrangement they can and do take part in both ionic and covalent bonding.

↓ **Figure 5:** The halogens all exist as molecules made up of pairs of atoms.

 F_2

 Cl_2

 Br_2

 I_2

Ionic bonding in the halogens

The halogens all react with metals, gaining a single electron to give them a stable arrangement of electrons in the outer level, and forming ions with a −1 charge, eg F^-, Cl^-, I^-. In these reactions salts known as metal halides are formed. Examples of the compounds formed are sodium chloride (NaCl), iron bromide ($FeBr_3$) and magnesium iodide (MgI_2).

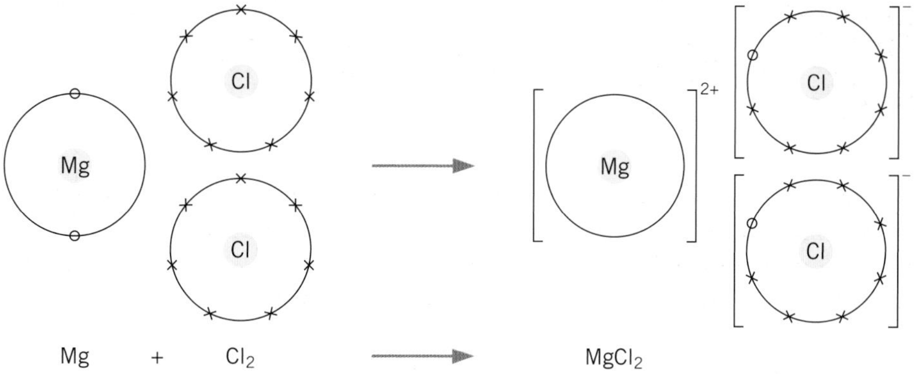

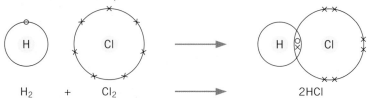

Mg + Cl_2 $\longrightarrow$ MgCl$_2$

↑ **Figure 6:** When a halogen and a metal react, the metal donates electrons to the halogen and ionic bonds are formed between the resulting ions. (Only the outer energy levels are shown here.)

Covalent bonding in the halogens

When the halogens react with themselves or with other non-metals, they share electrons to gain a stable outer energy level and so they form covalent bonds (see Section 1.8). Examples of these compounds are the halogen molecules (F_2, Cl_2, etc), hydrogen chloride (HCl) and tetrachloromethane (CCl_4, also known as carbon tetrachloride).

H_2 + Cl_2 $\longrightarrow$ 2HCl

↑ **Figure 7:** When a halogen and a non-metal react, they share electrons to form covalent bonds within the resulting molecules.

Hydrogen chloride is a dense colourless gas with a choking smell. Unlike many covalent compounds it dissolves readily in water to form hydrochloric acid. As it reacts with the water hydrogen ions and chloride ions are formed. It is these hydrogen ions which make the solution acidic.

$$HCl(g) \xrightarrow{\text{water}} H^+(aq) + Cl^-(aq)$$

Hydrogen fluoride, hydrogen bromide and hydrogen iodide all react in the same way with water – they are a family of very strong acids.

Key Ideas

- The Group 7 elements are called the halogens.

- The halogens have typical non-metal properties – they have low melting and boiling points and they are poor conductors of heat and electricity.

- The halogens consist of molecules made up of pairs of atoms.

- Halogens form ionic compounds when they react with metals (forming ions with a charge of −1) and covalent compounds when they react with non-metals.

? Questions

1 Produce a table to compare the properties of the halogens, from fluorine to iodine. Include in your table melting point, boiling point, state at room temperature and appearance.

2 Draw a graph to display the data given in the table (Figure 4).

3 Explain clearly the way in which the reactions of the halogens with metals differ from the reactions of the halogens with non-metals.

4 Produce dot and cross diagrams, along with balanced equations, for the following reactions between halogens and metals:

   a chlorine and magnesium

   b iodine and sodium

   c fluorine and aluminium

   d bromine and potassium.

5 Produce dot and cross diagrams, along with balanced equations, for the following reactions between halogens and non-metals:

   a fluorine atoms and hydrogen atoms

   b chlorine atoms and carbon atoms

   c chlorine atoms and iodine atoms

   d two bromine atoms.

It is not just the physical properties of the halogens which show a clear trend. The chemical reactivity of the elements changes too – they become less reactive moving down the group.

This change in reactivity becomes very clear when the reactions of the halogens with another element are observed. For example, when we look at the reactions of the halogens with hydrogen (Figure 1) very clear differences can be seen. The change from the explosive reaction of fluorine with hydrogen, to the slow and reversible reaction which takes place between iodine and hydrogen even at 300 °C and with a platinum catalyst, demonstrates clearly that the halogens become less reactive moving down the group.

Reaction of halogen with hydrogen	Conditions
Fluorine $F_2(g) + H_2(g) \rightarrow 2HF(g)$	explosive under all conditions
Chlorine $Cl_2(g) + H_2(g) \rightarrow 2HCl(g)$	explosive in sunlight · slow in dark
Bromine $Br_2(g) + H_2(g) \rightarrow 2HBr(g)$	300 °C + platinum catalyst
Iodine $I_2(g) + H_2(g) \rightleftharpoons 2HI(g)$	300 °C + platinum catalyst very slow and reversible

↑ **Figure 1:** The reactions of the halogens with hydrogen.

Displacement reactions

The more reactive halogens at the top of the group will displace the less reactive halogens from solutions of their salts. Bromine displaces iodine from solution because it is more reactive than iodine, whilst chlorine will displace both iodine and bromine. Obviously fluorine, the most reactive of the halogens, would displace all of the others, but because it reacts so strongly with water the displacement reactions cannot be carried out.

These displacement reactions take place between ions in solution. Although the halogens are easy to identify as elements because of their very different appearances, many of the metal halides form colourless solutions in water. To enable us to be sure which halide ion is present, there is a simple test involving silver nitrate. The nitrate ions displace the halide ions, forming silver halides. These are insoluble, so a silver halide precipitate is formed. For example:

silver nitrate + sodium chloride ⟶ silver chloride + sodium nitrate

$AgNO_3(aq) + NaCl(aq) \longrightarrow AgCl(s) + NaNO_3(aq)$

↑ **Figure 2:** Chlorine gas bubbled through potassium bromide solution displaces bromine from the solution:

$Cl_2 + 2KBr \longrightarrow 2KCl + Br_2$

The reddish brown colour of the bromine can be clearly seen in this photograph.

→ **Figure 3:** Silver chloride is white, silver bromide is cream and silver iodide is pale yellow. The colour of the precipitate allows us to identify the halide in the original solution.

Explaining the patterns

The patterns of behaviour of the elements in Group 7 can be explained by the arrangement of electrons in their highest occupied or outer energy level. The trend for the halogens is the opposite to that for the alkali metals. Moving down the group the elements become less reactive because electrons are gained, for ionic or covalent bonding, less and less easily. This is because the larger the atom becomes, the more layers of electrons there are screening the outer electrons from the attractive positive force of the nucleus. This means that the tendency to attract electrons gets less and less.

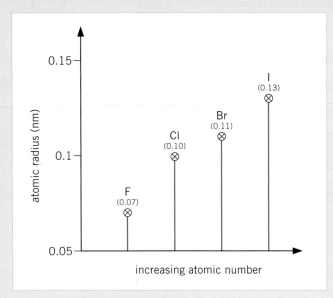

← **Figure 4:** The atomic radius of the halogen atoms gets larger moving down the group so electrons are gained less easily.

? Questions

1 Give a word equation and a balanced chemical equation for the reaction of:

   a fluorine   **b** iodine

   with hydrogen, showing the conditions under which the reactions take place.

2 **a** Explain why chlorine will displace bromine and iodine from solutions of their salts.

   b Give word and balanced chemical equations for the reactions between:

   i bromine and potassium iodide

   ii chlorine and magnesium bromide.

3 **a** Give balanced equations for the reactions between:

   i silver nitrate solution and potassium bromide

   ii silver nitrate solution and sodium iodide.

   b Explain how these reactions can be used to help identify an unknown solution.

H 4 Using the information given in Figure 4, explain the trend in the reactivity of the halogens down the group. Diagrams will make the explanation clearer.

Key Ideas

⊙ In Group 7, the further down the group an element is, the less reactive it will be and the higher its melting and boiling point will be.

⊙ A more reactive halogen can displace a less reactive halogen from an aqueous solution of its salt.

H ⊙ The decreased reactivity of halogens down the group is explained by the increased number of energy levels screening the outer electrons from the positive nucleus, so electrons are less easily gained down the group.

6.7 Group 0 – the noble gases

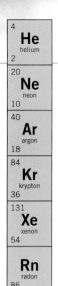

← **Figure 1:** The noble or inert gases make up Group 0 of the periodic table.

The elements in Group 0 of the periodic table are known as the **noble gases**. Another name for them is the *inert* gases, which is very appropriate as this group of elements is extremely inert (unreactive).

The non-reacting elements

Helium, neon, argon, along with krypton, xenon and radon are the least reactive elements known. It is very difficult to make them react with any other elements. They don't even react with themselves to form molecules. Most gases which are elements are diatomic – two atoms joined together to form a molecule. But the noble gases are monatomic – they exist as individual atoms because they will not form bonds of any sort with anything. So they are found simply as He, Ne, Ar, etc.

H Why are the noble gases so unreactive?

As in so much of the chemistry of the periodic table, the reason for the unreactive character of the noble gases lies in their electronic structure. The outer electron energy level of a noble gas atom is full. The atoms are therefore completely stable – they have no tendency to gain, lose or share electrons.

 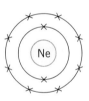 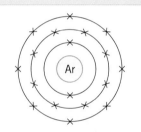

← **Figure 2:** The electronic structure of the noble gases explains their completely inert behaviour.

Typical non-metals

The noble gases are typical non-metals in many ways. They are colourless, odourless gases which have low melting and boiling points. They are poor conductors of heat and electricity, even when in the liquid form. Just like in other groups of the periodic table, there are clear trends in the melting and boiling points of the noble gases. The melting and boiling points increase down the group – although as the boiling point of radon is still only −62 °C, they all boil at pretty low temperatures.

The density of the noble gases also increases going down the group, the result of the atoms getting bigger all the time. Helium has the smallest and lightest atoms and so helium gas is less dense than air, a fact which is important when we look at its uses.

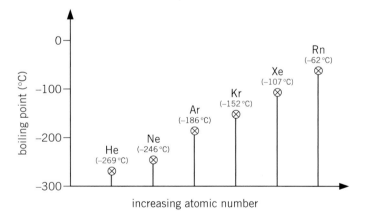

↑ **Figure 3:** The trend in the boiling point of the noble gases moving down the group can be clearly seen from this data.

Gas	Density (g/dm^3)
helium	0.17
neon	0.84
argon	1.66
krypton	3.49
xenon	5.47

← **Figure 4:** The density of the noble gases (at room temperature and pressure).

Using the noble gases

The noble gases do not take part in chemical reactions so we cannot use them to make useful materials for us. Instead, we use them in situations where their extreme lack of reactivity is useful in itself.

Helium is used in airships and in party balloons. Its low density means that it floats in air and its low reactivity means that it does not catch fire, unlike the only alternative gas, hydrogen. It is also used with oxygen as a breathing mixture for deep sea divers, as it reduces their chances of suffering from the 'bends'.

Neon is used in electrical discharge tubes – better known as neon lights. An electrical current is passed through the neon gas and it gives out a bright light as the electrons are excited without undergoing any chemical reaction. Neon lights are familiar as street lighting and in advertising. **Argon** is used in a different type of lighting – the everyday light bulb (or filament lamp). The argon provides an inert atmosphere so that when the electric current passes through the metal filament, making it very hot indeed, no chemical reaction takes place between the filament and the gas it is surrounded by. This stops the filament from burning away and makes light bulbs last longer. Helium, neon and argon are all used in lasers too.

↑ **Figure 5:** Helium balloons add colour and fun – yet are safe for the youngest child.

? Questions

1 a In what ways are the noble gases similar to the other non-metal elements?

 b In what ways do the noble gases differ from the other non-metal elements?

2 Draw a table to show the boiling points of the noble gases, using the data in Figure 3.

3 a Draw a graph of the data given in Figure 4.

 b What trend can you observe in the densities of the noble gases and how would you explain it?

4 How are the uses of the noble gases a reflection of their chemically inert nature?

In the centre of the periodic table there is a large block of metallic elements. They are known as the transition metals or transition elements. They include a wide variety of different elements, but many of them have characteristics in common.

45 Sc scandium 21	48 Ti titanium 22	51 V vanadium 23	52 Cr chromium 24	55 Mn manganese 25	56 Fe iron 26	59 Co cobalt 27	59 Ni nickel 28	63 Cu copper 29	64 Zn zinc 30
89 Y yttrium 39	91 Zr zirconium 40	93 Nb niobium 41	96 Mo molybdenum 42	Tc technetium 43	101 Ru ruthenium 44	103 Rh rhodium 45	106 Pd palladium 46	108 Ag silver 47	112 Cd cadmium 48
139 La lanthanum 57	178 Hf hafnium 72	181 Ta tantalum 73	184 W tungsten 74	186 Re rhenium 75	190 Os osmium 76	192 Ir iridium 77	195 Pt platinum 78	197 Au gold 79	201 Hg mercury 80
227 Ac actinium 89									

← **Figure 1:** The transition metals – the more common ones are shown in bold type.

Looking at the transition metals we do not find trends in the way that we did when we looked at the different groups of elements. However, they do have a number of important characteristics in common.

The properties of the transition metals

The transition metals have a typical metallic structure which explains most of their properties. The metals atoms exist in a giant structure held together by metallic bonds, and the outer electrons of each atom can move about freely within the metal.

Like all metals, the transition metals are very good conductors of electricity and heat – the free electrons carry the electrical current or the heat energy through the metal. The transition metals are also hard, tough and strong, yet they can easily be bent or hammered into useful shapes.

With the exception of mercury, which is a liquid at room temperature, the transition metals have very high melting points. This is very clear if they are compared to the alkali metals of Group 1.

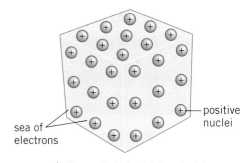

sea of electrons — positive nuclei

↑ **Figure 2:** It is this 'sea' of free electrons which explains many of the properties of typical metals.

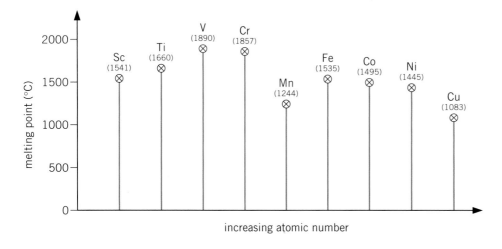

← **Figure 3:** Not only are the melting points of the transition elements generally much higher than those of the Group 1 elements (see Figure 5 on page 91), they also show much less variation.

The transition metals are much less reactive than the metals in Group 1. This means they do not react as easily with oxygen or water as the alkali metals – in other words, they only corrode very slowly. This makes the transition metals very useful as structural materials, particularly when they are mixed together or combined with other elements to make alloys. Iron mixed with carbon is certainly the best known of these (see Section 4.3). Other very useful combinations of transition metals are bronze, which is a combination of copper and tin, and cupro-nickel, the very hard alloy of copper and nickel which is used to make the coins we use in our currency.

Iron is the transition metal which is used most widely in the construction of buildings and vehicles. Copper, on the other hand, has another very important use. Copper is an excellent conductor of heat and electricity, and it can also be drawn out into long wires. Because of this it is very widely used for making electrical cables, and also for high quality cookware – it is a lot more expensive than the iron and steel usually used for cooking utensils. Copper is also used to make household water pipes, often replacing lead. Lead was used extensively for water pipes in the last century until people discovered it was poisonous – now old piping is being replaced with copper or plastic tubes to do the same job safely.

↑ **Figure 4:** Some of the transition metals which play so many important roles in our lives – copper (centre) and (clockwise from left) aluminium pellets, nickel–chrome ore, nickel bars, titanium rods, iron–nickel ore, niobium bars, chromium granules.

? Questions

1 Chose three properties of metals and explain them in terms of the 'sea of electron' model of metal structure.

2 **a** In Figure 3, what is the highest and lowest melting point shown for a transition metal?

   b In Section 6.3 Figure 5, what is the highest and lowest melting point shown for an alkali metal?

   c Basing your answer on the evidence from parts **a** and **b** alone, why would you chose a transition metal for making engines, boilers or cookers, rather than an alkali metal?

3 Why are transition metals more useful than alkali metals as structural materials?

⊙— Key Ideas

⊙ In the centre of the periodic table is a block of elements known as the transition metals.

⊙ They have many typical metal properties – they are good conductors of heat and electricity, are easily shaped, strong and tough, and have high melting points.

⊙ Compared to the alkali metals they are much harder, have higher melting points and are relatively unreactive with oxygen and water.

⊙ The uses of the transition metals reflect their individual metallic properties.

6.9 More about transition metals

The transition metals have many properties in common, so what you know about one or two of the elements can be applied to almost any of them. Transition metals have some quite unusual properties which in turn influence the way we use them.

Coloured compounds

Many of the transition metals form coloured compounds. These include some very common compounds which we use in the laboratory. For example, potassium manganate (VII) is purple – the purple colour is due to the manganese ion in the compound. Similarly, copper (II) sulphate is blue (from the copper ion) and potassium chromate (VI) is orange (from the chromium ion). These colours are shown in Figure 1.

The colours which are produced by the transition elements are important in the world around us – for example, the colours of many minerals, rocks and gem stones are the result of transition metal ions. A reddish brown colour in the rocks is often the result of the iron ions, whilst the blue colour of sapphires and the green of emeralds are due to transition metal ions within the structure of the crystal.

People make use of the coloured ions of the transition metals in a variety of ways. Many of the glazes which are applied to pottery contain transition metal ions which are the basis of the colour they produce. Also as copper weathers it produces a green film of basic copper carbonate. This green patina is very attractive and is generally known as verdigris, and this is one reason why copper is used for many statues. The green colour is a direct result of the copper ions in the compound.

↓ **Figure 1:** The bright colours of these compounds are the result of the transition metal ions they contain.

↖ **Figure 2:** The colours which result from transition metal ions may be dull (like the verdigris on this statue), shiny or sparkly (like these sapphires), but they are almost always regarded as attractive and desirable.

H When compounds containing transition elements are written down they usually include a Roman number as well as the name of the compound, eg potassium manganate(VII), copper(II) sulphate. This is because transition metals often have more than one form of ion. Examples include iron (Fe^{2+} and Fe^{3+}), copper (Cu^+ and Cu^{2+}) and chromium (Cr^{2+} and Cr^{3+}). Some of the metals have even more – vanadium has five different types of ion! The interesting thing is that the different ions usually cause different colours in the compounds. For example, iron(II) ions (Fe^{2+}) give compounds with a green colour, whilst iron(III) ions (Fe^{3+}) are usually the reddish brown colour we associate with rust!

Convenient catalysts

Most chemical reactions take place quite slowly – in fact left alone most of the chemical reactions in the chemical industries would take place so slowly that we would never get enough of the chemicals we need, and the people running the companies would never make any money. Fortunately most reactions can be speeded up. This might be brought about by an increase in temperature or pressure, or it might depend on a **catalyst** (see Section 8.3).

Catalysts speed up a chemical reaction without being changed themselves in any way. They do not change the proportion of the products made, and they can often be reused time after time. Many of the transition elements make very effective catalysts. In the Haber process for making ammonia (see Sections 4.8 and 9.6) iron is used as a catalyst. Platinum and nickel are important catalysts in the process by which vegetable oils such as olive oil and corn oil are turned into margarine. Manganese(IV) oxide is the catalyst often used in the decomposition of hydrogen peroxide. Another increasingly important role for transition elements such as platinum is in the catalytic converters attached to car engines. These catalytic converters remove most of the pollutant gases, produced by the engine of a car as it burns petrol, before they reach the atmosphere, so transition elements in their role as catalysts are helping us to combat pollution.

← **Figure 3:** Transition metals, as catalysts within the catalytic converters fitted to all new cars, can help to make air pollution like this a thing of the past.

Key Ideas

⊙ Most transition metals form coloured compounds.

⊙ The coloured compounds can be seen in different coloured pottery glazes, in weathered copper and in gem stones.

⊙ Many transition metals, including iron and platinum, are used as catalysts.

? Questions

1 a Give three examples of coloured transition metal compounds.

  b Give two examples of the role of coloured transition metal compounds in the natural world.

  c Give two examples of the ways in which people make use of coloured transition metal compounds.

2 a What is a catalyst?

  b Give examples of three transition metals which are used as catalysts and describe what they are used for.

1 The first airships were filled with hydrogen gas. Now helium gas is used in airships.

a The list gives some chemical symbols.

Ar   Cl   H   He   O

Choose from the list the correct chemical symbol for:

i hydrogen (1 mark)

ii helium. (1 mark)

b Choose **one** property from the list below which makes both hydrogen and helium useful for airships.

colourless   low density   no smell (1 mark)

c Explain why helium is now used in airships and why hydrogen is no longer used. (2 marks)

(Total 5 marks)
AQA specimen question

2 Part of the periodic table which Mendeleev published in 1869 is shown below.

	Group 1	Group 2	Group 3	Group 4	Group 5	Group 6	Group 7
Period 1	H						
Period 2	Li	Be	B	C	N	O	F
Period 3	Na	Mg	Al	Si	P	S	Cl
Period 4	K Cu	Ca Zn	* *	Ti *	V As	Cr Se	Mn Br
Period 5	Rb Ag	Sr Cd	Y In	Zr Sn	Nb Sb	Mo Te	* I

Use the periodic table at the back of the book to help you answer this question.

a Some elements in Group 1 of Mendeleev's periodic table are **not** found in Group 1 of the modern periodic table. Name **two** of these elements. (1 mark)

b Which group of elements in the modern periodic table is missing on Mendeleev's table? (1 mark)

c Mendeleev left several gaps in his periodic table. These gaps are shown as asterisks (*) on the table above. Suggest why Mendeleev left these gaps. (1 mark)

d Copy and complete the following sentence:

In the **modern** periodic table the elements are arranged in the order of their .... numbers. (1 mark)

(Total 4 marks)
AQA specimen question

3 One definition of an element is:

'A substance which cannot be broken down into simpler substances by chemical methods'.

The table shows some of the 'substances' which Antoine Lavoisier thought were elements. He divided the 'substances' into four groups. He published these groups in 1789.

The modern names of some of the substances are given in brackets.

Acid-making elements	Gas-like elements	Metallic elements	Earthy elements
sulphur	light	cobalt	lime (calcium oxide)
phosphorus	caloric (heat)	copper	magnesia (magnesium oxide)
charcoal (carbon)	oxygen	gold	barytes (barium sulphate)
	azote (nitrogen)	iron	argilla (aluminium oxide)
	hydrogen	lead	silex (silicon dioxide)
		manganese	
		mercury	
		nickel	
		platina (platinum)	
		silver	
		tin	
		tungsten	
		zinc	

a Name **one** 'substance' in the list which is **not** a chemical element or compound. (1 mark)

b **i** Name **one** 'substance' in the list which is a compound. (1 mark)

ii Suggest why Lavoisier thought that this 'substance' was an element. (1 mark)

c Dmitri Mendeleev devised a periodic table of the elements in 1869. A modern version of this table is shown at the back of the book.

Give **two** ways in which Mendeleev's table is more useful than Lavoisier's. (2 marks)

(Total 5 marks)

AQA specimen question

4 a The table gives the atomic numbers and boiling points of the noble gases.

Noble gas	Atomic number	Boiling point (°C)
helium	2	−269
neon	10	−246
argon	18	−186
krypton	36	
xenon	54	−107
radon	86	−62

i Draw a graph of boiling point against atomic number. Draw a line of best fit through the points. (3 marks)

ii Use the graph to help you complete the sentence.

The estimated boiling point of krypton is ...°C. (1 mark)

b Krypton is very unreactive.

i Explain, as fully as you can, why krypton is so unreactive. (3 marks)

ii Very few compounds of krypton have ever been made. One compound is krypton fluoride.

A sample of krypton fluoride was found to contain 0.42 g of krypton and 0.19 g of fluoride. Calculate the formula of krypton fluoride.

To gain full marks you must show all your working.

(Relative atomic masses: F = 19, Kr = 84) (4 marks)

(Total 11 marks)

AQA specimen question

5 a The transition elements have the typical properties of metals.

i Transition metals are good conductors of electricity.
Explain why. (2 marks)

ii Transition metals have high melting points.
Explain why. (2 marks)

b Iron is a transition metal. Iron, because of its strength, is used in the building of ship's hulls. The main problem with using iron is that it rusts unless protected.

Explain how attaching zinc blocks to an iron hull stops it from rusting. (2 marks)

(Total 6 marks)

AQA specimen question

6 Fluorine is more reactive than chlorine. Fluorine reacts with most elements in the periodic table. However, fluorine does not react with argon.

(Atomic numbers: F = 9, Cl = 17)

a To which group of the periodic table do fluorine and chlorine belong? (1 mark)

b Copy the diagram below. On your diagram, draw the electron arrangement of a chlorine atom. (2 marks)

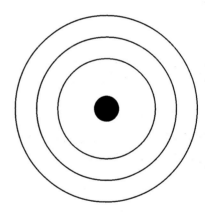

c Explain why fluorine is more reactive than chlorine. (3 marks)

(Total 6 marks)

AQA specimen question

7.1 Acids and bases

When a substance dissolves in water it forms an aqueous solution. That solution may be acidic, alkaline or neutral. **Bases** are chemicals which can neutralise **acids**, and **alkalis** are bases which dissolve in water. Pure water is neutral. To find out whether a given solution is acidic, basic or neutral we use a special chemical called an **indicator**.

Why are indicators important?

We need to be able to tell whether a solution is acidic, alkaline or neutral for a number of reasons. One is that during many chemical reactions, changes in acidity or alkalinity take place. If we can observe this change, then we can tell whether a reaction has happened at all, and whether it has finished or not. The other major reason why it is important for us to tell whether a solution is acidic or alkaline is safety. Both acids and alkalis are potentially dangerous chemicals which can break down and destroy not only clothing but human body tissues as well.

↑ **Figure 1:** Acids can be dangerously corrosive. This is the apparatus worn by John Haigh, the Acid Bath Murderer, to protect himself from the sulphuric acid he used to dissolve the bodies of his victims.

Acids

Acids include chemicals like citric acid, sulphuric acid and ethanoic acid. They all have a very sour taste, although many of them are too dangerous to put in your mouth. They are often used in chemical reactions in the laboratory, yet ethanoic acid (vinegar) and citric acid (the sour taste in citrus fruits, fizzy drinks and squashes) are examples of acids which we regularly eat.

One of the most commonly used laboratory acids is hydrochloric acid (HCl). This is formed when the gas hydrogen chloride dissolves in water. The other hydrogen halides – hydrogen fluoride, hydrogen bromide and hydrogen iodide – behave in a similar way, producing hydrofluoric, hydrobromic and hydroiodic acids respectively (Section 6.5).

$$HCl(g) \xrightarrow{\text{water}} H^+(aq) + Cl^-(aq)$$

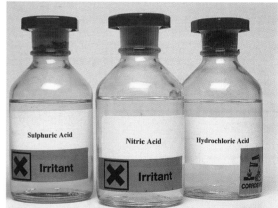

↑ **Figure 2:** The three most common laboratory acids.

Bases

Bases are the opposite of acids in the way they react. Because alkalis are bases which dissolve in water, they are the bases which are most commonly used. For example, ammonium hydroxide (NH_4OH), sodium hydroxide (NaOH) and potassium hydroxide (KOH) are often found in school laboratories. Ammonium hydroxide is formed when ammonia gas dissolves in water, the other two when solid sodium hydroxide or potassium hydroxide dissolve in water. They all form alkaline solutions. For example:

$$\text{ammonia} + \text{water} \longrightarrow \text{ammonium hydroxide}$$
$$NH_3(g) + H_2O(l) \longrightarrow NH_4OH(aq)$$

$$\text{sodium hydroxide} + \text{water} \longrightarrow \text{sodium hydroxide}$$
$$NaOH(s) + H_2O(l) \longrightarrow NaOH(aq)$$

The ionic basis of acidic and alkaline solutions is quite simple:

⊙ Acids are substances which form hydrogen ions (H^+) when added to water. Hydrogen ions make solutions acidic. For example:

$$H_2SO_4(aq) \longrightarrow 2H^+(aq) + SO_4^{2-}(aq)$$
$$HNO_3(aq) \longrightarrow H^+(aq) + NO_3^-(aq)$$

⊙ Alkalis are substances which form hydroxide ions (OH^-) when added to water. Hydroxide ions make solutions alkaline. For example:

$$NH_4OH(aq) \longrightarrow NH_4^+(aq) + OH^-(aq)$$
$$NaOH(aq) \longrightarrow Na^+(aq) + OH^-(aq)$$

Like strong acids, strong alkalis are corrosive and cause great damage to the skin by reacting with the fats and oils found in it. Both acids and alkalis only show their properties when they are dissolved in water.

Using indicators

Many acids and alkalis look very similar – most of them form colourless solutions so telling them apart would be very difficult without indicators. Indicators are special chemicals which change colour with acids and alkalis. Litmus paper is a well known indicator but there are many more, including some natural ones like the juice of red cabbage or beetroot.

The pH scale

We use the pH scale to tell us the strength of an acid or alkali. It runs from 1 (the strongest acid) to 14 (the strongest alkali). Universal indicator is a very special indicator made up of a number of dyes. It turns different colours in different strengths of acid and alkali. Anything in the middle of the pH scale (pH 7) is neutral – neither acid nor alkali.

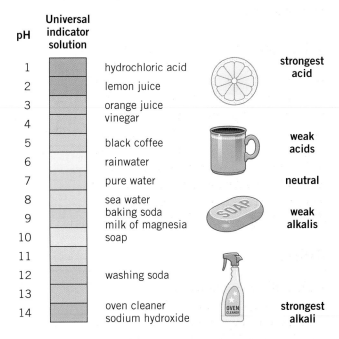

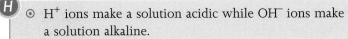

Universal indicator is also used in pH papers, which give different colours.

pH   1 2 3 4 5 6 7 8 9 10 11 12 13 14

↑ **Figure 3:** The pH scale.

? Questions

1 Why is it important to be able to find out if a colourless solution is acidic, basic or neutral?

2 a What is an indicator?

   b What is the pH scale?

   c How are indicators and the pH scale linked?

3 When the gas hydrogen fluoride reacts with water, a very unpleasant acid is formed. Give a word and balanced chemical equation for the formation of hydrofluoric acid.

4 When potassium hydroxide dissolves in water an alkaline solution is formed. Give a word and balanced chemical equation for this reaction.

🔑 Key Ideas

⊙ When a substance dissolves in water it forms an aqueous solution which may be acidic, alkaline or neutral.

⊙ Pure water is neutral.

⊙ Hydrogen halides are gases which dissolve in water to produce acidic solutions.

⊙ Ammonia dissolves in water to form an alkaline solution.

H ⊙ H^+ ions make a solution acidic while OH^- ions make a solution alkaline.

⊙ Indicators can be used to show if a solution is acidic, alkaline or neutral by the way the colours change.

⊙ The pH scale is used to show how acidic or alkaline a solution is.

7.2 | Neutralisation

When an acid reacts with a base or an alkali, it forms a neutral solution containing a salt and water. This is known as a **neutralisation** reaction. The general formula which describes all reactions of this type is:

acid + base $\longrightarrow$ salt + water

An indicator can be used to show when acidic and alkaline solutions have completely reacted to produce a neutral salt solution.

Examples of neutralisation reactions are:

hydrochloric acid + sodium hydroxide $\longrightarrow$ sodium chloride + water

$$HCl(aq) + NaOH(aq) \longrightarrow NaCl(aq) + H_2O(l)$$

sulphuric acid + ammonium hydroxide $\longrightarrow$ ammonium sulphate + water

$$H_2SO_4(aq) + NH_4OH(aq) \longrightarrow NH_4SO_4(aq) + H_2O(l)$$

↑ **Figure 1:** Universal indicator clearly shows that the acid and alkali have completely reacted together to form a neutral salt solution.

H Neutralisation reactions can be expressed in terms of what is happening to the acidic and alkaline ions. Hydrogen ions (H^+) combine with hydroxide ions (OH^-) to form water molecules:

$$H^+(aq) + OH^-(aq) \longrightarrow H_2O(l)$$

Ideas and Evidence

Everyday acids and alkalis

Although we learn about acids and alkalis in the context of the science laboratory, they play an important role in everyday life. Some of their everyday uses are outlined below.

⊙ Both acids and alkalis are used as household and industrial cleaners.

Acids dissolve lime scale. The acid reacts with the calcium carbonates and magnesium carbonates in the lime scale to produce soluble salts, carbon dioxide and water. All of the lime scale removers for toilets, sinks, kettles, washing machines, dishwashers and irons are basically acids.

Alkalis react with and remove grease and fat. So soaps, detergents and oven cleaners are all alkalis.

⊙ The reaction between alkalis and fat is used to make soap. Traditionally sodium hydroxide was boiled up with animal fats, but now a wide range of fats and oils are used.

↑ **Figure 2:** The reaction of acids with lime scale gives us a vital tool in the battle against the build-up of scale in pipes, kettles, toilets and washing machines.

- Our stomach makes quite powerful hydrochloric acid to help break down our food. But too much of this acid causes indigestion. Indigestion tablets rely on the reaction between alkalis (such as magnesium oxide) and acid, neutralising the excess acid and ending the discomfort.

- The soil can become very acidic because of the action of microorganisms or as a result of acid rain. Spreading lime (calcium hydroxide) adds an alkali to the acid and neutralises the excess acid in the ground.

- Lakes can become very acidic because of acid rain. Again, adding the lime neutralises the excess acid and keeps the water safe for animals and plants to live in.

Science people

The big problem with measuring the acidity or alkalinity of a solution is that the concentration of hydrogen ions varies so much, from about $12\,mol/dm^3$ at the high end to around $10^{-15}\,mol/dm^3$ at the low end. The problem caused by this awkward measuring system was solved in 1909 by a Danish chemist called Soren Peter Lauritz Sorensen, when he was working on methods to improve quality in the brewing industry. He suggested using a logarithmic scale for hydrogen ion concentration, which meant that the acidity or alkalinity could be measured using a simple scale running from 1 to 14. This is why the name pH is used – it stands for **p**ower of **H**ydrogen. Not surprisingly, Sorensen's idea was quickly welcomed and used by other chemists.

← **Figure 3:** Soren Sorensen, who made life easier for chemists everywhere!

Questions

1 When some fertilisers are added to soil they dissolve in the water in the soil and make it acidic. This means that some crops will not grow well in the soil. Farmers sometimes spread lime (calcium oxide, a base) over the soil after adding fertiliser to it.

   a Why do farmers spread lime on the soil?

   b What might happen if a farmer spreads too much lime onto the soil?

2 Write down the formulae of the following compounds:

   a lithium hydroxide   **d** potassium hydroxide

   b hydrochloric acid   **e** ammonium hydroxide

   c sulphuric acid   **f** nitric acid.

3 Give word and balanced chemical equations for the following neutralisation reactions:

   a hydrochloric acid and potassium hydroxide

   b nitric acid and sodium hydroxide

   c sulphuric acid and potassium hydroxide

   d hydrochloric acid and ammonium hydroxide.

H

4 For each of the reactions in question 3 show the neutralisation in terms of the ions involved. For example, for part **a**:

$$H^+ + Cl^- + K^+ + OH^- \longrightarrow KCl + H_2O$$

Key Ideas

- When an acid reacts with a base a neutralisation reaction takes place.

- An indicator can be used to show when acidic and alkaline solutions have completely reacted to produce a neutral salt solution.

H - In neutralisation reactions the H^+ of the acid reacts with the OH^- of the alkali to form neutral water (H_2O).

The alkali metals from Group 1 of the periodic table have oxides and hydroxides which dissolve in water to make alkaline solutions – which is why they are known as the alkali metals. The metals in Group 2 of the periodic table – metals like calcium and magnesium – also have hydroxides and oxides which dissolve in water to produce alkalis, although they are not so strongly alkaline as those involving Group 1 metals.

When an alkaline solution reacts with an acid solution, the neutralisation reaction that occurs produces a salt and water:

acid + alkaline hydroxide solution $\longrightarrow$ a neutral salt solution + water

↑ **Figure 1:** A soluble salt made by the reaction of an alkaline hydroxide solution with an acid can be extracted from the solution by evaporation of the water. This dish contains sodium chloride crystals.

Choosing a salt

By carefully choosing both the alkali and the acid, we can determine which salt will be made. The salt which results from a reaction depends on two things:

⊙ The metal in the alkali will determine which metal salt is produced. For example, if sodium hydroxide is used as the alkali, then whatever acid the alkali is reacted with, the salts produced will always be sodium salts.

⊙ The other factor is the acid used. When an alkali is reacted with **hydrochloric** acid to neutralise it, the salt formed will always be a **chloride**. Whatever alkali is reacted with **sulphuric** acid, the salt will always be a **sulphate**. Neutralising **nitric** acid always gives a **nitrate**.

In other words, it is the combination of the metal in the alkali and the acid used which decides which salt will be formed. For example:

hydro**chloric** acid + **potassium** hydroxide $\longrightarrow$ **potassium chloride** + water

$HCl(aq)$ + $KOH(aq)$ $\longrightarrow$ $KCl(aq)$ + $H_2O(l)$

sulphuric acid + **sodium** hydroxide $\longrightarrow$ **sodium sulphate** + water

$H_2SO_4(aq)$ + $2NaOH(aq)$ $\longrightarrow$ $Na_2SO_4(aq)$ + $2H_2O(l)$

nitric acid + **lithium** hydroxide $\longrightarrow$ **lithium nitrate** + water

$HNO_3(aq)$ + $LiOH(aq)$ $\longrightarrow$ $LiNO_3(aq)$ + $H_2O(l)$

The oxides of the transition metals are also bases, so very similar reactions take place when acids react with oxides. Again, a salt and water are the products of the reaction. For example:

sulphuric acid + zinc oxide $\longrightarrow$ zinc sulphate + water

$H_2SO_4(aq)$ + $ZnO(aq)$ $\longrightarrow$ $ZnSO_4(aq)$ + $H_2O(l)$

Making ammonium salts

Ammonium salts can be made in two ways. Ammonia may be bubbled through an acid – it forms an aqueous solution which combines with the acid to form an ammonium salt. For example:

hydrochloric acid + ammonia $\longrightarrow$ ammonium chloride

$HCl(aq)$ + $NH_3(aq)$ $\longrightarrow$ $NH_4Cl(aq)$

sulphuric acid + ammonia $\longrightarrow$ ammonium sulphate

$H_2SO_4(aq)$ + $2NH_3(aq)$ $\longrightarrow$ $(NH_4)_2SO_4(aq)$

copper sulphate crystal

zinc sulphate crystals

↑ **Figure 2:** If copper oxide and zinc are both reacted with sulphuric acid, the sulphates which result are easily distinguished!

On the other hand, the ammonia may be bubbled through water first to make ammonium hydroxide (see Section 7.1). This in turn reacts with an acid to give an ammonium salt and water. For example, with nitric acid:

ammonium hydroxide + nitric acid $\longrightarrow$ ammonium nitrate + water

$$NH_4OH(aq) + HNO_3(aq) \longrightarrow NH_4NO_3(aq) + H_2O(l)$$

The direct reaction of ammonia with nitric acid also gives ammonium nitrate, and these reactions are very important in the manufacture of nitrate fertilisers.

Ideas and Evidence

A special sort of salt!

When alkalis react with fatty acids, a very special type of neutralisation reaction takes place, and the 'sa.t' which is produced is what we know as soap! This reaction takes place when an alkali such as sodium hydroxide is boiled up with animal fats or vegetable oils, made up of long chain fatty acids:

alkali + fatty acid $\longrightarrow$ soap + water

Commercially the reaction is carried out in great 'soap kettles'. Brine is pumped into them after the fats and alkali have been boiled, and the insoluble soap precipitates out as a curd on the top. The pure soap is taken and processed – perfumes and colours may be added – before it is packaged for sale.

The reaction between alkalis and fatty acids is not confined to the soap factory. The reason that alkalis are so dangerous is that if they are spilled on your skin they react with the fatty acids present in all of your cells, destroying the structure and forming 'human soap' which makes your skin feel slimy as the tissue is broken down!

↑ **Figure 3:** Few people realise that the soaps they buy started life as a reacting mass of hot alkali mixed with animal fats or plant oils!

Questions

1 Give word and balanced chemical equations for the reactions between an acid and the hydroxide of an alkali metal which would result in the following salts:

  a lithium chloride

  b sodium nitrate

  c potassium sulphate.

2 State what salts you would expect from the following neutralisation reactions:

  a nitric acid and calcium hydroxide

  b nitric acid and ammonia

  c sulphuric acid and lithium hydroxide.

3 Explain why the making of soap can be described as a neutralisation reaction.

4 Design a leaflet, or produce a display to be put up in the laboratory, for the new intake of pupils in September giving them information about acids and alkalis and explaining why these should be treated with respect.

Key Ideas

⊙ The salts of alkali metals can be made by reacting solutions of their alkaline hydroxides with acids to form neutral salts and water.

⊙ The salt produced depends on the metal in the alkali and the acid used.

⊙ Neutralising hydrochloric acid produces chlorides.

⊙ Neutralising nitric acid produces nitrates.

⊙ Neutralising sulphuric acid produces sulphates.

Neutralisation reactions are not always as simple as adding a solution of a metal hydroxide to a solution of an acid. To make the salts of the transition metals we have to overcome the fact that although their oxides and hydroxides react with acids, they do not dissolve in water.

Making transition metal salts

The oxides and hydroxides of the transition metals are bases, so they will react with acids to form a salt and water. However, they will not dissolve in water, although the salts that are formed are usually soluble. To produce a soluble transition metal salt, the solid metal hydroxide (or oxide) is added to an acid until no more will react, so that the acid is completely neutralised. The excess metal hydroxide (or oxide) is then removed from the soluble salt solution by filtering, after which the soluble salt can be obtained by evaporation of the water. For example:

$$\text{copper(II) oxide} + \text{sulphuric acid} \longrightarrow \text{copper(II) sulphate} + \text{water}$$
$$CuO(s) + H_2SO_4(aq) \longrightarrow CuSO_4(aq) + H_2O(l)$$

↓ **Figure 1:** This method of making salts is common for most of the transition elements because of their insoluble oxides and hydroxides.

(a) Insoluble black copper oxide is added to a solution of sulphuric acid.

(b) As the reaction takes place the colourless acid solution turns blue, indicating the presence of copper sulphate.

(c) When the reaction is complete and all the acid is used up, the excess black copper oxide powder remains at the bottom.

(d) The solution of copper sulphate is filtered to remove the excess copper oxide.

(e) After evaporation of the water blue copper sulphate crystals are left.

Other transition metal salts are made in the same way, with the excess metal oxide or hydroxide always removed by filtering. The salt which is produced is determined by the metal in the hydroxide or oxide used and the acid which takes part in the reaction, just as for the other salts we have looked at (Section 7.3). For example:

$$\text{iron(III) oxide} + \text{hydrochloric acid} \longrightarrow \text{iron(III) chloride} + \text{water}$$
$$Fe_2O_3(s) + 6HCl(aq) \longrightarrow 2FeCl_3(aq) + 3H_2O(l)$$

$$\text{copper hydroxide} + \text{nitric acid} \longrightarrow \text{copper nitrate} + \text{water}$$
$$Cu(OH)_2(s) + 2HNO_3(aq) \longrightarrow Cu(NO_3)_2(aq) + 2H_2O(l)$$

The silver halides

The silver halides are a group of silver salts, silver being one of the most unreactive transition metals. The silver halides (silver chloride, silver bromide and silver iodide) are all relatively unstable, so the compounds are very easily split up (decomposed). In fact, the energy from ordinary visible light is sufficient to cause the silver halides to decompose to give silver and the halogen (chlorine, bromine or iodine). Because of this silver halides are used to make photographic film and photographic paper. Silver bromide and silver iodide are most commonly used.

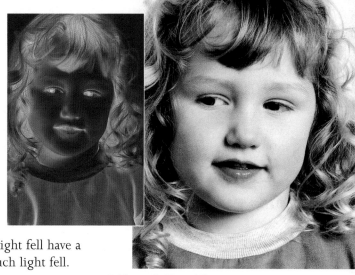

When a photographic film is exposed to light, a reaction known as **photochemical decomposition** takes place. The silver ions in the silver halide are reduced to silver atoms, whilst the halide ions are oxidised to form halogen gas. For example:

silver bromide $\xrightarrow{\text{light}}$ silver + bromine

$$2AgBr(s) \longrightarrow 2Ag(s) + Br_2(g)$$

The film now contains silver deposits of varying densities – depending on the amount of light which fell on the exposed film – and this forms a negative image. In other words, areas where lots of light fell have a heavier layer of silver (which appears black) than areas where not much light fell.

The silver halides don't just decompose in the presence of light. They are affected in the same way by X-rays and by the radiation from radioactive substances.

↗ **Figure 2:** The difference between a negative and the real appearance can clearly be seen here, with the heavy silver deposits in what are actually the lightest areas of the picture.

Ideas and Evidence

Silver halides, X-rays and radiation

In 1895 Wilhelm Röntgen discovered by accident that the silver halides are decomposed by X-rays, just as they are by light, and within three months X-ray photographs were being used by doctors to help diagnose and set broken bones.

Only a year after Röntgen had discovered X-rays, the Frenchman Antoine-Henri Becquerel tried to demonstrate that X-rays are produced by some chemicals after they are exposed to sunlight. He covered photographic plates with a thick layer of black paper to keep the light off them and placed a lump of uranium salt on top. After exposing the salt to the sunlight he developed the film and there was an image of the salt – made, he assumed, by X-rays. Becquerel set up more plates in the same way but the sun didn't shine so he put the plates in his desk drawer for several days. He then developed the photographic plate regardless, and was astonished to find a clear image of the salt. He had discovered radioactivity.

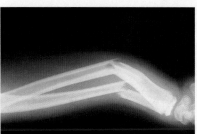

← **Figure 3:** X-rays depending on the decomposition of the silver halides are as important in medicine today as they were a hundred years ago for showing damage to bones.

← **Figure 4:** Antoine Becquerel discovered radioactivity in uranium through one of its properties – it affects photographic film, causing the silver bromide or iodide to decompose and the silver to be deposited to form a negative image.

Questions

1 a Produce an experimental procedure for making the transition metal salt of your choice, using a metal oxide or hydroxide and an acid.

b Give one advantage of using insoluble compounds in a reaction like this.

c Give one disadvantage of using insoluble compounds.

2 Explain how silver halides are used in photography.

Key Ideas

⊙ Salts of transition metals can be made by reacting their insoluble oxides or hydroxides with acids.

⊙ After reaction with the acid the excess metal oxide or hydroxide is filtered off.

⊙ Silver halides are reduced to silver by the action of light, X-rays and the radioactivity from radioactive substances.

⊙ Silver halides are used to make photographic film.

One salt is known to almost everyone because of its widespread use in everyday life. It is a compound of an alkali metal and a halogen, but sodium chloride is much better known simply as salt.

Salt has been important to people from the earliest times. It is actually vital for our health, and it is used around the world to enhance the flavour of food. The Romans valued it so highly that they were paid a certain amount of salt as part of their wages – the word salary comes from the Latin for salt, *salarium*. Salt is still of enormous importance in human life, not only as a seasoning and preservative for food, but as a major resource for the chemical industries.

Hundreds of thousands of tonnes of salt are used yearly around the world – but where does it all come from? One obvious source of salt is the oceans – sea water is salty. The other main source is in underground deposits – huge amounts of salt left behind millions of years ago when ancient seas evaporated as the climate changed.

↑ **Figure 1:** Sodium chloride (common salt) is an important factor in sea water, and in the cells of all the animals and plants that live either in the water or on the land above it.

← **Figure 2:** This vehicle is spraying rock salt – a mixture of salt, sand and grit – onto roads covered by ice and snow. The salt lowers the freezing point of water and so melts the ice, while the sand and grit provide more grip for car tyres.

How do we get salt?

In many of the hotter countries of the world salt is extracted from the oceans. The sea water is poured into big, flat open tanks and then the water evaporates away in the hot sun, leaving pure salt crystals behind. This method is even used on a very small scale in the UK, to produce high quality sea salt for eating, but the climate in the UK is simply not suitable for large scale salt production from the sea.

In many other countries, including the UK, salt is extracted from underground deposits. The salt is mined and brought to the surface in the form of rock salt, which is basically a mixture of sand and salt. Depending on the intended use, the pure salt may then have to be extracted, usually by dissolving it in water to make salt solution (known as brine).

↑ **Figure 3:** The salt extracted from these salt mines in Cheshire was once part of the sea water in a massive prehistoric sea.

Using the salt

Some of the salt extracted is used in the food production industry, while the rest is used for making chemicals. One very important industrial process is the electrolysis of sodium chloride solution (brine). Chlorine gas is formed at the positive electrode, hydrogen gas is formed at the negative electrode, and a solution of sodium hydroxide is also formed and collected:

sodium chloride + water $\longrightarrow$ hydrogen + chlorine + sodium hydroxide

These three products are all useful in different ways (see Section 7.6).

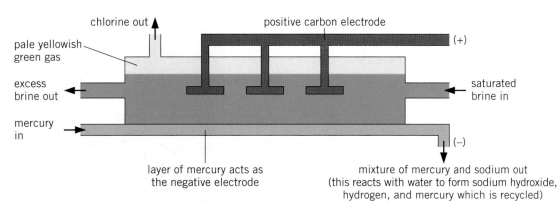

chlorine out

pale yellowish green gas

positive carbon electrode

(+)

excess brine out

saturated brine in

mercury in

(−)

layer of mercury acts as the negative electrode

mixture of mercury and sodium out (this reacts with water to form sodium hydroxide, hydrogen, and mercury which is recycled)

← **Figure 4:** The industrial electrolysis of brine is an almost waste-free chemical process. All of the products are collected and are useful, and any spare brine is simply sent around again.

Ideas and Evidence

Making it pay

The chlorine, hydrogen and sodium hydroxide produced by the electrolysis of brine are known as **co-products**. The amounts of each chemical produced are always in the same proportions. The good thing about this reaction is that all the products are useful (see Section 7.6). The difficult thing is that you cannot make one of the products without also making the others, so any company which electrolyses sodium chloride needs to be sure that it can sell all of the products that will result, not just one or two of them! What is more, it is vital that the value of the products

is substantially more than the cost of the raw materials, because the company has to pay for the chemical plant used, for the electricity to break down the sodium chloride and for the staff to look after the process. To be financially viable it has to do more than just cover these costs – it must make a profit as well.

↓ **Figure 5:** Although the costs of raw materials and the prices which can be charged for products change all the time, these figures give some idea of the balance of chemicals and costings in the electrolysis of brine.

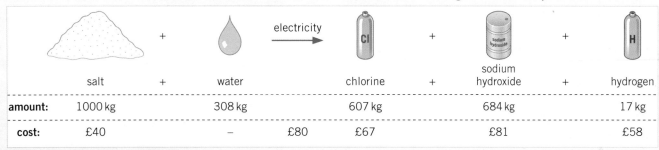

	salt	+	water		chlorine	+	sodium hydroxide	+	hydrogen
amount:	1000 kg		308 kg		607 kg		684 kg		17 kg
cost:	£40		–	£80	£67		£81		£58

? Questions

1 **a** What are the two main sources of salt for the chemical and food industries?

   b What are the advantages and disadvantages of the two methods of extraction?

2 Give a step-by-step description of the electrolysis of brine.

H 3 Give half equations for the reactions at the positive and negative electrodes in Figure 4.

4 Using the data in Figure 5, produce a pie chart to show the proportions of the different products of the electrolysis of brine.

H 5 If 117 g of sodium chloride were used in an electrolysis experiment, what mass of chlorine, sodium hydroxide and hydrogen would you expect to be produced?

Key Ideas

⊙ Sodium chloride (common salt) is found in large quantities in the sea and in underground deposits.

⊙ The electrolysis of sodium chloride solution (brine) is an important industrial process.

⊙ The products of the electrolysis are chlorine gas at the positive electrode, hydrogen gas at the negative electrode and sodium hydroxide in the tank.

7.6 Using brine products

The electrolysis of brine results in chlorine, hydrogen and sodium hydroxide. All of these products are useful in their own right and some of them can be reacted together to make yet more useful products.

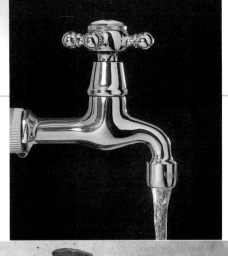

Chlorine

We know that chlorine is a poisonous green gas which bleaches damp litmus paper in the laboratory and causes great damage to the human body if it is inhaled in even tiny quantities. But it is also a tremendously useful chemical, both on its own and in combination with other elements. The chlorine produced by the electrolysis of brine plays a vital role in public health, because it is used to kill bacteria in drinking water and in swimming pools.

The chlorine may also be reacted with the sodium hydroxide produced in the electrolysis of brine to produce bleach (sodium chlorate(I)). Bleach is a strong oxidising agent which is very good at killing bacteria, and it is used extensively in homes, hospitals and industry to maintain hygienic conditions. Chlorine is also used in the manufacture of many other disinfectants, hydrochloric acid and the plastic (polymer) known as PVC.

Hydrogen

Hydrogen is a potentially explosive gas, yet once it has been produced, collected and stored in cylinders under pressure it has many important industrial uses. The Haber process for the production of ammonia (see Sections 4.8 and 9.6) depends on a ready supply of hydrogen. The manufacture of margarine involves bubbling hydrogen through vegetable oils under different conditions and in the presence of a catalyst to turn the oil into a soft spreadable solid. Finally hydrogen can be reacted with the chlorine also made by the electrolysis of brine to make hydrogen chloride which is then reacted with water to give hydrochloric acid. The acid made in this way is particularly pure and so it is widely used in the food and pharmaceutical industries.

↑ **Figure 1:** Chlorine is a chemical which has been put to terribly destructive use as a poisonous gas during wartime, yet it brings us clean, disease-free drinking water and keeps our homes, schools, industries and hospitals relatively free from infectious bacteria.

↓ **Figure 2:** Hydrogen is needed to make the vast amounts of margarine eaten every day all around the world. It is reacted with vegetable oils in equipment like this.

Sodium hydroxide

The sodium hydroxide which is left after the electrolysis of brine has to be purified because it is mixed with any remaining brine. Once that is done it is used for a variety of processes which include the manufacture of soap, paper and ceramics. Oven cleaners are based on sodium hydroxide too. The other major use of sodium hydroxide is to combine it with the chlorine produced to make bleach (see above).

Supply and demand

As we saw in Section 7.5, the quantities of the three co-products of the electrolysis of brine are inseparably linked. This can cause a problem for manufacturers, because demand for the products is not always the same. For example, there is a constant, all year demand for bleach from industry. But in the summer months, householders buy more bleach to put down smelly drains, and swimming pools use a lot more bleach as pool use increases.

To supply the chemicals to make more bleach the manufacturers have two choices. They may provide less chlorine and sodium hydroxide to other customers, which would not be good for business in the long term, or they might break down more sodium chloride by electrolysis to give the extra chemicals needed, although this would leave them with an excess of hydrogen. Making a bit more bleach all year round and storing it ready for the summer is not an option, because once sodium chlorate(I) is made it slowly breaks down, so bleach cannot be stored for long periods of time. Industrial chemists are constantly having to juggle with problems of supply and demand like these.

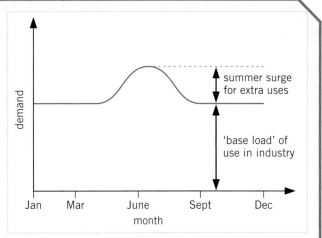

↑ **Figure 3:** The graph shows the seasonal changes in the demand for bleach.

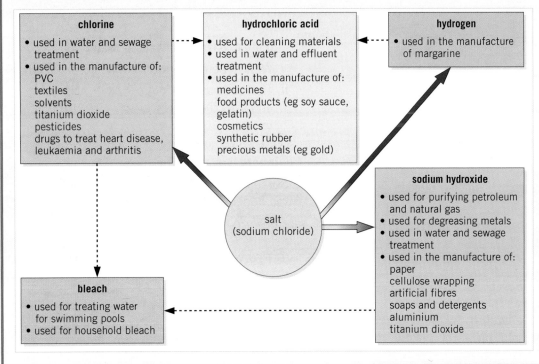

← **Figure 4:** Chemicals from salt are used in a wide variety of ways, and different demands for one chemical can put a strain on the supply of another one.

1 Make a table to summarise the uses of the products of the electrolysis of brine.

2 Explain how the price of electricity can affect the price of chemicals such as bleach, hydrochloric acid, and plastics such as PVC.

⊙ Chlorine is used to kill bacteria in drinking water and swimming pools and to manufacture hydrochloric acid, disinfectants, bleach and PVC.

⊙ Hydrogen is used in the manufacture of ammonia, margarine and hydrochloric acid.

⊙ Sodium hydroxide is used in the manufacture of bleach, soap, paper and ceramics.

1 A student was investigating the electrolysis of sodium chloride solution (brine) using this apparatus.

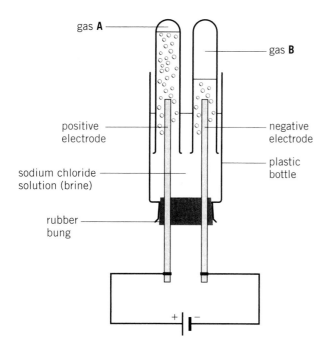

gas **A**

gas **B**

positive electrode

negative electrode

plastic bottle

sodium chloride solution (brine)

rubber bung

+ −

a Use the correct word from the list to answer this question.

   carbon dioxide   chlorine   hydrogen
   nitrogen   oxygen   sulphur dioxide

   i When damp blue litmus paper was held in gas **A** it lost its colour (was bleached). What is gas **A**? (1 mark)

   ii Gas **B** pops when a lighted splint is held above the tube. What is gas **B**? (1 mark)

b At the start of the experiment the sodium chloride solution was neutral. At the end of the experiment the solution in the plastic bottle had a pH of 10.

   What has happened to the solution? (1 mark)

c The table shows some of the products made from chlorine, hydrogen and sodium hydroxide. Copy and complete the table using words from the list.

   chlorine   hydrogen   sodium hydroxide

Substance	Used for
	hardening vegetable oil
	making PVC and solvents
	making soaps and detergents

(2 marks)

d Chlorine is used for treating water for drinking and in swimming pools. Why? (1 mark)

(Total 5 marks)

AQA specimen question

2 a A student knew that copper sulphate, $CuSO_4$, could be made by the following general reaction:

   acid + base ⟶ salt + water

   i What type of reaction is this? (1 mark)

   ii The base used is copper oxide. Name and give the chemical formula of the acid used. (2 marks)

b The student wrote about how the copper sulphate was made.

   'Some of the acid was warmed. Copper oxide was added. The mixture was stirred. More copper oxide was added until no more would react. The mixture was then filtered.'

   i Why was the acid warmed? (1 mark)

   ii Copper oxide was added until no more would react. Explain why. (2 marks)

(Total 6 marks)

AQA specimen question

3 The diagram shows the pH scale.

1	2	3	4	5	6	7	8	9	10	11	12	13	14

pH scale

   a What is the pH scale used for?   (1 mark)

   b Give an example of a chemical which you would expect to have a pH of around:

      i 1   (1 mark)

      ii 7   (1 mark)

      iii 14.   (1 mark)

   c If a substance has a pH of 7, what does this tell us?   (1 mark)

(Total 5 marks)

4 Acids and alkalis are useful in the home as well as in the laboratory.

   a Toilet cleaners and kettle descalers are used to remove lime scale.

      i Are they acids or alkalis?   (1 mark)

      ii Copy and complete this word equation to show how these products remove lime scale.

        ...... + lime scale $\longrightarrow$

        ...... + ... + ...   (3 marks)

   b How do oven cleaners remove fat and grease from the inside of ovens?   (2 marks)

(Total 6 marks)

5 a Give a word equation for the reaction between sulphuric acid (an acid) and sodium hydroxide (an alkali).   (2 marks)

   b This type of reaction is known as a .... reaction.   (1 mark)

   c **i** Soap is the result of the reaction between an alkali and a fatty acid. Suggest one source of the fatty acids used in the commercial production of soap.   (1 mark)

      ii Why is it so dangerous to spill alkalis on the skin?   (1 mark)

(Total 5 marks)

6 The oxides and hydroxides of the transition metals will react with acids to form salts.

   a What is the main difficulty in reacting the oxides and hydroxides of transition metals with acids?   (1 mark)

   b Give a word equation for the effect of sunlight on silver iodide.   (2 marks)

   c Give a chemical equation for the effect of sunlight on silver iodide.   (2 marks)

   d The picture shows a photographic negative.

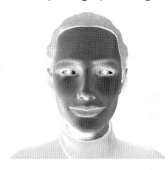

Explain how the reaction between the silver halides and sunlight is used in photography.   (3 marks)

(Total 8 marks)

Chapter 8: Reaction rates

Chemical reactions take place at all sorts of different rates. Some of them are incredibly fast – an explosion gives you no time to see what is going on! Other reactions, such as the rusting of iron in the presence of oxygen and water, take a very long time – it can be years before the iron is completely rusted away. Most reactions fall somewhere between these two extremes.

Why does rate matter?

The rate at which a reaction takes place is often very important. In the lab, if a reaction is particularly slow you won't get your results before the end of the session. In living organisms it is vital that all the chemical reactions take place at rates which supply the cells with the things they need exactly when they need them.

Reaction rate is also extremely important in the chemical industry. In any industrial process the ultimate purpose is to make money by producing useful products. In the chemical industry this means it is important to make as much of the desired product as possible as cheaply as possible. Cost is very important, because if it costs too much to make a product it will be hard to make much profit when it is sold. The rate of the reaction must be fast enough to make as much of the product as quickly as possible without risking overheating or explosions and without costing too much! So successful chemistry, whether at the microscopic level of the cell or on the massive scale of a major chemical plant, depends on controlling the rate of the reactions going on.

↑ **Figure 1:** In a massive chemical plant like this one, the rate of the chemical reactions must be carefully controlled to make sure they are taking place as fast as possible, under conditions which are as cheap as possible to run and as safe as possible both for the workers and the community – not an easy task!

Measuring reaction rates

In order to understand what affects the rate of chemical reactions and how we can control them we need to be able to measure the rate of any given reaction. There are two ways in which we can do this – *either* we can observe how quickly the reactants are used up, *or* we can observe how quickly the products are formed. Once we have a measurement for the reaction rate under one set of conditions, we can change the conditions and make comparisons of the changing reaction rate under different conditions.

There are three main ways in which we can make measurements of this sort.

⊙ We can measure a **change in mass** over time. Any reaction which involves a gas being given off can be carried out on a mass balance. As the gas is given off, the mass disappearing over a period of time can easily be measured and recorded.

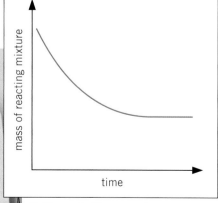

↖ **Figure 2:** The rate of a reaction can be measured by recording a change in mass over time.

- We can measure the **rate of precipitation**. When one of the products of a reaction is an insoluble solid which forms as a solid in solution (a precipitate), the solution will gradually become more and more opaque. The reaction is set up in a flask over a mark on paper underneath it, and the time taken for the marker to become invisible through the reacting mixture is recorded. Another method is to use a light meter and data logger to record the amount of light transmitted as the reaction proceeds.

- We can measure the **volume of gas** given off – but obviously only in reactions where gas *is* actually given off. The gas can be collected in a gas syringe and the increase in volume with time recorded.

Once we have the tools which will allow us to measure the rate of chemical reactions, we can move on to look at what actually affects the rate of the reactions we are observing.

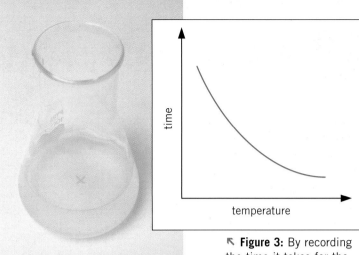

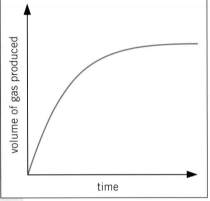

↖ **Figure 3:** By recording the time it takes for the marker to disappear under different conditions, the effect of different factors on the rate of reaction can be determined.

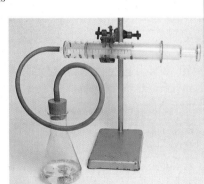

↖ **Figure 4:** Observations of the amount of gas produced with time gives us the rate of reaction.

? Questions

1 a What do we mean by the rate of a chemical reaction?

b Give two everyday examples of:

   i a very fast reaction

   ii a slow reaction.

c What are the two aspects of a chemical reaction which can be used to measure the rate?

2 Three different chemical reactions are given below:

   i calcium carbonate with hydrochloric acid

   ii magnesium ribbon with sulphuric acid

   iii sodium thiosulphate with hydrochloric acid.

a Write a word equation for the reactions in **i** and **ii**.

b Suggest a way in which the rate of each reaction might be measured.

3 Look at the graphs which result from using the three different methods of measuring the rates of a reaction (Figures 2–4).

a How are they similar to each other?

b How do they differ from each other and how might this affect their usefulness?

0—π Key Ideas

- The rate of a chemical reaction is important in living cells, in the laboratory and in industry.

- The rate of a chemical reaction can be followed by measuring the rate at which the reactants are used up or the rate at which the products are formed.

The rate at which chemical reactions take place is very important – and very variable. There are four main factors which affect the rate of chemical reactions:

- temperature
- concentration or pressure
- surface area
- presence of a catalyst.

How do reactions take place?

Reactions can only take place when different particles come together. The reacting particles don't just have to bump into each other, they need to collide with sufficient energy as well, otherwise they do not react. This is known as **collision theory**. The minimum amount of energy that particles must have in order to react is known as the **activation energy**. So anything which increases the likelihood of reacting particles bumping into each other, or which increases the force with which they collide, will make it more likely that reactions will happen. If we increase the chance of individual particles reacting we will also increase the rate of reaction.

In everyday life we control the rates of chemical reactions – cooking cakes in ovens, spraying a mixture of fuel and air into our car engines – often without any idea what we are doing and why! But in chemistry we need to know exactly how to control the rate of chemical reactions and why our control method works.

Temperature control

Increasing the temperature at which a reaction takes place – in other words, heating the reactants – speeds up the reaction. For most reactions a 10 °C increase in the temperature will double the rate of the reaction, for temperatures around room temperature. Increasing the temperature increases the speed of the reacting particles as they move around. This speeds up the reaction in two ways – the particles collide more frequently and they have more energy when they collide, and both of these changes increase the likelihood that the particles will react.

Increasing concentration or pressure

Many of our loveliest buildings are made of calcium carbonate in the form of limestone or marble. Often they have lasted for centuries, reacting only slowly with the slightly acid rain, but in the last 50 years or so they have begun crumbling away increasingly fast. The rate of this reaction seems to have speeded up. This is because the concentration of sulphuric and nitric acids found in rain water as a result of human pollution has been steadily increasing.

↓ Figure 1: There is no doubt that ammonia and hydrochloric acid have reacted together here in a spectacular manner to produce white ammonium chloride – but how do reactions happen?

↓ Figure 2: As this graph shows, the increased and more energetic collisions between reacting particles as the temperature increases lead to a clear increase in the rate of the reaction.

volume of gas produced

25 °C   15 °C   5 °C

time

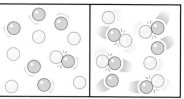

cold – slow movement, few collisions, little energy

hot – fast movement, more collisions, more energy

← Figure 3: Many statues and buildings have been increasingly damaged by acid rain – one result of the effect of increased concentration on the rate of a reaction.

A common way of increasing the rate of chemical reactions is to increase the **concentration** of the reactants. (Obviously this only applies if the reactants are in solution!) Similarly, if the reactants are gases, increasing the **pressure** at which they are reacting has the same effect.

If a solution is more concentrated it will have more particles of the reactants moving around in it. The more 'crowded' the reactant particles are, the more likely it is that they will bump into each other and a reaction will take place. In the same way, increasing the pressure of a mixture of gases squashes the gaseous particles more closely together. This increases the chance that they will collide and react, and so speeds up the rate of the reaction.

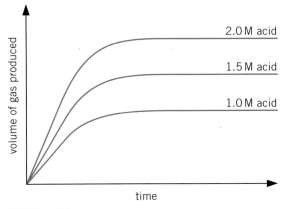

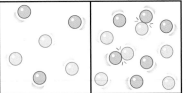

low concentration/ high concentration/
low pressure   high pressure

↖ **Figure 4:** The rate of reaction between calcium carbonate and sulphuric acid increases as concentration increases because the rate at which particles collide increases.

Questions

1 The data in this table is from a reaction carried out at two different temperatures:

Time of reading (minutes)	Total volume of gas given off at 30 °C (cm³)	Total volume of gas given off at 40 °C (cm³)
1	5	10
2	10	20
3	15	30
4	20	40
5	25	40
6	30	40
7	35	40
8	40	40
9	40	40

a Draw a graph of this data, plotting time along the x-axis.

b What does this data tell you about the effect of temperature on the rate of a reaction?

c Explain how temperature affects the rate of a reaction like this one.

2 Acid toilet cleaners designed to remove lime scale work better if they are used neat than if they are diluted with water. Explain why, using ideas about collision theory in your answer.

3 How does increasing the pressure of a gas mixture have the same effect on the rate of a reaction as increasing the concentration of reactants in solution?

4 Use your chemical knowledge to explain why acid rain damage on marble statues has increased significantly in the last few years.

Key Ideas

⊙ The rate of a chemical reaction increases if the temperature increases.

⊙ The rate of a chemical reaction increases if the concentration of dissolved reactants increases or if the pressure of gaseous reactants increases.

⊙ Increasing the temperature increases the speed of reacting particles so they collide more frequently and more energetically.

⊙ Increasing the concentration or pressure increases the frequency of collisions between reacting particles.

⊙ The minimum amount of energy that particles must have in order to react is known as the activation energy.

We can increase the rate of a chemical reaction by increasing the temperature or the effective concentration of the reacting particles, but there are other ways of changing reaction rates as well.

Increasing surface area

When you eat a piece of food, you chew it to break it up into small pieces – you don't usually swallow it whole, even though this would get it into your stomach more quickly! Digesting food is a chemical reaction, so by doing this you are controlling the rate of reaction.

If you want to boil potatoes quickly, you can cut them up into small pieces first. Cooking is a chemical reaction, so by doing this you are controlling the rate of reaction. Similarly, if you are trying to light a fire, you don't pile large logs together and try to set them alight – you use small pieces of kindling to begin with and then add the larger pieces of wood later, once the fire is going.

When a solid reactant is involved in a chemical reaction with a solution, the size of the pieces of the solid material make a big difference to the speed of the reaction. The inside of a large lump of a chemical is not in contact with the solution it is reacting with, so it can't react – it has to wait for the outside to react first. In smaller lumps or in a powder each grain is surrounded by solution and so reactions can take place easily.

↑ **Figure 1:** Without small pieces of kindling to get it going, a roaring fire like this would be almost impossible.

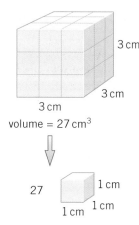

3 cm

3 cm

3 cm

volume = 27 cm³

Surface area of one side
= 3   3 = 9 cm².

Surface area of whole cube
= 6   9 = **54 cm²**.

27

1 cm

1 cm   1 cm

27 of these small cubes have the same volume as the large cube

Surface area of one side
= 1   1 = 1 cm².

Surface area of whole cube
= 6   1 = 6 cm².

Surface area of 27 small cubes
= 27   6 = **162 cm²**.

↑ **Figure 2:** When a solid reacts, the size of the pieces of it make a big difference to the rate of the reaction – the smaller the pieces, the faster the reaction. This is shown very clearly when equal masses of magnesium ribbon and magnesium powder are added to 250 cm³ of 1 molar HCl!

↑ **Figure 3:** Although flour seems harmless enough, it can react rapidly with air if the particles of flour are small enough. This flour mill in London was wrecked when flour dust caused a violent explosion.

Using a catalyst

Sometimes it is impossible to change the rate of a reaction using any of the ways we have looked at so far. In other cases none of these methods has sufficient effect without expensive extremes of temperature or pressure being used. However there is another way in which reactions may be speeded up, and that involves using a special chemical known as a **catalyst**. A catalyst is a substance which increases the rate of a chemical reaction but it is not affected by the reaction in any way. It is not used up in the reaction, so it can be used over and over again to speed up the conversion of reactants to products. Different reactions need different catalysts, and many of the catalysts commonly used are transition metals and their compounds – iron is used in the Haber process (see Section 4.8), while platinum is used in the production of nitric acid and also in the catalytic converters found in cars.

Catalysts have their effect by providing a surface for the reacting particles to come together and by lowering the activation energy needed before they can react (see Section 9.3), so more of the collisions between particles result in a reaction taking place. Catalysts are usually used in the form of powders, pellets or fine gauzes – these give them the maximum surface area for their catalytic action.

Catalysts are particularly important in industry. They save money because they speed up the process of making the product without the need to spend money increasing the temperature of the reacting chemicals. Although catalysts have to be bought (and they are not usually cheap), if they are well looked after and kept clean they will increase the rate of a reaction for a long time without further investment. What is more, using a catalyst almost always means that much lower temperatures, pressures and concentrations are needed to keep the reaction going at an ideal rate.

It is important to remember that although there are several ways of speeding up the rate of a reaction there is really only one way of increasing the total amount of product formed – put more reactants in at the beginning of the process.

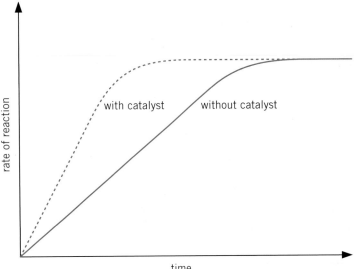

↑ **Figure 4:** Anything which makes it easier for a reaction to take place will speed up the rate of that reaction. By lowering the activation energy so that more collisions between particles result in reactions taking place, catalysts clearly increase the reaction rate.

? Questions

1 Explain why soluble painkillers work more quickly than tablets which are taken whole.

2 Plan an experiment to demonstrate the effect of the size of solid particles on the rate of a reaction.

3 a What is a catalyst?

  b Use this book or other resources to find three examples of catalysts along with the reaction that is catalysed.

  c Why are catalysts so widely used in industrial chemical reactions?

Key Ideas

⊙ The speed of a chemical reaction increases if the surface area of solid reactants increases (the solids are in smaller pieces).

⊙ The speed of a chemical reaction increases if a catalyst is used.

⊙ The only way to increase the amount of product is to increase the amount of the reactants.

For life to carry on successfully it is important that the hundreds of chemical reactions which occur in every living cell, making new materials and breaking things down, take place in a rapid and controlled way. This control is brought about by biological catalysts known as **enzymes**. Enzymes are made of protein, and like any catalyst they are not affected by the reaction they speed up, so they can be used many times.

Enzymes are very specific – each type of reaction which takes place in the cell is controlled by a specific enzyme which does not catalyse any other type of reaction.

Enzymes and temperature control

Leave a bottle of milk at the back of your fridge for a week or two and then pour it over your cornflakes and you'll find it is pretty disgusting. The milk will have 'gone off' as enzymes in bacteria break down the protein structure. Leave your milk in the sun for a day and the same thing will happen – but much faster. Temperature affects the rate at which chemical reactions take place even when the reactions are controlled by biological catalysts – in fact, *especially* when they are controlled by biological catalysts.

Biological reactions are sensitive to the same sort of things as inorganic reactions – concentration, temperature and particle size all affect them. But in living organisms an increase in temperature only works up to a certain point. Why is this?

The chemical reactions which take place fast in living cells happen at relatively low temperatures (warm rather than hot). In the human body this is around 37 °C. The catalytic action of the enzymes makes this possible. However, if the temperature increases too much then enzymes cannot work.

Because enzymes are made of long chain proteins, they unravel and **denature** if they get too hot – most enzymes are damaged by temperatures above 45 °C. Once the protein structure is damaged, the catalytic effect of the enzyme is lost and so the reaction which it controls cannot continue properly.

↑ **Figure 1:** A piece of meat is broken down by hydrochloric acid in a few days – but we can't wait that long to get energy and useful chemicals from our food. In the human stomach a similar piece of meat is broken down in a few hours, thanks to the action of the enzyme pepsin.

↙ **Figure 2:** Like most chemical reactions, the rate of the enzyme-controlled breakdown of starch by the enzyme amylase increases as the temperature rises – but only until the point is reached where the complex protein structure of the enzyme (left) breaks down.

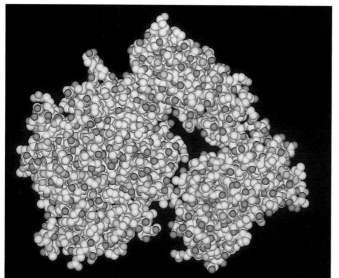

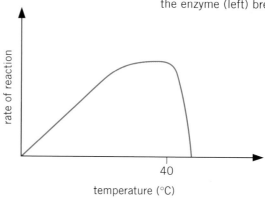

pH sensitivity

In enzyme-controlled reactions the reactants are known as **substrates**. Enzymes have their effect by binding the substrates to a specially shaped **active site** in the protein molecule. Anything which changes the shape of this active site stops the enzyme from working. Temperature is obviously one factor which changes the shape of the protein molecule. The surrounding pH is another.

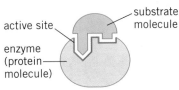

The enzyme and the substrate molecule fit together exactly like a lock and key.

The activation energy for the reaction is reduced once the substrate is in place. The substrate molecule reacts and changes shape.

The products leave the active site and the enzyme is unchanged, and ready to catalyse another reaction.

↑ **Figure 3:** Enzymes have their effect as catalysts using the 'lock-and-key' mechanism shown here. Anything which changes the shape of the protein molecule may change the shape of the active site and stop the enzyme from working.

The shape of an enzyme is the result of intramolecular forces between the different parts of the protein molecule. A change in the pH affects these forces and changes the shape of the molecule so that it can no longer act as a catalyst. Different enzymes have different ideal pHs.

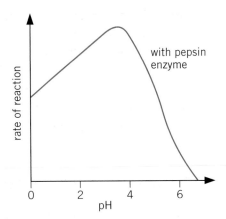

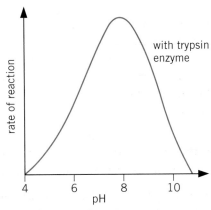

↑ **Figure 4:** The graphs show the rate of reaction for the breakdown of protein by two different enzymes. These enzymes are found in quite different parts of the human gut, and they need very different conditions of pH to work at their maximum rate. Pepsin is found in the stomach, along with hydrochloric acid, whilst trypsin is in the small intestine, along with alkaline bile.

Science people

In 1897 the German chemist Eduard Buchner accidentally discovered that a cell-free yeast extract could still convert sugar to alcohol and carbon dioxide. He had discovered the first free enzyme which he called zymase. This was really the beginning of the study of enzymes and the science of biochemistry – before Buchner's discovery scientists had believed that the reactions of life could only take place within living cells.

? Questions

1 What are enzymes and why are they so important?

2 Explain the following in terms of enzyme action:

   a When making home-made wine, if the jars of fermenting grape juice are overheated no fermentation takes place.

   b In bread making, dough left out in a cold store room can take 24 hours to rise, while similar dough in a warm kitchen rises in an hour or two.

3 **a** Using the information from Figure 4, what is the optimum pH for each of the enzymes pepsin and trypsin?

   b Explain what happens to the action of these enzymes as the pH goes higher than the optimum level.

Key Ideas

⊙ The chemical reactions in living cells occur quite rapidly in warm conditions rather than hot ones.

⊙ Cells use biological catalysts, known as enzymes, which are made of protein.

⊙ Enzymes are damaged (denatured) by heat.

⊙ Different enzymes work best at different pH values.

Living organisms are made up of individual cells. Each cell is like a minute chemical factory, as hundreds of chemical reactions take place which produce new materials and sometimes break down old ones. These chemical reactions are obviously vital for our existence as living organisms, but throughout human history we have also made use of some of them to improve our quality of life.

Making use of microorganisms – yeast

Yeast is a form of fungus which has been used by human civilisations for centuries. When they are short of oxygen, yeast cells convert sugar into carbon dioxide and alcohol (ethanol):

$$\text{sugar} + \text{yeast} \longrightarrow \text{ethanol} + \text{carbon dioxide}$$

This very specialised process is known as **fermentation** and is the result of the action of an enzyme called zymase.

The best known uses of the fermentation reaction include the making of alcoholic drinks, such as beer and wine, and bread making. In the production of beer and wine it is the alcohol which is important, although the carbon dioxide produced is also sometimes used to make the drink fizzy (sparkling). In bread making it is the bubbles of carbon dioxide, produced as the sugar is broken down, which are used to make the bread dough rise, giving bread its very typical light, airy texture. When the bread is cooked the ethanol evaporates, the yeast is killed and the reaction stops.

↑ **Figure 1:** Dating from 2250 BC, these statues of people making beer show clearly that the Ancient Egyptians knew about using yeast to make alcoholic drinks. Nowadays, the use of living organisms to make new materials is called *biotechnology*.

← **Figure 2:** The rising of bread dough is a clear indication of carbon dioxide being produced by the action of yeast on sugar. The process of bread making has been fundamental to the human diet for centuries.

Fermentation in the lab

In the laboratory, fermentation can easily be set up by mixing yeast, sugar and a little warm water in a test tube. The effect of fermentation can be observed as the mixture grows and becomes frothy. More scientifically, the presence of carbon dioxide gas can be used to show that fermentation is taking place – a simple test is that carbon dioxide gas turns clear limewater milky.

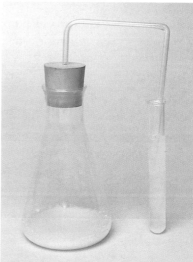

← **Figure 3:** Limewater looks just like water until carbon dioxide is bubbled through it. The yeast in this flask is clearly breaking down the sugar to produce ethanol and the carbon dioxide which has turned the limewater in the tube cloudy.

For centuries people knew that sugar was needed for the formation of alcoholic drinks, but they thought that the sugar simply broke down to form alcohol. They did not know that wild yeasts were already present on the skins of the grapes (or other fruits being fermented) so yeast did not need to be added separately. Louis Pasteur knew that although sugar is an optically active molecule (it rotates polarised light), when it breaks down the optical activity is lost. Yet in the 1850s Pasteur showed that a fermented mixture was optically active. He knew that (at that time) only living organisms were capable of creating new molecules which affected polarised light. So he reasoned that fermentation must be a process involving living organisms – the yeast cells he found in the brews. If people provided the living yeast with ideal conditions to grow, brewing and wine-making could move from small scale operations to larger factory-based operations. This is exactly what happened, and now specific types of yeast are added to produce reliable and distinctive products.

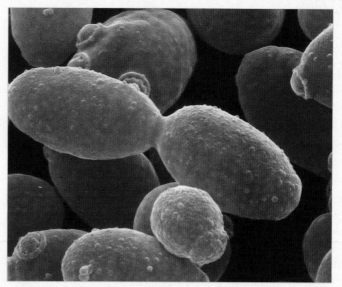

↑ **Figure 4:** This micrograph shows yeast cells, magnified over 4000 times. It was Louis Pasteur who first recognised the role of yeast in the production of alcohol, paving the way for a major change in the management of brewing beer and wine-making.

Enzymes and milk

Sometimes milk 'goes off' as a result of the action of bacteria, and it looks, tastes and smells disgusting. At other times we actually want our milk to go off – but in the way and at the speed we choose. Yoghurt and cheese are the result of milk that has gone off in very controlled conditions. In yoghurt making, specific bacteria are allowed to grow in milk which has been pasteurised (heat treated) to get rid of the unwanted bacteria which would otherwise give it an unpleasant taste and smell. The mixture of milk and bacteria is kept at a temperature of around 45 °C and the yoghurt-making bacteria convert **lactose**, the natural sugar found in milk, to **lactic acid**, the chemical which gives yoghurts their slightly sharp taste. Cheese making is very similar, except that the bacteria and milk are kept at much lower temperatures and only the solid curds produced are used to make the cheese.

1 Explain why enzymes are so important and give three examples of their use in the food industry.

2 Explain the importance of the work of Louis Pasteur in developing our understanding of the fermentation process and of enzymes.

3 Produce an information leaflet on one of the following industries, explaining the processes by which the product is made:

  brewing/wine-making

  the baking industry

  yoghurt production.

  The leaflet is to be used with pupils in years 6 and 7.

- ⊙ Living cells use chemical reactions to produce new materials.

- ⊙ In fermentation, yeast cells convert sugar to carbon dioxide and alcohol (ethanol).

- ⊙ Carbon dioxide turns limewater cloudy.

- ⊙ Milk is turned into yoghurt by the action of bacteria which convert lactose to lactic acid.

Since the end of the 19th century, when enzymes were first isolated from living cells, we have found more and more ways of using enzymes in industry. The application of this new science is an example of biotechnology.

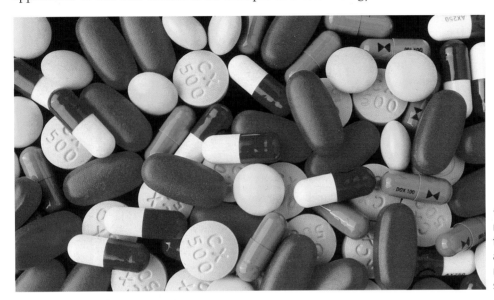

← **Figure 1:** A surprising number of the medicines we take, including the important antibiotic penicillin, are made using enzymes supplied by microorganisms.

Advantages and disadvantages of enzymes

In a chemical industrial process, one of the main problems is getting the reactions to happen at relatively normal temperatures and pressures. Constantly supplying heat, and building plants that can withstand high pressures, require expensive and energy-demanding equipment. So there is a constant quest for ways of carrying out reactions under relatively normal conditions. Enzymes can provide the perfect answer, safely catalysing reactions so that they occur at relatively low temperatures and pressures.

The main problem with using enzymes is that they are very sensitive to their surroundings (see Section 8.4). For enzymes to function properly the temperature must be kept down, below around 45 °C, and the pH also needs to be kept within closely monitored limits which suit the particular enzyme.

Enzymes are used industrially in two main ways. Some processes use the whole microorganism to provide the enzyme. These include brewing and the production of antibiotics like penicillin. However, whole microorganisms use up a lot of the substrate simply making new microorganisms, so some industrial processes use pure enzymes – enzymes which have been isolated from the microorganisms in which they were made. Pure enzymes use the substrate much more efficiently, although they are more expensive to produce.

What are enzymes used for?

The number of different uses for microorganisms and the enzymes they produce is growing all the time. The production of human insulin by enzymes in genetically engineered bacteria is one example of a relatively new use of whole microorganisms in biotechnology.

Pure enzymes (such as proteases, carbohydrases and isomerase) have many uses too. **Proteases** (protein digesting enzymes) are used in the manufacture of baby foods. They 'pre-digest' some of the protein, making it easier for a baby's digestive system to cope with.

Carbohydrases (carbohydrate digesting enzymes) are used to convert starch syrup into sugar (glucose) syrup. Huge quantities of sugar syrup are used in food production – just look at the ingredients labels of all sorts of foods. Using enzymes to convert plant starch into sweet sugar provides a cheap source of sweetness for food manufacturers. It is also important in the process of making fuel from plants such as maize.

Sometimes the glucose syrup made from starch is passed into another process using a different set of enzymes. **Isomerase** is used to convert glucose syrup into fructose syrup, by rearranging the atoms within the glucose molecule. The fructose syrup is much sweeter than glucose, and therefore smaller amounts of it are needed to make food taste sweet. As a result, fructose is widely used to sweeten 'slimming' foods – the food tastes sweet yet contains fewer calories.

Some uses of enzymes are very mundane – for example in biological detergents. The detergents contain proteases and **lipases** (fat digesting enzymes) which break down the proteins and fats in the dirt we get on our clothes – and so help provide a cleaner wash.

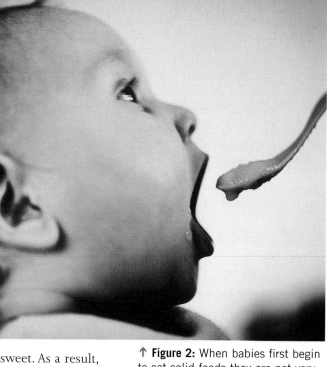

↑ **Figure 2:** When babies first begin to eat solid foods they are not very good at it. They may be given foods containing protein which has been pre-digested by enzymes, so it is easier for them to extract the goodness they need from their food.

← **Figure 3:** Millions of people in the UK, the US and around the world are overweight – and many of them are trying to slim. The market for slimming foods is enormous – and so more and more glucose syrup is converted to fructose syrup using enzyme technology.

? Questions

1 Make a table to show the advantages and disadvantages of using enzymes as catalysts to bring about chemical reactions in an industrial process.

2 Why are pure enzymes sometimes used instead of whole microorganisms in industrial processes?

3 Biological washing powders contain enzymes in tiny capsules. Explain why they are more effective than ordinary washing powders at lower temperatures.

4 Carry out a survey of the 'ingredients' labels of a number of different foods. Find how many foods in your sample contain sugar or glucose syrup and how many contain fructose syrup. Show your results graphically in some way.

0— Key Ideas

⊙ Enzymes are used in industry to bring about reactions at normal temperatures and pressure that would otherwise require expensive, energy-demanding equipment.

⊙ Whole microorganisms or pure enzymes may be used in industrial processes.

⊙ Enzymes are used in a wide range of different processes including the manufacture of baby foods, producing sugar from starch, producing slimming foods, as biological detergents and for making antibiotics and human insulin.

Industrial processes based on enzymes as catalysts may use whole microorganisms in the process or they may use pure, isolated enzymes extracted from microorganisms. Whichever method is used, care has to be taken to ensure that the enzymes work as effectively and economically as possible.

When the whole microorganism is used, a successful industrial process will depend on stabilising the organism and maintaining optimum conditions for its growth and survival, so that it keeps on functioning for as long as possible. The temperature must be correct, the right balance of nutrients supplied, oxygen levels maintained, and waste products removed if possible to control the pH levels.

Batch and continuous processes

Industrial processes using microorganisms usually operate either a **batch** process or a **continuous** process. In a batch process the microorganisms are cultured with a fixed volume of food medium, and they grow and use up the nutrients until they have reached a maximum population and have manufactured lots of the desired product. At this stage the whole process is halted, since the rate at which the products are produced starts to slow down as the nutrients run out. The products (often antibiotics or enzymes for another process) are then harvested and the culture tanks cleaned and sterilised before a new batch culture is started up.

→ **Figure 1:** The manufacture of penicillin, which takes place in an enormous chemical plant like the one above, is an example of batch culture. The graph shows the typical pattern for this type of process.

Science people

The penicillin story

In 1928 Alexander Fleming noticed that a mould which had grown accidentally on a culture of bacteria had stopped them growing. Eleven years later Howard Florey and Ernst Chain managed to develop the antibiotic penicillin from penicillium mould, but it was virtually impossible to extract enough of the drug from the mould to cure patients on a large scale.

With the onset of the Second World War, the need for penicillin became even more urgent with the casualties on the battlefield. But mass production of the miraculous-seeming drug was not possible until several big American pharmaceutical companies stepped in with huge fermentation plants which they had developed for other processes. These plants, combined with the lucky discovery of another type of penicillin mould (found by one of the scientists on a mouldy melon in a market!) which gave a much higher yield of penicillin drug than the original type, meant that large scale production of the antibiotic began in earnest, saving the lives of millions of soldiers and civilians in the years that followed.

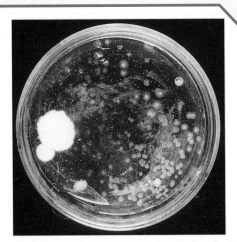

↑ **Figure 2:** The realisation that a chemical compound made by a mould could destroy bacteria – seen here on Fleming's original plate – led eventually to the development of antibiotics, drugs which still save millions of lives every year.

In a continuous process extra nutrients are added at regular intervals during the growth of the colony of microorganisms. At the same time some of the products along with microorganisms and wastes are removed, so the volume within the system stays the same. Continuous production is used for making single-celled protein (sold as Quorn ™) and in some forms of waste-water treatment. This system has many advantages, not least because it allows for production without breaks for cleaning and setting up new cultures, but batch production has other advantages – it is more flexible if demand is variable, and it is less prone to contamination. With the increasing use of pure enzymes more continuous processes are being developed, because the growth of the microorganisms is no longer a factor and so a much better yield is obtained.

Using pure enzymes

Increasingly scientists are looking at using isolated pure enzymes in industrial processes instead of whole microorganisms. This has lots of advantages – for example, all of the substrate provided will be converted into product (whereas whole microorganisms use a lot of substrate just for growing new microorganism), and ideal conditions for the specific enzyme can be used. What is more, only one pure product is formed because each enzyme only catalyses one reaction.

However, using pure enzymes can be very wasteful. They are quite expensive to produce, yet at the end of the process when the products are harvested, they cannot usually be recovered and so they are simply lost. This is why the newest areas of enzyme technology are involved in developing *immobilised* enzymes. The enzymes are immobilised (trapped and held) in an inert solid which does not interfere with their catalytic action. This holds them stationary while they catalyse the desired reaction. The enzymes can then be recovered from the reaction mixture at the end of the process and reused time after time. This makes the whole process more economical, much easier to control, and also means that the enzymes do not contaminate the end product.

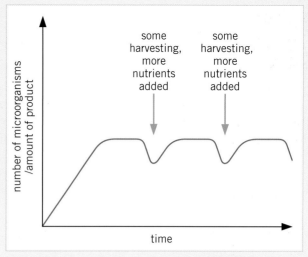

↑ **Figure 3:** Continuous culture is an ideal situation – but it does not give the best results with all microorganisms.

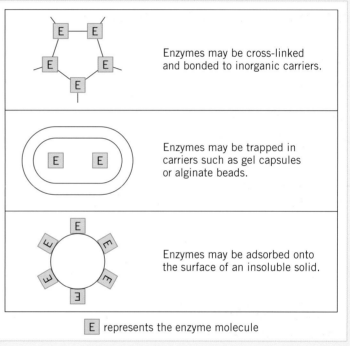

Enzymes may be cross-linked and bonded to inorganic carriers.

Enzymes may be trapped in carriers such as gel capsules or alginate beads.

Enzymes may be adsorbed onto the surface of an insoluble solid.

E represents the enzyme molecule

↑ **Figure 4:** Immobilised enzymes can be used time and time again. The enzymes may be trapped in a solid sheet or in a carrier such as inert alginate beads (made from an extract of seaweed).

1 a Indigestion tablets called **antacids** can be taken to react with excess hydrochloric acid in the stomach. A student investigated two different antacid tablets labelled **X** and **Y**.

Both tablets **X** and **Y** contained calcium carbonate.

   i Calculate the formula mass (M_r) of calcium carbonate, $CaCO_3$.
(Relative atomic masses: Ca = 40, C = 12, O = 16) (2 marks)

   ii Name the gas formed when calcium carbonate reacts with hydrochloric acid. (1 mark)

b The student first reacted tablet **X**, and then tablet **Y**, with 100 cm^3 of a hydrochloric acid solution. The student measured the volume of gas produced during the first five minutes. The results are shown in the table.

Time in minutes	Volume of gas in cm^3 Tablet X	Volume of gas in cm^3 Tablet Y
0	0	0
1	38	31
2	48	54
3	48	67
4	48	72
5	48	72

   i Draw a graph of the results for tablet **Y**.
(A graph of the results for tablet **X** has been drawn for you. Copy it onto your graph for tablet **Y**.) (3 marks)

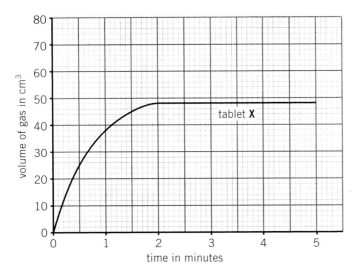

ii Tablet **X** contains less calcium carbonate than tablet **Y**.
How do the results show this? (1 mark)

iii Explain why the rate of reaction slows down for both tablets. (2 marks)
(Total 9 marks)
AQA specimen question

2 a What are enzymes? (1 mark)

b Explain why enzymes are used in industry. (3 marks)
(Total 4 marks)
AQA specimen question

3 The drawing shows a reaction carried out by a student.

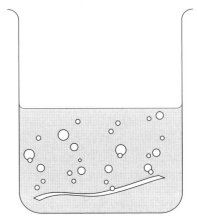

The experiment involved reacting a piece of magnesium ribbon with 1 M sulphuric acid.

a Suggest **one** way in which the student could measure the rate at which this reaction takes place. (1 mark)

b Suggest **three** ways in which the student could increase the rate of the reaction. (3 marks)

c Explain how each of these methods has its effect on the rate of the reaction. (6 marks)
(Total 10 marks)

4 The following data shows the results obtained by two students when they reacted the same mass of calcium carbonate with 0.5 M acid. In one reaction the calcium carbonate was kept in lumps, in the other it was ground to a powder.

Time of reading in minutes	Total volume of gas given off in cm³ (lumps of calcium carbonate)	Total volume of gas given off in cm³ (powdered calcium carbonate)
1	5	15
2	10	30
3	15	40
4	20	43
5	25	45
6	30	45
7	35	45
8	40	45
9	43	45
10	45	45
11	45	45

a Plot a graph of these results, with time on the x-axis. (4 marks)

b What do these results show about the effect of surface area on reaction rate? (1 mark)

c Why does the surface area of a solid reactant have such an effect on the rate of a reaction? (2 marks)

d Although the rates of the two reactions were different, the total amount of gas produced was the same. Why? (1 mark)

(Total 8 marks)

5 The use of enzymes in industrial processes is increasing all the time.

a What is an enzyme? (1 mark)

Use the information in the diagram to help you answer the rest of this question.

The diagram shows a graph of the rate of an enzyme-controlled reaction at different temperatures.

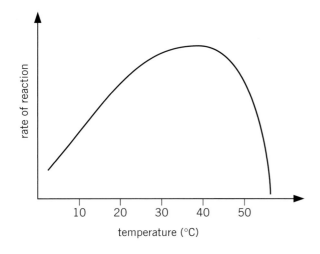

b At what temperature is this enzyme most effective? (1 mark)

c **i** What happens to the level of enzyme activity after 50 °C? (1 mark)

ii Why does this happen? (2 marks)

d The pH of the reacting mixture also affects the rate of an enzyme-controlled reaction. Explain why. (2 marks)

(Total 7 marks)

Ⓗ 6 a When whole microorganisms are used in an industrial process they are grown in large fermenters like this one.

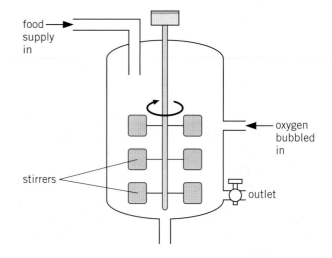

Explain the importance of:

i the food supply (1 mark)

ii the oxygen supply (1 mark)

iii the stirrers. (1 mark)

b Industrial processes using microorganisms are usually run either as **batch** processes or **continuous** processes. What is meant by:

i a batch process (2 marks)

ii a continuous process? (2 marks)

c What are the advantages of using isolated enzymes instead of whole organisms in industrial processes? (2 marks)

(Total 9 marks)

Whenever chemical reactions take place energy is involved, as chemical bonds are broken and formed. Energy is usually transferred either to or from the surroundings.

⊙ Reactions which transfer energy, often as heat, to the surroundings are known as **exothermic reactions** and we can measure a rise in temperature as the reaction progresses.

⊙ On the other hand, reactions which transfer energy, again often as heat, from the surroundings to the reacting chemicals are known as **endothermic reactions** and we can measure a drop in temperature as the reaction progresses.

Exothermic reactions

← **Figure 1:** When a fuel like this wood burns in oxygen we get a very clear illustration of what is meant by an exothermic reaction – we don't need a thermometer to measure the temperature change!

Fuels burning are a clear example of exothermic reactions, but there are a number of others which we often meet in the laboratory. Neutralisation reactions between acids and alkalis are exothermic, and the rise in temperature can easily be measured. Similarly the addition of water to white anhydrous copper(II) sulphate (anhydrous means 'without water') produces blue hydrated copper(II) sulphate crystals and heat – another exothermic reaction.

Respiration is a very special form of burning fuel. It involves the burning of sugar with oxygen, within the cells of every living organism, to produce the energy needed for all the reactions of life along with water and carbon dioxide as waste products. Respiration is another exothermic reaction.

↑ **Figure 2:** Warm-blooded animals such as this harvest mouse – and humans – depend on the heat generated by exothermic respiration to maintain the body temperature at a constant level, regardless of the weather.

Endothermic reactions

Endothermic reactions are less common than exothermic ones, but there are a number which are quite familiar. For example, when certain salts such as potassium chloride and ammonium nitrate dissolve in water they take in heat from the surroundings and the temperature of the solution drops. Also, any thermal decomposition reaction is endothermic, because the reaction only takes place if heat is put into the system. The breakdown of calcium carbonate to calcium oxide and carbon dioxide is one example – the reaction only takes place if the calcium carbonate is heated up to 800 °C, so the reaction takes in a great deal of energy from the surroundings. Another enormously important endothermic reaction is photosynthesis. Photosynthesis is the reaction by which plants turn carbon dioxide and water into sugar and oxygen, using energy from the sun.

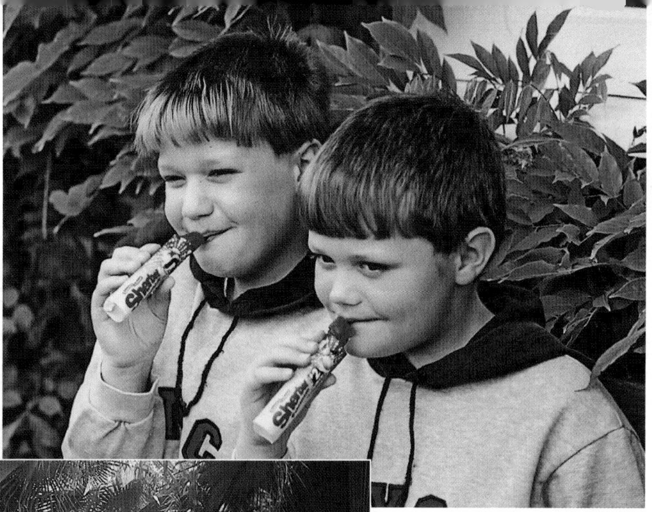

↑ **Figure 3:** Sherbet dissolving in water is an endothermic reaction – the slight cooling sensation on the tongue adds to the fizzy sour effect of these sweets.

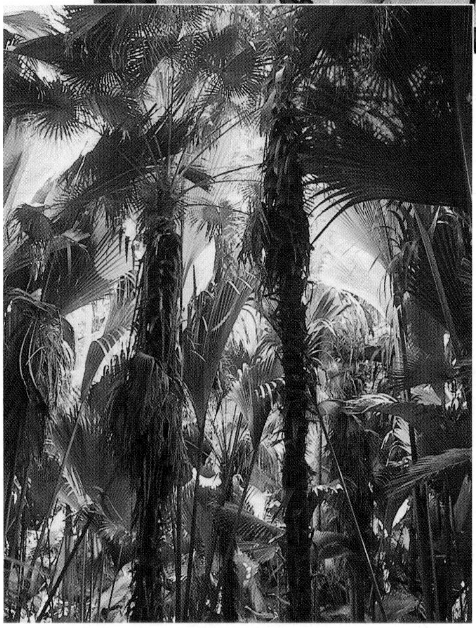

← **Figure 4:** Photosynthesis takes place in the green parts of plants all over the world – it is probably the most common endothermic reaction on Earth.

Questions

1 Which of the following chemical changes and reactions are exothermic and which are endothermic?

a a candle burning

b a firework exploding

c photosynthesis

d potassium chloride dissolving

e respiration

2 The sweets we know as sherbet are made of a mixture of sodium hydrogen carbonate and sugar. You have been told that sherbet dissolving is an endothermic reaction. Devise an experiment which would show that this is the case – or prove that it is not!

3 One of these graphs shows the course of an endothermic reaction and the other shows the course of an exothermic reaction.

a State which is which and explain your reasoning.

b What was the temperature change in:

i the exothermic reaction

ii the endothermic reaction?

c What is happening in the region labelled C in each graph?

Key Ideas

- When chemical reactions occur energy is usually transferred to or from the surroundings.
- An exothermic reaction transfers energy to the surroundings.
- An endothermic reaction takes in energy from the surroundings.

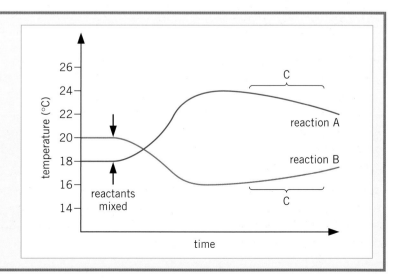

During any chemical reaction, existing chemical bonds are broken and new bonds are formed. Energy has to be supplied to break chemical bonds, so breaking bonds is an endothermic process – energy is taken in. However, when new bonds are formed, energy is released, so bond formation is an exothermic process.

In an exothermic reaction the energy released when new bonds are formed is greater than the energy used in breaking existing bonds, so overall energy is transferred from the reaction into the surroundings, usually meaning heat is given out.

In an endothermic reaction the energy required to break existing bonds is greater than the energy released when new bonds are formed, so overall energy is transferred from the surroundings to the reacting chemicals, usually meaning heat is taken in.

It is the *balance* between the energy which must be supplied to break existing bonds and the energy which is released when new bonds are formed, which determines whether a reaction is endothermic or exothermic. We can find out more about what is happening in a particular reaction by looking at energy level diagrams.

Energy level diagrams

Energy level diagrams show us the relative energy contained in the molecules of the reactants and the products of a reaction. This energy is expressed in kJ/mole – it represents the energy needed to make or break the bonds within 1 mole of the chemical elements or compounds involved in the reaction.

Diagrams like Figure 1 show us three different, important things.

⊙ This is an exothermic reaction – the products are at a lower energy level than the reactants, so energy has been given out in the reaction.

⊙ The difference between the energy of the reactants and the products indicates the amount of energy given out during the reaction (per mole). In an exothermic reaction, because the products contain less energy than the reactants, this number is always *negative*. This difference in energy between the reactants and the products is shown as **ΔH**, so we can say that in an exothermic reaction ΔH will always be negative.

⊙ Thirdly, we can see that to begin with, the energy line rises higher than the energy of the reactants. This represents the energy which has to be put into the reaction initially to break the existing bonds. This is the **activation energy** which has to be supplied before the reaction takes place at all.

In an energy level diagram for an endothermic reaction (Figure 2) we can see that the situation is reversed. The products are at a higher energy level than the reactants. This means that the difference between the energy levels (ΔH) is positive. The difference in the height represents the energy taken in during the reaction. As in Figure 1, the energy line goes higher than the level of the products, representing the energy needed to break down the existing bonds – again this is the activation energy.

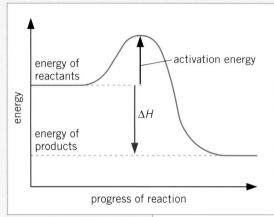

↑ **Figure 1:** This is a typical energy level diagram for an exothermic reaction.

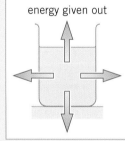

↓ **Figure 2:** This is a typical energy level diagram for an endothermic reaction.

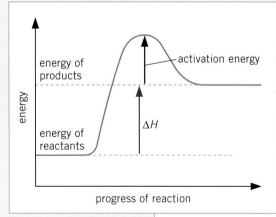

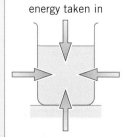

Energy transfers in practice

We can look at some energy level diagrams for real reactions and see what they have to tell us.

Example 1

Sodium and chlorine react together violently to give sodium chloride. Is this a reaction where energy is taken in or given out?

As we can see from Figure 3, the products have much less energy than the reactants. ΔH is strongly negative, so we can tell that the reaction between sodium and chlorine is strongly exothermic.

Example 2

Solid ammonium chloride dissolves in water. The energy level diagram for the reaction is shown Figure 4.

In this case the diagram shows us that when ammonium chloride dissolves in water the energy of the products is higher than that of the reactants. ΔH is positive and the reaction is endothermic.

ammonium chloride solution

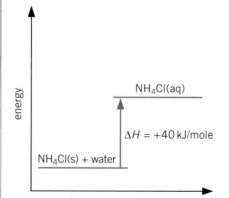

→ **Figure 4:** Energy level diagram for the formation of ammonium chloride solution.

sodium chloride crystals

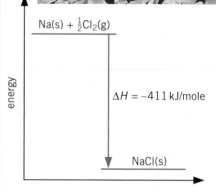

↑ **Figure 3:** Energy level diagram for the formation of sodium chloride.

Key Ideas

⊙ During chemical reactions energy must be supplied to break bonds and is released when bonds are formed.

⊙ In an exothermic reaction the energy released from forming new bonds is greater than the energy needed to break existing bonds.

⊙ In an endothermic reaction the energy needed to break existing bonds is greater than the energy released from forming new bonds.

⊙ Energy level diagrams show the relative energy levels of the reactants and the products of a reaction.

? Questions

1 Sketch energy level diagrams for the following reactions:

a $6CO_2 + 6H_2O \longrightarrow C_6H_{12}O_6 + 6O_2$ $\quad \Delta H = +2880\,\text{kJ/mole}$

b $C + O_2 \longrightarrow CO_2$ $\quad \Delta H = -394\,\text{kJ/mole}$

c $H_2 + I_2 \longrightarrow 2HI$ $\quad \Delta H = +26.5\,\text{kJ/mole}$

d $C_5H_{12} + 8O_2 \longrightarrow 5CO_2 + 6H_2O$ $\quad \Delta H = -3500\,\text{kJ/mole}$

2 a During all chemical reactions energy needs to be supplied for the reaction to take place. Why?

b At some point during all chemical reactions some energy is released – when?

c Explain how the balance of the energy taken in and given out affects the type of reaction taking place.

The activation energy is the minimum amount of energy needed by the reacting particles in any particular reaction for that reaction to take place. Unless particles collide with sufficient energy to supply the activation energy they simply don't react. The activation energy must be supplied before a reaction can take place. For example, when fireworks explode a strongly exothermic reaction is taking place, yet the chemicals which react so violently sit harmlessly in the cardboard tube until we 'light the blue touch paper and retire'! The heat from the burning of the blue fuse paper supplies the activation energy needed to start the reaction of the chemicals in the tube.

The activation energy needed for a reaction to take place is quite separate from the energy difference between the reactants and the products (ΔH). This is why even exothermic reactions often need heating to get them started.

The catalyst contribution

Catalysts are extremely important in the laboratory and particularly in the chemical industries because they speed up the rate of a reaction (see Section 8.3). Catalysts speed up the rate of reactions by lowering the activation energy needed for each reaction to take place. This means that many more of the collisions which occur between reacting particles actually result in a reaction taking place, and this in turn results in an increased reaction rate. A catalyst effectively makes it easier for the reactants to react together and form the product.

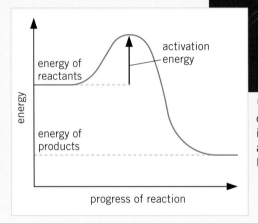

Figure 1: The spectacular chemistry of a firework display is stored safely until the activation energy is supplied by lighting the fuse.

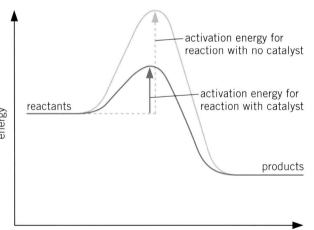

Figure 2: A catalyst has its effect by lowering the activation energy, making it easier for the reaction to take place and so speeding up the rate.

Whatever effect the catalyst has on lowering the activation energy of a reaction, the overall energy change (ΔH) remains the same. Enzymes, the biological catalysts which are so important in living cells and increasingly in industrial processes, work on the same principle of lowering the activation energy of the reaction which they catalyse.

Nanotechnology and catalysis

The use of catalysts and enzymes has been increasingly developed over the last century. So far most of the uses have involved speeding up industrial reactions to make them faster and more economic. Catalysts are also being used in an attempt to 'clean up' some of our modern technology, helping to reduce the pollution from car exhausts in catalytic converters.

Some new and quite mind-boggling uses of catalysts and enzymes are beginning to emerge from science laboratories around the world. For example, there is an enzyme called ATPase, which releases the energy stored in a molecule called ATP and makes it available to cells – it is vital for all the reactions of life. Scientists have isolated this enzyme and used it to create a nanomotor. (*Nanotechnology* is the science of building tiny machines no bigger than 100 nanometres in size – 100 nanometres is one ten-thousandth of a millimetre.) They have fixed one end of the enzyme to a sheet of metal a few atoms thick, and attached a microscopic propeller to the other end of the enzyme molecule. When supplied with ATP, the enzyme catalyses the breakdown of ATP and the energy released is used to turn the propeller. These minute 'motors' are so powerful that, if they were the size of a human being, they would be able to rotate a propeller 1 km long even if it was in water! When the enzymes are flooded with ATP the propellers turn, and when the ATP runs out they stop. More ATP starts them up again. Because ATP is found naturally in cells this development is seen as a step towards biomachines, where in the future the join between biological systems and mechanical devices may be completely undetectable.

↑ **Figure 3:** Enzymes trapped in microscopic capsules like this speed up the process of getting our clothes clean when they are used in biological washing powders. Some of these capsules are open to reveal the enzymes within.

1 In any chemical reaction energy has to be supplied to make the reaction happen.

  a What is this energy needed for?

  b What is it called?

2 Explain why:

  a a high activation energy means a chemical reaction takes place slowly

  b a low activation energy means a chemical reaction tends to take place fast.

3 Catalysts speed up the rate of chemical reactions without being changed themselves. They are often found as very small beads or pellets with holes in them. Use your knowledge of chemical reactions and the factors affecting the rate of those reactions to answer the following questions.

  a How do catalysts increase the rate of chemical reactions?

  b Why are catalysts usually found as tiny beads or pellets with holes in them?

⊙ The activation energy is the minimum energy needed by reacting particles for a reaction to occur.

⊙ Catalysts have their effect by lowering the activation energy, making it easier for a reaction to take place and so speeding up the rate of a reaction

Bond energies

We don't actually need to carry out reactions and measure the energy changes which take place to decide whether the reaction is endothermic or exothermic. Every single type of chemical bond has a particular bond energy associated with it, and this allows us to calculate exactly how much energy will be taken in and released in a particular reaction.

The bond energy for a particular type of bond is always the same, no matter which compound it is found in. The bond energy is measured in kJ/mole. This represents the amount of energy in kilojoules needed to break 1 mole of that particular type of bond.

We can use known bond energies to work out the overall energy change in almost any reaction. To do this we need to have a list of the bond energies of some of the most commonly found chemical bonds. (The list is shown in the table.)

Working things out

To calculate the energy change in a reaction we need to work out how much energy is needed to break the existing bonds in the reactants, and then how much energy is released on the formation of the new bonds in the products.

It is very important to remember that the data in the table is the energy required for **breaking** bonds. Energy is taken in and the measurement is positive. However when we want to know the amount of energy released when those same bonds are **formed**, although the figure is the same, the sign is reversed. For example, the bond energy for the breaking of a carbon–carbon bond is +347 kJ/mole, and the bond energy for forming a C–C bond is −347 kJ/mole.

Example 1

When hydrogen and chlorine react together they form hydrogen chloride. We can work out the energy changes as follows.

⊙ First we need to know the balanced equation for the reaction:

$$H_2 + Cl_2 \longrightarrow 2HCl$$

⊙ This tells us that 1 mole of hydrogen molecules react with 1 mole of chlorine molecules to form 2 moles of hydrogen chloride molecules.

⊙ From our table of data we know that the energy needed to break apart 1 mole of hydrogen molecules (H–H bonds) is 436 kJ/mole, and the energy needed to break 1 mole of chlorine molecules (Cl–Cl bonds) is 242 kJ/mole. So the energy needed to break existing bonds in the reactants is:

$$436 + 242 = +678 \text{ kJ/mole}$$

C — H

413 kJ/mole

glucose

methane

↖ **Figure 1:** Whether it is part of a small methane molecule or a larger glucose molecule, the average bond energy of the carbon–hydrogen bond is 413 kJ/mole.

Bond	Bond energy (kJ/mole)
C–C	347
C–O	358
C–H	413
C–N	286
C–F	467
C–Cl	346
Cl–Cl	242
H–Cl	431
H–O	463
H–N	388
H–H	436

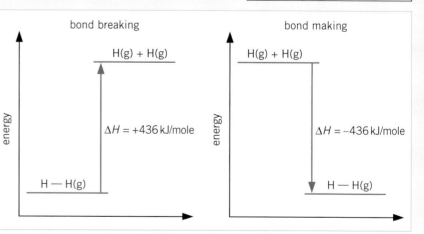

↑ **Figure 2:** The diagrams show the difference between the energy needed for the breaking and making of the same bond.

From our table of data we also know how much energy will be released in the formation of 2 moles of hydrogen chloride (H–Cl bonds). As bonds are being formed, energy is released. So to form two moles of H–Cl the bond energy will be:

$$2 \times (-431)\,\text{kJ/mole} = -862\,\text{kJ/mole}$$

To find the net energy transfer (overall energy change) for the reaction we combine the amount of energy taken in to break the bonds and the amount of energy released in bond formation:

$$\begin{array}{ccc} \text{energy taken in} & & \text{energy released} & & \text{total energy transfer} \\ \text{during bond breaking} & + & \text{during bond formation} & = & \text{during the reaction} \end{array}$$

$$678 \quad + \quad (-862) \quad = \quad -184\,\text{kJ/mole}$$

or $\quad \Delta H = -184\,\text{kJ/mole}$

The negative number shows that more energy was released in bond formation than was needed to break existing bonds, telling us that the reaction is **exothermic**.

↑ **Figure 3:** We don't need calculations to tell us that some reactions – like the dynamite exploding inside this building – are exothermic!

Example 2

When steam is blown through white hot coke, the carbon is oxidised to carbon monoxide.

The balanced equation for the reaction is:

$$C(s) + H_2O(g) \longrightarrow CO(g) + H_2(g)$$

1 mole of carbon reacts with 1 mole of water to form 1 mole of carbon monoxide and 1 mole of hydrogen.

The carbon already exists as atoms so there are no C–C bonds to be broken. The energy needed to break the two bonds in the water (H–O bonds) is:

$$2 \times 463 = 926\,\text{kJ/mole}$$

The energy released in the formation of carbon monoxide and hydrogen is −358 kJ/mole for the C–O bond and −436 kJ/mole for the H–H bond, making a total of −794 kJ/mole.

To find the net energy transfer for the reaction we combine the amount of energy taken in to break the bonds and the amount of energy released in bond formation:

$$926 + (-794) = +132\,\text{kJ/mole}$$

or $\quad \Delta H = +132\,\text{kJ/mole}$

The positive number shows that less energy was released in bond formation than was needed to break existing bonds, telling us that the reaction is **endothermic**.

Bond energy calculations like this always follow the same pattern. You use this method to find the net energy transfer in reactions if an energy transfer diagram is not available.

? **Questions**

1 a What is meant by the term 'bond energy'?

  b What is the difference between the bond energy for making and breaking bonds and how do we indicate this difference?

2 Write balanced equations and then work out the net energy transfer for the following reactions:

  a   hydrogen   + bromine   ⟶ hydrogen bromide

  b   carbon   + hydrogen   ⟶   methane

  c carbon monoxide   +   oxygen   ⟶   carbon dioxide

  d   nitrogen   + hydrogen   ⟶   ammonia.

0—π Key Ideas

- During a chemical reaction, energy must be supplied to break bonds and is released when bonds are formed.

- The net energy transfer in reactions can be calculated using known bond energies.

In some chemical reactions, the products formed immediately react together to produce the original reactants. This is what is known as a **reversible reaction**. Because a reversible reaction can go in both directions, when it is written down it is represented by a special double arrow with one half going in the forwards direction and the other backwards, like this:

A + B ⇌ C + D
reactants   products

Examples of reversible reactions

When solid ammonium chloride is heated it decomposes into ammonia and hydrogen chloride (thermal decomposition). When these gases cool down they react and recombine to form ammonium chloride again:

ammonium chloride ⇌ ammonia + hydrogen chloride

$NH_4Cl(s)$ $NH_3(g) + HCl(g)$

(white solid)   (colourless gases)

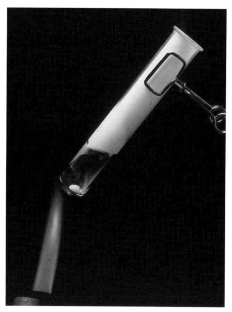

↑ **Figure 1:** The decomposition of ammonium chloride is a typical reversible reaction because the reaction goes in both directions very easily.

Another example of a reversible thermal decomposition is the reaction of hydrated copper sulphate with heat. When the familiar blue crystals of hydrated copper(II) sulphate are heated, the water is driven out of the crystals and evaporates, leaving white anhydrous copper(II) sulphate (hydrated means 'with water' and anhydrous means 'without water'):

hydrated copper(II) sulphate ⇌ anhydrous copper(II) sulphate + water

$CuSO_4.xH_2O$ ⇌ $CuSO_4$ $+ xH_2O$

(blue)   (white)

If a few drops of water are then added to the white anhydrous copper(II) sulphate, the blue colour of the hydrated compound immediately returns. This reaction can be used as a laboratory test for water.

Yet another good example of a reversible reaction is the one between iodine monochloride (ICl) and chlorine gas. Iodine monochloride is a brown liquid, while chlorine is a green gas. They react together to form yellow crystals of iodine trichloride (ICl_3). In an atmosphere containing plenty of chlorine gas, iodine trichloride will be made and remain stable. If the concentration of chlorine falls then the iodine trichloride decomposes back to iodine monochloride and chlorine:

iodine monochloride + chlorine ⇌ iodine trichloride

$ICl(l)$ $+ Cl_2(g)$ ⇌ $ICl_3(s)$

(brown)   (green)   (yellow)

→ **Figure 2:** Iodine trichloride crystals decompose to give the iodine monochloride and chlorine gas from which it was formed.

Energy transfers in reversible reactions

If a reversible reaction is exothermic in one direction it will be endothermic in the other. The same amount of energy will be transferred in both cases. For example, hydrated copper sulphate needs energy supplied in the form of heat to give anhydrous copper sulphate and water. When water is added to anhydrous copper sulphate, energy in the form of heat is produced.

H Equilibrium in reversible reactions

When a reversible reaction takes place in a closed system – one in which nothing can get in or out – then a state of equilibrium between the reactants and the products will be reached when the reaction occurs at exactly the same rate in each direction. Once this equilibrium is reached then the proportion of products and reactants in the mixture will stay the same. This situation is known as a **dynamic equilibrium**. The reactions are still going on – it is simply that the forward reaction is making products at exactly the same rate as the backward reaction is converting products back to reactants.

However, by changing the reaction conditions it is possible to change the position of the equilibrium – which changes the relative proportions of the reactants and products in the mixture. This is very important, because if we want to collect the products of a reaction we need as much product as possible in the reacting mixture.

Key Ideas

- In reversible reactions the products of the reaction can react to produce the original reactants.

- If a reversible reaction is exothermic in one direction it will be endothermic in the opposite direction. The same amount of energy is transferred in each case.

- When a reversible reaction takes place in a closed system an equilibrium is reached where the reaction takes place at exactly the same rate in each direction.

? Questions

1 What does the sign $\rightleftharpoons$ mean when it is used in a reaction?

2 What is the main difference between a reversible reaction and an ordinary reaction? (Compare the reaction between iodine monochloride and chlorine with the reaction between hydrogen and chlorine to help with your explanation.)

3 In a reversible reaction, if the reaction in one direction is exothermic, the reaction in the opposite direction will be endothermic. Using ideas of energy and chemical bonds, explain why the *amount* of energy transferred is always exactly the same in the forward and reverse directions.

4 a What is meant by a closed system?

   b In a closed system reversible reactions reach a dynamic equilibrium. What does this mean?

In a reversible reaction, the equilibrium position determines the relative amounts of reactants and products that will be present in the reacting mixture. For each reaction the equilibrium position depends very strongly on the conditions of temperature and pressure under which the reaction is taking place. It was a French chemist, Henri Le Chatelier, who first realised that by changing the reacting conditions (in particular the temperature and pressure) we can change the equilibrium position to give more product and less reactants in the final mixture. If we can shift the equilibrium position to the right, we will increase the yield of products (the proportion of products to reactants). This ability to manipulate the balance of reactants and products is very important when we look at industrial processes.

Moving the equilibrium – the rules

If a reaction is endothermic:

⊙ an increase in temperature supplies extra energy and so the yield of the products increases

⊙ a decrease in temperature decreases the yield of products.

If a reaction is exothermic:

⊙ a decrease in temperature increases the product yield

⊙ an increase in temperature decreases the product yield.

So in a reversible reaction we can alter the temperature to change the yield of chemicals in the equilibrium mixture.

But temperature is not the only important factor. Many reactions involving gases have a greater volume on one side of the reaction than the other. If we **raise** the pressure it encourages the reaction which produces less volume, while if we **lower** the pressure it encourages the reaction which produces more volume. So by choosing the appropriate pressure for our reaction we can increase the proportion of product in our final mixture.

The easiest way to understand these principles is to look at a real-life example. A typical case is that of the Haber process (see Section 4.8).

Equilibrium and the Haber process

The Haber process involves the reversible reaction between nitrogen and hydrogen to form ammonia:

$$N_2(g) + 3H_2(g) \rightleftharpoons 2NH_3(g)$$

ΔH is negative, so the forward reaction is exothermic

↓ **Figure 2:** The Haber process is remarkably efficient, because whatever the proportions of chemicals in the final reaction mixture, any unreacted nitrogen and hydrogen can be recycled and used again.

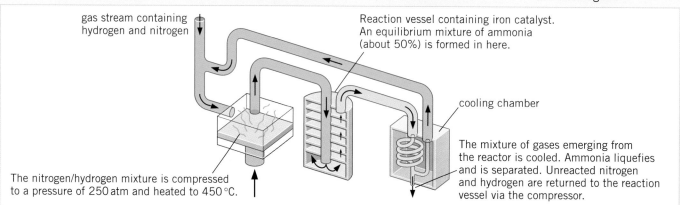

gas stream containing hydrogen and nitrogen

Reaction vessel containing iron catalyst. An equilibrium mixture of ammonia (about 50%) is formed in here.

cooling chamber

The nitrogen/hydrogen mixture is compressed to a pressure of 250 atm and heated to 450 °C.

The mixture of gases emerging from the reactor is cooled. Ammonia liquefies and is separated. Unreacted nitrogen and hydrogen are returned to the reaction vessel via the compressor.

On the left side of the equation there are 4 moles of gas ($N_2 + 3H_2$). On the right side there are only 2 moles of gas ($2NH_3$). (As 1 mole of gas always takes up 22.4 litres at 0° C and atmospheric pressure, the volume is directly related to the number of moles.) So the volume of the reactants is much greater than the volume of the products. This means that an increase in pressure will favour the production of ammonia – as it has the smaller volume. To get the maximum possible yield of ammonia the pressure would be as high as possible. In an industrial situation a compromise has to be made between high pressure and the expense of building a chemical plant capable of withstanding the high pressures, so the production of ammonia in the Haber process is usually carried out at pressures between 200 and 350 atmospheres.

The effect of temperature on the Haber process is more complex. Because the forward reaction is exothermic, a low temperature would maximise the proportion of ammonia in the final mixture. However, the overall rate of the reaction would be very slow because the particles would collide less often and would have less energy. To make ammonia commercially the reaction needs to be as fast as possible. To manage this, another compromise is reached. A reasonably high temperature is used because it is better to get a lower proportion of ammonia but a very fast turnover. The use of the iron catalyst also helps speed up the reaction rate but has no effect at all on the proportion of chemicals in the equilibrium mixture. If the product is removed as soon as it is formed, the yield will be improved because the reaction will keep chasing equilibrium. This can't be done in the Haber process because the whole reacting mixture has to be cooled to condense out and collect the ammonia.

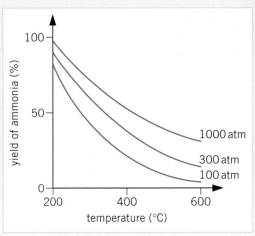

↑ **Figure 3:** In an industrial process like the Haber process compromises are made between getting the maximum amount of product in the equilibrium mixture and the reaction taking place at a reasonably fast rate.

? Questions

1 Henri Le Chatelier said 'If the conditions of a reversible reaction are changed, the position of the equilibrium will shift to oppose that change.' Explain in terms of this statement the effect of:

  a temperature on the products of an exothermic reaction

  b increased pressure on the products of the Haber process

  c temperature on the products of an endothermic reaction.

2 **a** In a theoretical process, a 10% yield of a chemical is obtained in 20 seconds while to get a 20% yield of the same chemical for the same process takes 60 seconds. Explain why it makes economic sense to go for the conditions which give a 10% yield rather than the 20% yield.

  b Explain why the normal operating conditions of 200–350 atm and 450 °C are chosen for the Haber process.

3 An imaginary chemical reaction has the equation:

$$A_2B_2 \rightleftharpoons 2AB$$

The graph shows the amount of AB at equilibrium at different temperatures.

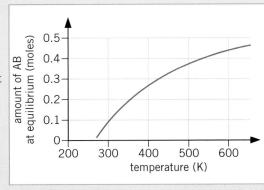

  a How much AB is there at:

  i 300 K **ii** 400 K

  iii 500 K **iv** 600 K?

  b What does this tell you about the energy changes in this reaction?

  c A company wishes to build a factory to make AB from A_2B_2. What conditions would you advise them to choose for the reaction and why?

🔑 Key Ideas

⊙ The relative amounts of the reacting substances at equilibrium depend on the conditions of the reaction.

⊙ If a reaction is endothermic, an increase in temperature increases the product yield.

⊙ If a reaction is exothermic a decrease in temperature increases the product yield.

⊙ If a reaction involves gases an increase in pressure will favour the reaction which produces the smallest volume.

⊙ Factors like these, along with the overall reaction rate, are important for determining the optimum conditions for industrial processes.

1 Chemical reactions are either **endothermic** or **exothermic**.

  a **i** What is an exothermic reaction?   (1 mark)

      ii Give **one** example of an exothermic reaction.   (1 mark)

  b **i** What is an endothermic reaction?   (1 mark)

      ii Give **one** example of an endothermic reaction.   (1 mark)

  c State which line on this graph represents an exothermic reaction and give the reasons for your choice.   (2 marks)

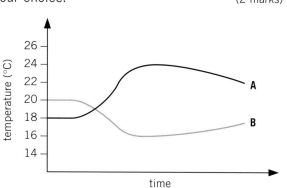

(Total 6 marks)

H 2 The energy level diagram shown here represents the energy changes in the reaction between the chemicals X and Y, which react together to give a compound known as XY.

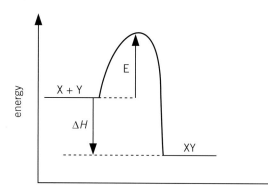

  a Is this reaction exothermic or endothermic? Explain your answer.   (2 marks)

  b **i** What does ΔH represent?   (2 marks)

      ii Will ΔH be positive or negative for this reaction?   (1 mark)

  c **i** What is represented by the arrow marked E on the graph?   (1 mark)

(Total 6 marks)

3 **a** What is meant by the **activation energy** of a reaction?   (2 marks)

  b How does a catalyst affect the activation energy of a reaction?   (2 marks)

  c Sketch the graph shown in the diagram.

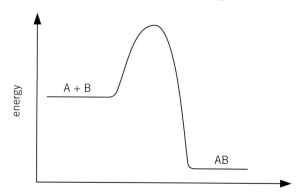

    Add another line to the graph showing the course of the same reaction if a catalyst was used.   (1 mark)

  d 'Whatever effect the catalyst has on the activation energy of a reaction, ΔH for that reaction remains the same.' Explain this statement, sketching diagrams if necessary.   (3 marks)

(Total 8 marks)

H 4 Hydrogen and chlorine are reacted together to form hydrogen chloride:

$$H_2(g) \; + \; Cl_2(g) \longrightarrow 2HCl(g)$$

The table shows bond energies for different types of bond.

Bond	Bond energy (kJ/mol)
Cl—Cl	242
H—Cl	431
H—H	436

  a Use the bond energies to calculate the energy change for the formation of hydrogen chloride in kJ/mol.   (3 marks)

  b Is this reaction exothermic or endothermic? Explain your answer.

(2 marks)

(Total 5 marks)

AQA specimen question

H 5 Ammonia is produced by the Haber process. In the process nitrogen and hydrogen are mixed. The pressure is increased to about 200 atmospheres. The gases are passed over an iron catalyst at about 450°C. The equation for the reaction is

$$N_2(g) + 3H_2(g) \rightleftharpoons 2NH_3(g)$$

The reaction between nitrogen and hydrogen is reversible. This affects the amount of ammonia that it is possible to obtain from the process. The graph below shows how the pressure and temperature affect the percentage of ammonia that can be produced.

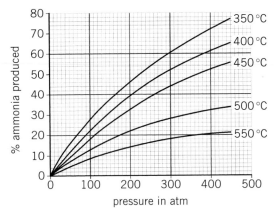

To gain full marks you should write down your ideas in good English. Put them in a sensible sequence and use the correct scientific words.

Use this information, together with your knowledge of the process, to explain why many industrial ammonia plants operate at 200 atmospheres and 450 °C. (5 marks)

(Total 5 marks)

AQA specimen question

H 6 Sugar is found in many foods, such as cakes and biscuits.

Sugar is broken down in the body to produce water and carbon dioxide.

$$C_{12}H_{22}O_{11} + 12O_2 \longrightarrow 12CO_2 + 11H_2O$$

a Why must the body *supply* energy in order to break down a sugar molecule? (1 mark)

b When the body breaks down sugar, energy is released.

   i What name is given to a reaction in which energy is released? (1 mark)

   ii Explain where this energy comes from in terms of the bonds in the molecules. (2 marks)

c The body can obtain about 1.7×10^6 kJ of energy by breaking down 100 g of sugar.

   i If a heaped teaspoon of sugar contains 5 g of sugar, how much energy does this sugar produce when broken down by the body? (1 mark)

   ii If a person has two teaspoons of sugar in each cup of tea that they drink, how much energy does this produce in one week if they drink five cups of tea a day? (2 marks)

   iii To lose 0.5 kg of fat, an average person needs to eat about 3.2×10^6 kJ of food energy less than they need. If this person puts only *one* teaspoon of sugar in their tea instead of two teaspoons, approximately how much fat could they expect to lose in one week? (3 marks)

(Total 10 marks)

Most of the chemistry we have looked at so far involves the reactions of the 91 naturally occurring elements and their compounds. In this chapter we will be looking simply at the reactions of carbon and its compounds – a branch of chemistry known as **organic chemistry**.

Science people

The term 'organic chemistry' comes from the early days of chemistry as a science. In 1807 Jöns Jacob Berzelius decided that all chemicals could be divided into two groups, depending on the way they behaved when they were heated. Anything which charred or burned when it was heated (he noticed these were mainly from living things) he called **organic chemicals**. Anything which melted or vaporised when heated he called **inorganic**.

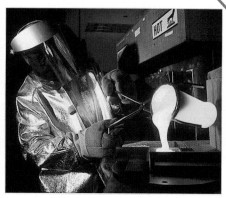

↑ **Figure 1:** Heating materials and observing what happened to them was the basis of Berzelius' classification of materials. Wood is an example of an organic substance, while glass is inorganic.

Other scientists adopted and used Berzelius' classification and decided that organic chemicals were formed under the influence of a 'vital force' found only in living things, so for many years people were convinced that organic chemicals could never be synthesised in the laboratory.

Although we now know that Berzelius' definition and the idea of vital force have some major weaknesses, the two main categories of chemicals which he suggested, inorganic and organic, remain with us today. Organic chemistry involves the study of carbon compounds whilst inorganic chemistry deals with the remaining naturally occurring elements and their compounds. Amazingly, the number of known organic compounds – around 7 million – is far greater than all known compounds of the other elements!

Sources of organic chemicals

Although the idea that organic chemicals can only be formed by the vital force of living organisms is not correct – many organic chemicals are synthesised in laboratories and chemical plants every day – it is true that living organisms contain many organic chemicals. Fossil fuels like coal, crude oil, and natural gas, which have formed over millions of years from plants and marine animals, and living fuels like wood are also rich in organic compounds.

Burning organic compounds

Organic compounds almost always contain hydrogen as well as carbon (see Section 3.5). Many organic compounds burn easily in air, and this is why they are frequently used as fuels. In a plentiful supply of air combustion is complete. The carbon in the compound reacts with the oxygen in the air and is oxidised to form

↑ **Figure 2:** The plant origins of this slab of coal are clearly visible.

carbon dioxide, while the hydrogen also reacts with the oxygen and is oxidised to form water. A clear example of this is when natural gas (methane, CH_4) is burned in air:

methane + oxygen $\longrightarrow$ carbon dioxide + water

$$CH_4 + 2O_2 \longrightarrow CO_2 + 2H_2O$$

As long as compounds like methane burn in a plentiful supply of air they make excellent fuels. However, if the supply of air is limited – which in turn means that the supply of oxygen is limited – then problems can arise. **Incomplete combustion** takes place and instead of just carbon dioxide being formed, carbon monoxide and/or carbon itself will be the result:

methane + insufficient oxygen $\longrightarrow$ carbon dioxide + carbon monoxide + carbon + water

When carbon monoxide is formed then the situation can become life threatening because carbon monoxide is a poisonous gas.

The silent killer

Carbon monoxide is poisonous because it attaches to the red pigment (haemoglobin) in the red blood cells which carries oxygen around the body. This reduces the ability of the blood to carry oxygen to the cells where it is needed. If the concentration of carbon monoxide in the blood gets too high, insufficient oxygen gets to vital organs like the heart and the brain, and the person breathing in the carbon monoxide will die. Faulty gas fires and boilers can release carbon monoxide into a room as the methane burns incompletely, particularly if the windows and doors are shut so only a very limited supply of air comes into the room. Carbon monoxide has no colour or smell, and the first symptoms of breathing it in are drowsiness – which makes it very likely that someone breathing air containing carbon monoxide may simply fall asleep and then die. Sadly there are deaths from carbon monoxide poisoning almost every year. Often sooty marks from incomplete combustion could have given a warning if people knew what to look for – but an inexpensive carbon monoxide detector is an even better way of avoiding tragedy.

Incomplete combustion in car engines means that carbon monoxide is one of the gases produced in the exhaust fumes – a form of pollution which is removed by the catalytic converter fitted to modern cars.

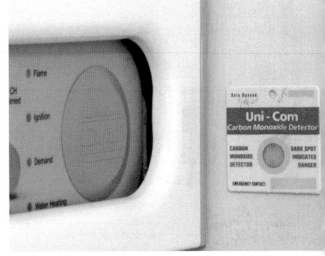

↑ **Figure 3:** Students and others who live in rooms with gas fires have to make sure that the appliance is regularly checked for carbon monoxide leaks – otherwise the source of comforting warmth may become a source of silent death. A simple carbon monoxide detector like this can warn people of the dangers and prevent anyone in the room being poisoned by this invisible, odourless gas.

? Questions

1 What is the difference between organic and inorganic compounds?

2 Originally it was thought that organic compounds were only found in living organisms.

  a Explain how this idea was disproved.

  b Give three examples of organic compounds found in living organisms.

  c Give three examples of organic compounds which are not from living organisms.

3 Design a leaflet which could be given to all students as they begin their time at college or university, warning them of the possible dangers of gas fires in their rooms and telling them what precautions they might take to prevent accidents.

Key Ideas

⊙ All organic compounds contain carbon.

⊙ When organic compounds are burned in a plentiful supply of air the carbon is oxidised to carbon dioxide and the hydrogen is oxidised to water.

⊙ When organic compounds are burned in a limited supply of air the carbon is incompletely oxidised to carbon monoxide.

⊙ Carbon monoxide is poisonous because it reduces the oxygen-carrying capacity of the blood.

Burning fossil fuels

The tables in Figure 1 show the primary energy consumption of fossil fuels (oil, gas and coal) from 1995 to 1999 in different areas of the world. Figure 2 shows similar data for China (which uses a distinctive mix of fossil fuels). The energy consumption is measured in 'million tonnes of oil equivalent' – in other words, the amount of energy in one million tonnes of oil. This is a unit used by the energy industry to enable the comparison of different types of fuels. One tonne of oil equivalent is about 40 thousand million joules.

Figures 3 and 4 compare the prices of different types of fuel and the amounts of carbon dioxide produced when they are burned.

→ **Figure 1:** Amounts of the three types of fossil fuels used in different areas of the world.

Year	Fossil fuel consumption (million tonnes of oil equivalent)			
	Oil	Gas	Coal	Total fossil fuels
1995	161	16	636	813
1996	174	16	677	867
1997	186	17	649	852
1998	190	17	614	821
1999	200	19	511	730

↑ **Figure 2:** Amounts of the three types of fossil fuels used in China.

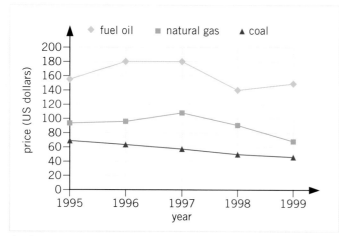

↑ **Figure 3:** Graph of the price of fuel oil, natural gas and coal from 1995 to 1999. The price is given per tonne of oil equivalent to enable fair comparison of the fuels.

Area	Fossil fuel consumption (million tonnes of oil equivalent)			
	1995			
	Oil	Gas	Coal	Total fossil fuels
North America	956	649	535	2140
Central & South America	194	66	19	279
Europe	723	343	387	1453
Former Soviet Union	217	492	193	902
Middle East	191	123	6	320
Africa	105	40	85	230
Asia / Pacific	849	196	994	2039
Total	3235	1909	2219	7363
	1996			
	Oil	Gas	Coal	Total fossil fuels
North America	989	663	559	2211
Central & South America	203	71	20	294
Europe	741	380	385	1506
Former Soviet Union	188	498	179	865
Middle East	200	136	6	342
Africa	107	43	90	240
Asia / Pacific	888	213	1059	2160
Total	3316	2004	2298	7618
	1997			
	Oil	Gas	Coal	Total fossil fuels
North America	1007	664	573	2244
Central & South America	213	76	21	310
Europe	749	374	373	1496
Former Soviet Union	187	466	175	828
Middle East	204	147	6	357
Africa	110	42	92	244
Asia / Pacific	920	222	1045	2187
Total	3390	1991	2285	7666
	1998			
	Oil	Gas	Coal	Total fossil fuels
North America	1029	648	578	2255
Central & South America	219	81	21	321
Europe	761	385	367	1513
Former Soviet Union	182	477	167	826
Middle East	207	154	7	368
Africa	113	44	91	248
Asia / Pacific	896	228	1013	2137
Total	3407	2017	2244	7668
	1999			
	Oil	Gas	Coal	Total fossil fuels
North America	1047	652	581	2280
Central & South America	219	84	21	324
Europe	755	400	348	1503
Former Soviet Union	182	483	171	836
Middle East	215	158	7	380
Africa	116	47	89	252
Asia / Pacific	929	242	913	2084
Total	3463	2066	2130	7659

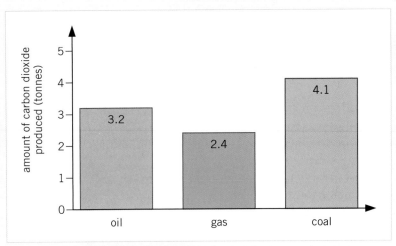

← **Figure 4:** Graph of the amount of carbon dioxide produced by oil, gas and coal when they are burned to produce the same amount of energy. The values given are the amounts produced per tonne of oil equivalent burned.

1 a Use the information in Figure 4 to put the three fossil fuels in order of the amount of carbon dioxide produced when each fuel is burned to produce the same amount of energy.

  b Use your knowledge of the chemical composition of these three fuels to explain why this order occurs.

2 a Use the information in Figures 1 and 3 to produce two tables like the one below, showing the cost of fossil fuels from 1995 to 1999 in: **i** Central & South America **ii** the Former Soviet Union.

	Oil			Gas			Coal			
	A	**B**	**C**	**D**	**E**	**F**	**G**	**H**	**I**	
Year	**million tonnes oil equivalent**	**price per tonne**	**cost (A × B)**	**million tonnes oil equivalent**	**price per tonne**	**cost (D × E)**	**million tonnes oil equivalent**	**price per tonne**	**cost (G × H)**	**total cost (C + F + I)**
1995										

  b Use the information in your tables to plot a graph showing the total cost of fossil fuels from 1995 to 1999 in: **i** Central & South America **ii** the Former Soviet Union.

  Comment on the pattern of costs that you see.

3 a Use the information in Figures 1 and 4 to produce two tables like the one below, showing the amount of carbon dioxide produced by the burning of fossil fuels from 1995 to 1999 in:
  i North America **ii** Europe.

	Oil			Gas			Coal			
	A	**B**	**C**	**D**	**E**	**F**	**G**	**H**	**I**	
Year	**million tonnes oil equivalent**	**CO_2 per tonne**	**CO_2 from oil (A × B)**	**million tonnes oil equivalent**	**CO_2 per tonne**	**CO_2 from gas (D × E)**	**million tonnes oil equivalent**	**CO_2 per tonne**	**CO_2 from coal (G × H)**	**(C + F + I) ÷ (A + D + G)**
1995										

  b What does the figure in the final column represent?

  c Use the information in your tables to plot a graph showing the figures in the final column for:
  i North America **ii** Europe.
  Comment on any patterns that you see.

4 Repeat your calculations for question 3 using the data for China in Figure 2. Comment on your results.

There are around 7 million organic compounds in the world – so many that it might seem an impossible task to understand anything about them. Fortunately however, the structure of the carbon atom and the way it joins to other atoms means that organic compounds can be classified in much the same way as we classify things in the living world. Organic compounds exist in large families of substances which all have the same general formula and which have similar chemical properties. Each organic family is known as a **homologous series**.

The members of a homologous series have the same **general formula**. This describes the number of carbon atoms and their relationship with the other atoms in the molecule. The physical appearance and chemical properties of the members of a homologous series can vary quite a bit between very short carbon chain molecules and very long carbon chain molecules (see Section 3.2) but the general formula always applies to all of them, whatever their size.

↑ **Figure 1:** Crude oil is the source of many different organic chemicals belonging to a number of homologous series.

Alkanes and alkenes

The simplest homologous series of organic compounds is the **alkanes**, consisting simply of carbon and hydrogen molecules joined by single covalent bonds (see Section 3.5 for more on the hydrocarbons). Because there are no double or triple bonds in alkanes, they are referred to as **saturated**. Methane has the formula CH_4, whilst ethane is C_2H_6 and propane is C_3H_8. These formulae can be worked out by drawing out the number of carbon atoms and working out how many hydrogen atoms would be attached:

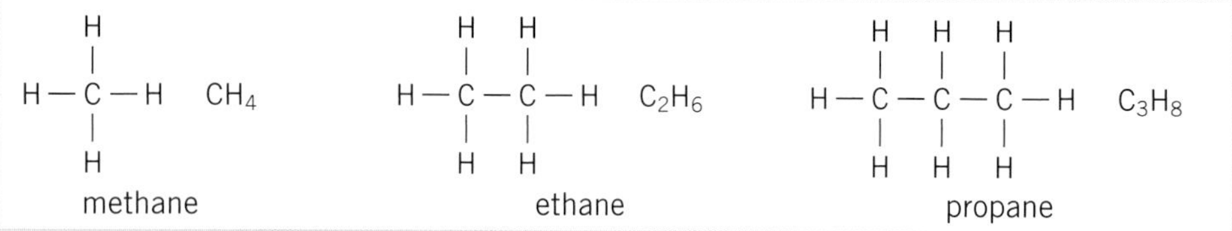

↑ **Figure 2:** Naming organic compounds – the number of carbon atoms in an organic molecule is often indicated in its name.

However, it is simpler to use the general formula for the alkanes: C_nH_{2n+2}

This makes it possible to work out the formula of any alkane as long as you know either the number of carbon atoms or the number of hydrogen atoms it contains.

Another simple example of a homologous series is the **alkenes** (see Section 3.5). The alkenes are a homologous series of **unsaturated** hydrocarbons – their molecules contain a carbon–carbon double bond.

The general formula of the alkenes is: C_nH_{2n}

We can use this to work out the molecular formula (and therefore the structural formula) of any member of the homologous series of alkenes.

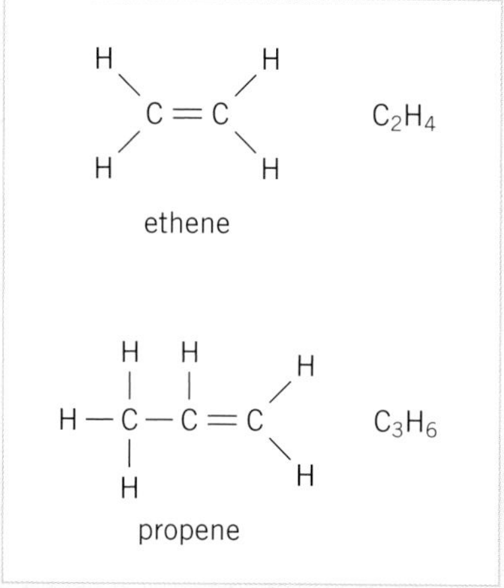

Number of carbon atoms	Name
1	meth-
2	eth-
3	prop-
4	but-
5	pent-

Combustion reactions

Both alkanes and alkenes can undergo combustion reactions – they burn in the presence of air to form carbon dioxide and water (see Section 3.5). However, the alkenes are more reactive than the alkanes because they have a carbon–carbon double bond. This means that the alkenes have many uses in making other chemicals since they undergo many more chemical reactions than the alkanes.

↑ **Figure 3:** Ethene and propene – represented by their structural formulae, which show the carbon–carbon double bond, and by their molecular formulae.

However, the alkanes are much more commonly used as fuels than alkenes – their lower carbon to hydrogen ratio (C:H) makes them burn much more cleanly.

$$\text{ethane} + \text{oxygen} \longrightarrow \text{carbon dioxide} + \text{water}$$
$$2C_2H_6 + 7O_2 \longrightarrow 4CO_2 + 6H_2O$$
$$\text{ethene} + \text{oxygen} \longrightarrow \text{carbon dioxide} + \text{water}$$
$$2C_2H_4 + 6O_2 \longrightarrow 4CO_2 + 4H_2O$$

Reactions with hydrogen

The alkanes are fully saturated hydrocarbons and so they do not react with hydrogen at all. The alkenes are rather different, because of the presence of the double bond. They do not react with hydrogen under normal conditions of temperature and pressure, but in the presence of a catalyst (finely divided nickel) and at a fairly high temperature (about 200 °C) they undergo an **addition** reaction. One of the carbon–carbon bonds breaks, allowing each carbon to form a covalent bond with another atom – in this case hydrogen. The molecule which results from this addition reaction is an alkane.

$$\text{ethene} + \text{hydrogen} \xrightarrow{\text{Ni catalyst at 200 °C}} \text{ethane}$$
$$C_2H_4 + H_2 \longrightarrow C_2H_6$$

Reaction with bromine

When bromine is dissolved in water a yellow-brown liquid known as bromine water results. This is a convenient way to use bromine in the laboratory.

If an alkane, a saturated hydrocarbon, is bubbled through yellow-brown bromine water nothing happens. However, if an alkene is bubbled through bromine water the liquid becomes colourless as the bromine reacts with the unsaturated hydrocarbon to form a compound (Section 3.5). This is a useful test for distinguishing between alkanes and alkenes.

? Questions

1 Give the structural and molecular formula for an alkane containing:

   a 3 carbon atoms   **b** 5 carbon atoms   **c** 8 carbon atoms.

2 Give the structural and molecular formula for an alkene containing:

   a 3 carbon atoms   **b** 5 carbon atoms   **c** 8 carbon atoms.

3 Use the general formula of the alkanes to work out how many hydrogen atoms will be present in an alkane with the following numbers of carbon atoms:

   a 6   **b** 10   **c** 7   **d** 15.

4 Use the general formula of the alkenes to work out how many hydrogen atoms will be involved in alkenes with the following numbers of carbon atoms:

   a 6   **b** 12   **c** 20   **d** 17.

5 Explain in terms of the structure of the molecule why butane is used as a fuel and butene is not.

🔑 Key Ideas

- A homologous series is a family of organic compounds which have the same general formula and similar chemical properties.

- Saturated hydrocarbons have the general formula C_nH_{2n+2} and are known as alkanes.

- Unsaturated hydrocarbons have the general formula C_nH_{2n} and are known as alkenes.

- Alkanes and alkenes undergo combustion reactions (react with oxygen).

- The alkenes undergo addition reactions: they react with bromine to decolourise bromine water and they react with hydrogen in the presence of a catalyst to form an alkane.

10.4 Isomers (H)

Organic molecules are well known for forming long chain molecules, long carbon backbones with other atoms attached to them. Because of the way the molecules are arranged they often form **isomers**. Isomers are molecules which contain the same numbers of each atom but have different arrangements of the atoms. They have the same chemical formula but different structures. These different structures can give rise to very different physical and chemical properties.

Figure 1: The fresh, minty taste of spearmint is very different from the flavour of caraway seeds – yet both plants get their distinctive aromas from different isomers of the same organic chemical, carvone.

Working out isomers

Structural isomers are the simplest form of isomers to understand. They consist of molecules which have the same number of atoms in each molecule, but they differ in the way the atoms are connected up. The easiest way to understand this is to see it in action:

For example, butane has the chemical formula C_4H_{10}. The simplest form of butane is shown as a simple straight chain molecule, in Figure 2. However, these same atoms can be rearranged differently to give 2-methylpropane, the structural isomer of butane, shown in Figure 3. These molecules are both still alkanes but their properties differ. For example, the boiling point of butane is −0.5 °C while the boiling point of 2-methylpropane is −11.7 °C.

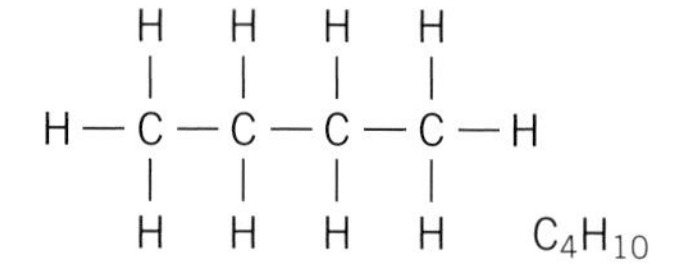

Isomers usually have different physical properties which depend on the strength of the intermolecular forces (the forces between the molecules). The strength of the intermolecular forces increases as the carbon chain length increases. Long chain molecules can pack closely together which means that the forces between the molecules are very large. Long chains can also become tangled together, which also increases the size of the intermolecular forces. Similarly, as the amount of branching of the chain increases, so the strength of the intermolecular forces decreases. The shape of the molecules means they cannot pack closely together, so the molecules are held less closely together and the forces between them are weaker. The stronger the intermolecular forces, the higher the melting and boiling points of the isomer.

How many isomers?

The longer the carbon chain becomes, the more structural isomers are possible. So while butane, with four carbon atoms in the chain, has two possible isomers, pentane with its five carbon atoms has three different isomers.

Just as with butane, the different arrangements of the atoms in the isomers of pentane lead to very different properties. The chains of the pentane molecules are relatively long, with strong intermolecular forces, whilst 2,2-dimethylpropane is an almost spherical molecule. The 2-methylbutane molecule is intermediate in chain length – so the forces holding the molecules together are intermediate in strength. The effect can be clearly seen when the boiling points of the different isomers are compared:

Isomer	pentane	2-methylbutane	2,2-dimethylpropane
Boiling point	36.3 °C	28 °C	10 °C

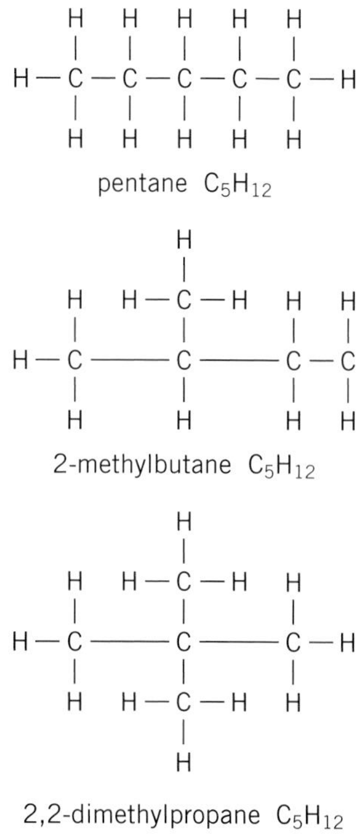

Figure 2: Butane

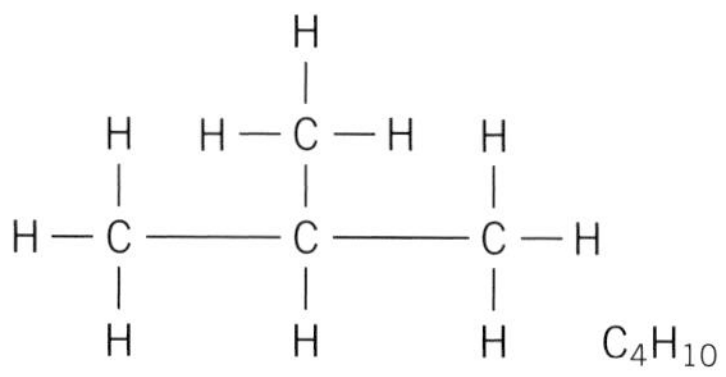

Figure 3: 2-methylpropane

pentane C_5H_{12}

2-methylbutane C_5H_{12}

2,2-dimethylpropane C_5H_{12}

Figure 4: The three isomers of pentane.

Predicting isomers

Alkanes with fewer than four carbon atoms in their chains cannot form isomers. This is because, however we draw them, they are still exactly the same molecule.

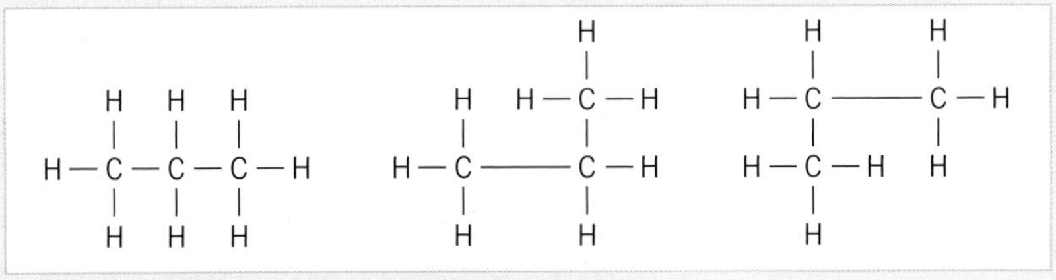

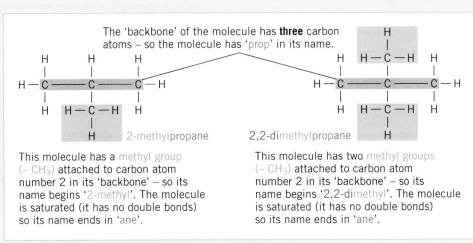

← **Figure 5:** These drawings of propane may look different at first glance, but they all involve the same three atoms in a line and so they all represent the same molecule –they are not isomers.

Similarly, when we try to work out the isomers of larger alkanes, we have to be very careful not to simply duplicate arrangements. For example, when we look at the two structures in Figure 6 it would be easy to think we had discovered an extra isomer of pentane – in fact the molecules in Figure 6 are chemically and physically identical, with one turned the other way around.

However, bearing these points in mind we can predict the isomers from a wide range of alkanes.

Naming isomers

The names of the basic alkanes are relatively straightforward. However, the names of the isomers can seem complex. In fact, the names simply tell us exactly what the isomer looks like. In the two examples in Figure 7, the names have been broken down and related to the structure of the isomer to show how it is done.

↓ **Figure 6:** Two identical molecules of 2-methylbutane.

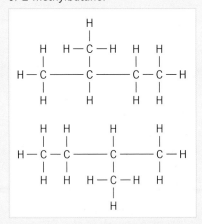

The 'backbone' of the molecule has **three** carbon atoms – so the molecule has 'prop' in its name.

2-methylpropane

2,2-dimethylpropane

This molecule has a methyl group (– CH₃) attached to carbon atom number 2 in its 'backbone' – so its name begins '2-methyl'. The molecule is saturated (it has no double bonds) so its name ends in 'ane'.

This molecule has two methyl groups (– CH₃) attached to carbon atom number 2 in its 'backbone' – so its name begins '2,2-dimethyl'. The molecule is saturated (it has no double bonds) so its name ends in 'ane'.

↑ **Figure 8:** The name of an alkane depends on its structure.

? Questions

1 What is an isomer?

2 Draw at least three isomers for hexane (C_6H_{14}).

3 How many isomers can you draw for octane (C_8H_{18})?

4 a Using the data from the table on page 156, draw a bar chart showing the boiling points of the three isomers of pentane.

   b What causes the differences in the boiling points of these three compounds which all have the same molecular formula, C_5H_{12}?

5 Take the isomers you have worked out in question 2 and name each one systematically.

Key Ideas

⊙ Isomerism occurs when two or more compounds have the same chemical formula but different structures.

⊙ Isomers have different properties which depend on the strength of the intermolecular forces.

⊙ The strength of the intermolecular forces increases as the chain length increases, and decreases as the amount of chain branching increases.

The hydrocarbons contain only carbon and hydrogen atoms. However, many homologous series of organic compounds also contain other elements, such as oxygen, nitrogen and sulphur. One of the best known of these organic families is the **alcohols**.

Ethanol

Ethanol is a member of the alcohol family. It has a number of uses but is probably best known for its use in alcoholic drinks. It is a poisonous chemical which in high doses causes death, but in lower doses it has a relaxing effect on the brain, releasing inhibitions, so people use it as a social drug which helps them enjoy their leisure time.

Ethanol is also a very useful solvent, which can be found in substances such as perfume and some types of paints and other decorative finishes. Another use which is becoming increasingly important is as a fuel for cars. The combustion of ethanol is clean and it is a renewable resource, because it can be made from plants.

↑ **Figure 1:** The alcohols are a very well known group of organic chemicals, mainly because one member of the family is a widely used social drug!

The production of ethanol

The natural fermentation of fruits is harnessed and used in a controlled way in the making of beers, wines, and ethanol for fuel. In each case, sugars have to be supplied to act as an energy source for yeast. The raw materials (grapes or other fruit for wine, malted barley for beer, sugar cane or maize for fuel, or just plain sugar) are mixed with yeast and water and kept at just above room temperature, at 20–30 °C. The yeast contains enzymes, which are biological catalysts (see Sections 8.4 and 8.5). If there is plenty of oxygen the yeast will break down sugar to carbon dioxide and water. However, in conditions without oxygen the enzymes in the yeast catalyse the breakdown of sugar into ethanol and carbon dioxide. The carbon dioxide is allowed to escape so it does not poison the yeast, but air is not allowed into the reaction vessel so that the yeast continues to produce ethanol:

$$\text{sugar} \xrightarrow{\text{yeast}} \text{ethanol} + \text{carbon dioxide}$$
$$C_6H_{12}O_6 \longrightarrow 2C_2H_5OH + 2CO_2$$

↑ **Figure 2:** When fruits fall to the ground and begin to decay, wild yeasts present on the skin break down the fruit sugar and form ethanol and carbon dioxide. These fermented fruits can cause animals to become intoxicated – and probably our ancestors discovered ethanol in the same way.

← **Figure 3:** Fractional distillation may be used to increase the ethanol content of alcoholic drinks. In this equipment, wine is being distilled to make brandy, an alcoholic spirit.

If the product is to be wine or beer the yeast will be removed and the drink bottled at this stage. To make spirits, where the ethanol content is higher, or to get pure ethanol for use as a solvent or a fuel, the ethanol is separated from the reaction mixture by fractional distillation.

Q Ideas and Evidence

Alcohol – fuel of the future?

↑ **Figure 4:** In areas where there is plenty of sun and rain, plants such as this sugar cane grow very rapidly and have a high sugar content. The problem is turning them into fuels.

If sugar-rich products from sugar cane and maize are fermented with yeast but without oxygen, the sugars are broken down incompletely to give alcohol (ethanol) and water. The ethanol is extracted from the products of fermentation by distillation, and it can then be used in motor vehicles as a fuel.

Car engines need special modification to be able to use pure ethanol as a fuel, but many cars can run on a mixture of the two fuels without problems.

The pros and cons of ethanol as a fuel

Ethanol is efficient and produces far lower amounts of pollutant gases like carbon monoxide, sulphur dioxide and nitrogen oxides when it burns, so it is much cleaner than conventional hydrocarbon fuels. In addition, ethanol reduces pollution even when it is simply mixed with conventional petrol to make a fuel such as gasohol (a mixture of 10% alcohol and 90% petrol), which is produced in large quantities in North and South America.

The biggest problem with gasohol is that a large mass of plant material is needed to produce the ethanol. This means that the use of ethanol as a fuel has so far been limited to those countries with enough space and a suitable climate to grow lots of the right sort of plant material as fast as possible, such as Brazil and the US.

In America, the use of gasohol, distilled from maize grown within the US itself, is becoming an increasingly important factor in the battle against air pollution in major cities and across the country.

? Questions

1 List three common uses for ethanol, giving a specific example in each case.

2 Why is it so important that the fermentation of sugar takes place without oxygen?

3 Make a flow chart to summarise the stages in the production of pure ethanol from sugar.

4 Using the information on these pages, and other resources, prepare a presentation on the use of ethanol as a fuel for the future, explaining the advantages and the difficulties involved.

0–π Key Ideas

⊙ Ethanol is used as a solvent and as a fuel, and is present in alcoholic drinks.

⊙ Ethanol is produced by the fermentation (by yeast) of sugars in the absence of oxygen.

⊙ Ethanol can be extracted from the reaction mixture by fractional distillation.

The homologous series of organic chemicals known as the alcohols contains a wide range of important and useful chemicals, although most people are only aware of ethanol. The alcohols consist of a hydrocarbon chain with a reactive –OH group attached. This characteristic group of the family – known as the **functional group** – affects the chemistry of all the members of the family.

The structure of the alcohols

The main part of an alcohol molecule is a hydrocarbon chain – the name of the alcohol comes from the number of carbon atoms in the chain. Every alcohol has an –OH functional group.

Many of the shorter chain alcohols, including ethanol, are clear, colourless liquids which are used in a variety of ways in industry. However, the ethanol used in alcoholic drinks is highly taxed to raise revenue, making it relatively expensive, whilst ethanol for use in industry as a solvent or a fuel is not taxed in the same way. To prevent people from trying to drink cheap industrial ethanol, poisonous methanol is added to it, along with a bright purple dye which has a very unpleasant smell. This makes methylated spirits, sometimes known as 'meths'.

↑ **Figure 1:** In each alcohol, the final hydrogen molecule has been replaced with an –OH group.

← **Figure 2:** Two bottles of ethanol – but the packaging emphasises the fact that one is for human consumption while the other is not.

Producing alcohols

Ethanol for drinking purposes and as a fuel for cars is usually made by fermentation of plants, as we saw in Section 10.5. However, most of the alcohols needed for industrial use, including ethanol, are manufactured from alkenes produced from the refining of crude oil. The conditions needed to produce alcohols in this way are quite extreme. Ethanol, for example, is produced when ethene is mixed with steam in the presence of a strong acid catalyst (phosphoric acid) at a moderately high temperature (around 300 °C) and a high pressure (70 atm):

ethene + steam ⟶ ethanol

The two different methods of producing ethanol have a number of advantages and disadvantages which need careful evaluation before deciding which is the appropriate production method. The fermentation of plant material is a long and relatively slow process. It cannot be speeded up by raising the temperature because this would kill the living yeast cells which bring about the production of ethanol.

However, once it is set up on a large scale, almost continuous production of ethanol can be achieved. In contrast, the rate of the reaction in production of ethanol from ethene is very rapid and can respond easily to changes in demand for the product – if extra ethanol is needed, it can be produced almost immediately.

At the end of the natural fermentation process the ethanol which has been produced forms only a relatively small proportion of a mixture which contains mainly water, together with yeast and debris from the original plant material. For use in alcoholic drinks the additional flavours and colours provided by the other chemical substances in the mixture are wanted, but for industrial usage pure ethanol has to be extracted by fractional distillation, adding an extra stage to the process. In the industrial production of ethanol from ethene, pure ethanol is the direct product.

Fermentation involves a batch process – the yeast, plant material or sugar and water mixture has to be set up and left for ethanol to be made. However, this is overcome by having many different batches so that ethanol production can be almost constant. The industrial production of ethanol from ethene can be a continuous process if demand is high.

Making ethanol by fermentation from plants uses a natural and renewable resource. Plants are used to provide the raw material for the process, and new plants can be grown continuously. The only limit to the production of ethanol in this way is the amount of land which can be dedicated to growing plants for fuel rather than for food. In contrast the ethene used in the industrial production of ethanol is derived from crude oil. This is a fossil fuel and is a non-renewable resource. Once all the oil has been used up there will be no more available, and current estimates suggest that there is enough crude oil left in the Earth's crust to last us with our current usage for about 40 years.

↑ **Figure 3:** Making ethanol on a large scale always involves massive industrial processes – whether it is made by fermentation (top photograph) or from ethene in a petrochemical plant (bottom photograph). These two processes use very different raw materials, and raise very different issues for us to think about.

Key Ideas

⊙ The alcohols form a homologous series with the –OH functional group giving them their characteristic properties.

⊙ Ethanol can be produced by the fermentation of sugars using yeast, and by the reaction of steam and ethene in the presence of a strong acid catalyst at a moderately high temperature and pressure.

? Questions

1 Draw the molecular and structural formulae for butanol and pentanol.

2 Alcohols with longer carbon chains have isomers. Draw the possible isomers of propanol and butanol.

3 a Make a table to evaluate the two different methods of producing ethanol in terms of the rate of reaction, the quality of the product, the use of finite resources, and the choice of a batch versus a continuous process.

   b Which method would you support for future development to produce large quantities of ethanol? Give reasons to support your choice.

The way the alcohols react with other chemicals is partly decided by the –OH functional group which they all possess and partly by the length of the carbon chain – as the chain gets longer, it has a bigger and bigger effect on the way the alcohol reacts. But for the alcohols with short carbon chains, the –OH group is the most important factor in their reactions.

Reactions with carboxylic acids

We are all familiar with mineral acids like hydrochloric acid and sulphuric acid, but there are many organic acids as well. An important group of organic acids is the **carboxylic acids**, which include many well known chemicals like ethanoic acid (vinegar) (see Section 10.8). Alcohols react with carboxylic acids to form compounds called **esters** and water, in the presence of an acid catalyst like concentrated sulphuric acid. The reaction is known as **esterification** – it is the organic equivalent of a mineral acid and a base reacting to form a salt and water. Esterification is a reversible reaction, so it is not necessarily the most economic way of forming esters, and other methods are usually used in industry. When ethanol reacts with ethanoic acid the ester formed is known as ethyl ethanoate.

| ethanoic acid | + | ethanol | $\rightleftharpoons$ | ethyl ethanoate | + | water |

Esters are another homologous series of organic compounds. There are weak intermolecular forces between their molecules, so they have low melting and boiling points. They are known for having pleasant smells. In nature many of the scents of fruits and flowers are due to esters, and they are often made industrially for use in the food and cosmetic industries as flavourings and fragrances. They are also important solvents, particularly for adhesives.

← **Figure 1:** Flowers like these produce attractive scents. We often try to mimic the natural smells of flowers and fruit in our food, cosmetics and cleaning products. One important industrial use of alcohols is to produce the esters which provide these smells.

Reactions with sodium

The alcohols react with sodium to form hydrogen. We know (from Section 6.4) that if we add sodium to water it floats on the water and reacts very vigorously, rushing around on the surface producing hydrogen gas and sodium hydroxide:

$$2Na(s) + 2H_2O(l) \longrightarrow H_2(g) + 2NaOH(aq)$$

When sodium is added to ethanol it sinks – the sodium is more dense than ethanol – and then a steady stream of hydrogen is produced. As well as the hydrogen, the reaction results in the formation of a solid known as sodium ethoxide. It is a very similar reaction to that between sodium and water, but considerably less vigorous:

$$2Na(s) + 2C_2H_5OH(l) \longrightarrow H_2(g) + 2C_2H_5ONa(s)$$
$$\text{ethanol} \qquad\qquad \text{sodium ethoxide}$$

↑ **Figure 2:** In the reaction between sodium and ethanol, hydrogen gas is given off and solid sodium ethoxide forms.

Oxidation reactions

Ethanol, like many other alcohols, is very easily oxidised. This is a process which takes place in two stages, when alcohols are exposed to the air or to other oxidising agents. The alcohol is first oxidised to form an aldehyde (another family of organic molecules with distinctive smells) and then further oxidised to form a carboxylic acid. This reaction is seen clearly in the case of ethanol. It can be oxidised to form ethanoic acid – better known as vinegar. This is why it is so important that wine and beer bottles are carefully sealed. If they are not, air gets in and the ethanol in the drink is oxidised to ethanoic acid. This has a sharp acidic taste, and the drink becomes extremely unpleasant tasting. The same reaction is used deliberately in the vinegar industry, where wine is deliberately oxidised to ethanoic acid to provide us with the well known essential addition to fish and chips!

↑ **Figure 3:** It is the oxidation of ethanol to ethanoic acid which turns alcoholic drinks sour and vinegary – not a pleasant experience!

H H | | H — C — C — OH | | H H ethanol	H O | ∥ H — C — C | \\ H OH ethanoic acid

oxidation by oxygen in air

The carboxylic acids are a homologous series of organic acids. They have the functional group –COOH attached to the hydrocarbon chain, and it is this which determines their properties. Carboxylic acids are common in the natural world, and they also play an important role in industrial chemistry.

Methanoic acid is produced by ants – it is the action of the methanoic acid on our skin that makes ant bites so unpleasant. Ethanoic acid, as we saw in Section 10.7, is the main ingredient in vinegar, whilst the sour taste of citrus fruits like lemons and limes comes from yet another member of the family, citric acid.

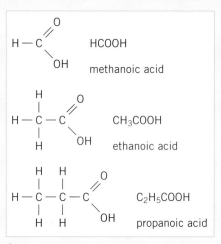

↑ **Figure 1:** The structures of some common carboxylic acids.

Reactions of the carboxylic acids

The carboxylic acids are weak acids, and in many ways they react with other compounds just as a mineral acid would. For example, they react with an alkali to form a salt and water. When ethanoic acid reacts with sodium hydroxide, sodium ethanoate (a carboxylic acid salt) and water are formed:

$$CH_3COOH + NaOH \longrightarrow CH_3COONa + H_2O$$

ethanoic acid	+	sodium hydroxide	⟶	sodium ethanoate	+	water
acid		base		salt		water

The carboxylic acids react with carbonates, forming carboxylic acid salts, carbon dioxide and water. For example, ethanoic acid reacts with sodium carbonate:

$$2CH_3COOH + Na_2CO_3 \longrightarrow 2CH_3COONa + CO_2 + H_2O$$

| ethanoic acid | + | sodium carbonate | ⟶ | sodium ethanoate | + | carbon dioxide | + | water |

↑ **Figure 2:** When we see ants close up like this, they can look intimidating. Their weaponry of concentrated methanoic acid can have an uncomfortable effect even on animals like ourselves, so many times bigger than they are.

A similar reaction takes place between ethanoic acid and hydrogencarbonates:

$$CH_3COOH + NaHCO_3 \longrightarrow CH_3COONa + CO_2 + H_2O$$

| ethanoic acid | + | sodium hydrogencarbonate | ⟶ | sodium ethanoate | + | carbon dioxide | + | water |

Other carboxylic acids react in just the same way. For example, methanoic acid (HCOOH) forms sodium methanoate (HCOONa):

$$HCOOH + NaOH \longrightarrow HCOONa + H_2O$$
$$2HCOOH + Na_2CO_3 \longrightarrow 2HCOONa + CO_2 + H_2O$$
$$HCOOH + NaHCO_3 \longrightarrow HCOONa + CO_2 + H_2O$$

As we saw in Section 10.7, carboxylic acids also react with alcohols to form esters – compounds which often have a characteristic smell and are used as food flavourings and to make perfumes. To make this reaction happen at a detectable rate, concentrated sulphuric acid is added to act as a catalyst:

| butanoic acid | + | butan-1-ol | ⇌ | butyl butanoate | + | water |

Everyday carboxylic acids

Carboxylic acids are an integral part of many everyday substances like vinegar, ant bites and citrus fruits. Ethanoic acid (vinegar) is used not only as a preservative and flavouring, but also in the manufacture of the fibre acetate rayon, widely used in clothing.

The carboxylic acid citric acid is an important part of the taste of oranges and lemons. It also plays a major role in the taste of soft drinks such as colas and squashes – just check on the labels of bottles and cans to see how frequently it appears.

Citric acid is not the only carboxylic acid to appear in citrus fruits. Ascorbic acid (better known as vitamin C) is also found not only in oranges, lemons and limes but in many other fruits and vegetables too. Ascorbic acid is vital for human health. In the days before this was realised, thousands of sailors died from scurvy, the disease which develops if people do not eat enough vitamin C. In 1795 lime juice was issued to all British naval vessels on the advice of the Scottish doctor James Lind, who realised that citrus fruits, rich in ascorbic acid, had been used by the Dutch to prevent scurvy for many years.

Another carboxylic acid which has a familiar role in 21st century life is aspirin. Aspirin is a drug which is widely used for pain relief from headaches and the symptoms of flu. It has also been shown to slow down the rate at which blood clots. As a result of this, the carboxylic acid contained in aspirin tablets is taken regularly by people who are at risk of heart attacks, to reduce the likelihood of their blood clotting.

↑ **Figure 3:** Citric acid and ascorbic acid are just two of the carboxylic acids found in a lemon like this.

? Questions

1 Give the molecular and structural formula of propanoic acid and pentanoic acid.

2 Give the molecular and structural formulae for the following reactions:

   a methanoic acid and potassium hydroxide

   b propanoic acid and sodium hydrogencarbonate

   c ethanoic acid and magnesium carbonate.

3 **a** Give an example of a reaction between a carboxylic acid and an alcohol.

   b What catalyst is usually needed for this reaction to take place?

   c What are the products of this type of reaction usually used for?

4 Design a poster for the chemistry lab to illustrate the importance of the carboxylic acids – include as much chemistry as you can.

🔑 Key Ideas

- ⊙ Carboxylic acids have the functional group –COOH.

- ⊙ Carboxylic acids are weak acids.

- ⊙ Carboxylic acids are neutralised by alkalis and react with carbonates and hydrogencarbonates to form carboxylic acid salts, carbon dioxide and water.

- ⊙ Carboxylic acids react with alcohols in the presence of a concentrated sulphuric acid catalyst to form esters.

- ⊙ Many carboxylic acids play important roles in everyday life.

The human heart is basically a bag of muscle. It beats about 70 times a minute from before we are born until we die, tirelessly pumping blood around our bodies. This circulation of the blood is vital to carry oxygen and food to all the cells of the body, including organs like the brain, and to remove the poisonous wastes which build up as the body works.

When things go wrong

As long as our hearts keep beating regularly, we tend to ignore them. However, for thousands of people each year their heart becomes very important indeed when they suffer the pain of an angina attack or, even more frighteningly, a heart attack. Very often heart problems like this are the result of the build-up of a chemical known as **cholesterol** in the arteries that supply the heart itself with blood. Cholesterol is an organic chemical known as a steroid, a large and complicated molecule which contains the −OH functional group of the alcohols.

Cholesterol is essential for the proper functioning of the human body – it is needed for the nerves to carry messages properly and to make some of the hormones (chemical messengers) which control the way the body works. But if the levels of cholesterol in the blood build up too high then some of the excess cholesterol gets deposited on the linings of the blood vessels. They become 'furred up' rather like pipes with lots of lime scale, and as the blood vessels supplying the heart get narrower and narrower, less blood can get through to the working muscles. Eventually, the cholesterol deposits cause blood clots to form around them, and the blood vessel becomes completely blocked. Starved of oxygen, the heart cannot work properly and the person suffers the severe pain of angina or a heart attack, when the muscle of the heart actually dies from lack of oxygen.

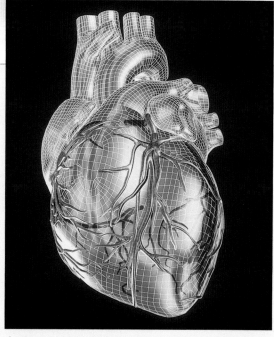

↑ **Figure 1:** The beating of the heart is vital to life. This computer image shows the coronary arteries in a healthy human heart.

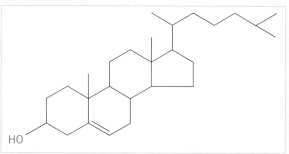

↑ **Figure 2:** A molecule of cholesterol – although the molecule is very large the alcohol group still affects its chemistry.

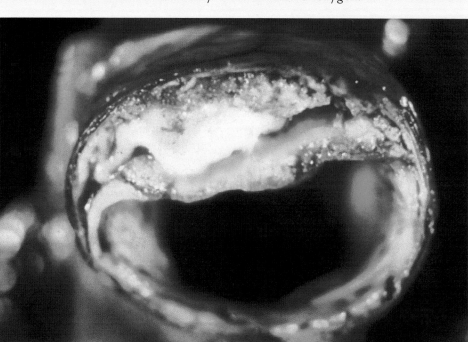

← **Figure 3:** When the arteries taking blood to the heart get blocked by cholesterol like this, it is only a matter of time before the heart stops working.

The production of high levels of cholesterol in the blood is often linked to high levels of fat in the diet. A few people will have raised blood cholesterol whatever they eat, but most people are advised to reduce the amount of fat that they eat to lower the amount of cholesterol in their blood. This in turn reduces the build-up of cholesterol in the blood vessels, which helps to reduce the risk of heart disease.

Good fat or bad fat?

Although it is widely known that a low fat diet is healthier than a high fat diet, not all of the fats we eat are the same, and some are thought to be more damaging to the heart than others. Fats are made by the reaction of organic acids known as fatty acids with an alcohol called glycerol. Animal fats – the sort found in meat and dairy products – are thought to be the most damaging. They are all **saturated** fats – the fatty acids from which they are made all contain only single carbon–carbon bonds, to which no more hydrogen atoms can be added (see Section 3.5). Saturated fats are all relatively hard fats which are solid at room temperature. In contrast, vegetable oils – like olive oil and corn oil – contain **unsaturated** fats made from fatty acids which have some carbon–carbon double bonds in their structure. Although they are better for our health, these compounds are often liquids so they cannot be spread on bread! However, vegetable oils can be hardened by adding hydrogen to some of the carbon–carbon double bonds in the presence of a catalyst. This makes the fatty acids slightly less unsaturated, but also turns them into soft solids at room temperature. With additional colourings and flavourings they become margarine, often regarded as a healthier alternative to butter. Reducing all types of fat in the diet and maintaining a healthy body weight are still the surest ways to reduce the level of cholesterol in the blood, although there are now some margarines which claim to contain compounds which will actually help to lower it for you.

↑ **Figure 4:** There is plenty of choice about what to put on bread and use in cooking, and it seems that some fats might be better for the heart than others.

Preventing problems

One of the reasons that a build-up of cholesterol on the walls of the blood vessels increases the risk of heart disease is that blood gets trapped in the cholesterol and clots. This clot may block the whole blood vessel, causing a heart attack, or it may travel to somewhere else in the body (like the brain), where it can cause a stroke. For this reason doctors often advise patients with any tendency to heart disease to take a small dose of the carboxylic acid aspirin each day. Aspirin makes the blood less likely to clot, so reducing the risk of heart disease. Given after a heart attack, it can increase the chance of survival.

? Questions

1 Explain the role of cholesterol in the body and in the development of heart disease.

2 **a** How are carboxylic acids linked with heart disease?

   b How do carboxylic acids play a role in ways to reduce the risk of heart disease?

3 Design a poster or leaflet explaining the importance of a low fat diet for a healthy heart, including as much chemistry as you can in a way that the general population is likely to understand.

🔑 Key Ideas

⊙ The steroid cholesterol contains the alcohol –OH group. It is essential for human health but if too much is produced it can cause heart disease.

⊙ Vegetable oils contain unsaturated fats and can be hardened to form margarine by adding hydrogen to some of the carbon–carbon double bonds.

⊙ The carboxylic acid aspirin is a drug used to reduce the likelihood of heart attacks.

Plastics form an important part of our material world. As we saw in Section 3.4, they are often formed from organic compounds derived from crude oil. Plastics are polymers – large molecules formed by joining together many small molecules known as monomers. Many polymers are made from compounds which contain a carbon–carbon double bond (–C=C–) in a process known as **addition polymerisation**. Examples include polythene (poly(ethene)) made from ethene monomers, poly(propene) made from propene monomers, and poly(chloroethene) which is made from chloroethene but is usually called polyvinylchloride or PVC.

↓ **Figure 1:** No matter what the monomer, when a carbon–carbon double bond is involved the polymer is formed by a simple addition reaction across the double bond.

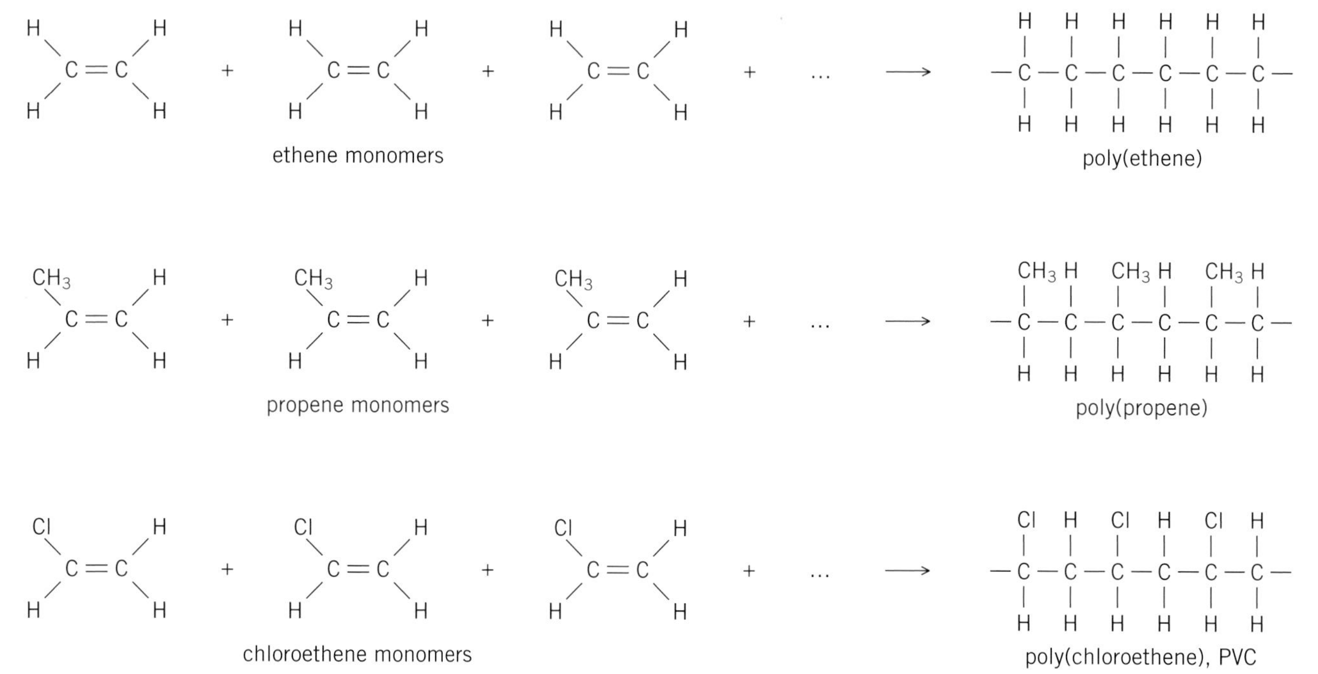

ethene monomers

poly(ethene)

propene monomers

poly(propene)

chloroethene monomers

poly(chloroethene), PVC

Different types of plastics

All polymers (plastics) consist of a tangled mass of very long molecules, in which the atoms are joined together in long chains by strong covalent bonds. Although the bonds holding the atoms together *within* the individual molecules are strong, the strength of intermolecular forces *between* the molecules in different polymers can vary considerably.

In some plastics the forces between the polymer chains are weak. As a result, when the plastic is heated these weak intermolecular forces are broken and the plastic can soften. Then as the plastic cools the intermolecular forces are reformed and the plastic hardens again. Plastics like this are known as **thermosoftening plastics**. Poly(ethene), poly(propene) and PVC are all examples of thermosoftening plastics. This property makes them useful to us in many ways, because they can be melted and remoulded into whatever shape we want. These are the sorts of plastics that can be recycled (see Section 3.4).

↑ **Figure 2:** Poly(chloroethene) – better known as PVC – is a typical addition polymer with a wide range of uses.

However, not all plastics soften in this way when they are heated. Some plastics form covalent bonds between the adjacent chains when they are first heated. These strong cross-linkages are permanent, and they prevent the plastic from softening when it is heated in the future. Known as **thermosetting plastics**, these polymers cannot be remoulded. As a result, thermosetting plastics cannot easily be recycled, but they can be used for all sorts of jobs which would be impossible with a thermosoftening plastic. Melamine (used in furniture and plastic cups and plates) and many glues are examples of thermosetting plastics.

A disposal problem

As we saw in Section 3.4, plastics are extremely hard-wearing and long-lasting chemicals. They do not break down naturally and many are not affected by the action of microorganisms. While some plastics like poly(ethene) and poly(propene) contain only carbon and hydrogen, many other plastics – and other organic molecules – contain other elements like chlorine and nitrogen as well. One of the reasons it is so hard to get rid of these plastics is that when they are burned, particularly if the supply of air is limited, they can produce poisonous fumes. All plastics form the combustion products of carbon and hydrogen – carbon dioxide and water. However those containing chlorine, like PVC, produce hydrogen chloride as well, while those containing nitrogen in their molecules produce hydrogen cyanide as they burn. This is why disposal of plastics by incineration causes so many problems – any poisonous gases which are produced have to be extracted before the fumes are allowed to escape into the air.

↑ **Figure 3:** The disadvantage of a thermosoftening plastic. Anything made of it placed too near a source of heat will melt and change shape.

↑ **Figure 4:** Thermosetting plastics can safely be used to make cheap and effective containers for very hot liquids – this kettle is one example.

? Questions

1 **a** Explain what is meant by a polymer.

b Why are plastics such useful materials?

2 **a** What is the difference in the way a thermosoftening and a thermosetting plastic respond to heat?

b Explain the chemistry behind their very different responses.

3 Polymers are not always made as a result of addition reactions across a carbon–carbon double bond – sometimes the double bond will be between carbon and another atom such as oxygen. Poly(methanal) is a thermosetting plastic often used to make objects such as kettles. The monomer unit is methanal, CH_2O. Using the structural formula given below to help you, show the addition polymerisation of methanal to make poly(methanal).

4 Suggest as many ways as possible of dealing with the problems of plastics in the environment.

0⊓ Key Ideas

- Most polymers (plastics) are made from compounds containing the carbon–carbon double bond by addition polymerisation.

- PVC is made from chloroethane monomers.

- Thermosoftening plastics have weak intermolecular forces and soften when heated so they can be reshaped.

- Thermosetting plastics have strong covalent cross-linkages so they do not soften when they are heated.

- Plastics and other organic compounds containing chlorine and nitrogen produce poisonous fumes of hydrogen chloride and hydrogen cyanide when burned, particularly in a limited supply of air.

1 a Using words from the list below, copy and complete the passage about organic compounds.

> **carbon** **carbon dioxide** **electricity**
> **energy** **fuels** **neutral** **water** **wood**

Some organic compounds are used as ....
because they release energy when they are
burned.

All organic compounds contain the element
.... Many also contain the element
hydrogen.

When organic compounds containing hydrogen
are burned in a plentiful supply of air, the
two substances formed are .... and water.

(3 marks)

b Why is it dangerous to burn organic compounds
in a limited supply of air? (2 marks)

(Total 5 marks)

AQA specimen question

2 Propene is a hydrocarbon molecule containing
three carbon atoms and six hydrogen atoms.

a What is meant by the term **hydrocarbon**? (1 mark)

b Draw the structural formula of propene. (1 mark)

c Is propene a **saturated** molecule or an
unsaturated molecule? Explain your answer.

(2 marks)

d Test tubes **X** and **Y** are identical. One test tube
contains propane, while the other test tube
contains propene.

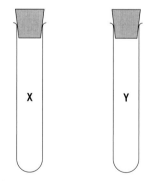

Explain clearly what test you could carry out to
find out which tube contains which compound,
stating clearly the results obtained in each
case. (3 marks)

e Propene molecules will react together to form
long chains.

i What is this kind of reaction called? (1 mark)

ii What properties does this new substance
have? (2 marks)

iii Why does the widespread use of substances
like this present an environmental problem?

(2 marks)

(Total 12 marks)

3 Molecule **A** contains carbon, hydrogen and oxygen
atoms.

$$A \quad H-\overset{\overset{\displaystyle H}{|}}{\underset{\underset{\displaystyle H}{|}}{C}}-\overset{\overset{\displaystyle H}{|}}{\underset{\underset{\displaystyle H}{|}}{C}}-C\overset{\displaystyle O}{\underset{\displaystyle O-H}{}}$$

a To which group of organic compounds does
molecule **A** belong? (1 mark)

b Suggest a name for compound **A**. (1 mark)

c Compound **A** is added to some sodium
carbonate solution. What would you expect
to observe? (2 marks)

Under the right conditions, compound **A** reacts
with ethanol to form compound **B**.

d What conditions are needed for this reaction to
take place? (1 mark)

e To what group of compounds does compound **B**
belong? (1 mark)

f Write a balanced equation, including structural
formulae, to show the reaction between
compounds **A** and **B**. (3 marks)

(Total 9 marks)

4 This question is about hydrocarbons.

The table on the next page gives some information
about the first ten members of a homologous
series. It includes their melting points and boiling
points. It was taken from a German Chemistry
textbook.

a i What is meant by a **homologous series**?

(2 marks)

ii Use the information in the table to predict
the boiling point of C_9H_{20}. (1 mark)

iii What is the formula of the twelfth member of
the series? (1 mark)

Name	Summenformel	Strukturformeln (Kurzform)	Schmelz-temperatur (°C)	Siede-temperatur (°C)
Methan	CH_4	CH_4	−182	−162
Äthan	C_2H_6	$CH_3–CH_3$	−183	−89
Propan	C_3H_8	$CH_3–CH_2–CH_3$	−188	−42
Butan	C_4H_{10}	$CH_3–(CH_2)_2–CH_3$	−138	0
Pentan	C_5H_{12}	$CH_3–(CH_2)_3–CH_3$	−130	+36
Hexan	C_6H_{14}	$CH_3–(CH_2)_4–CH_3$	−95	+69
Heptan	C_7H_{16}	$CH_3–(CH_2)_5–CH_3$	−90	+98
Octan	C_8H_{18}	$CH_3–(CH_2)_6–CH_3$	−57	+126
Nonan	C_9H_{20}	$CH_3–(CH_2)_7–CH_3$	−54	
Decan	$C_{10}H_{22}$	$CH_3–(CH_2)_8–CH_3$	−30	+174

b There are **three** hydrocarbons which have the molecular formula C_5H_{12}. The structural formula of one of these is shown below (**A**).

A $H-\overset{H}{\underset{H}{C}}-\overset{H}{\underset{H}{C}}-\overset{H}{\underset{H}{C}}-\overset{H}{\underset{H}{C}}-\overset{H}{\underset{H}{C}}-H$

i Draw the structural formula of the other two compounds (**B** and **C**). (2 marks)

ii What name is given to compounds which have the same molecular formula but different structures? (1 mark)

iii Which of the compounds, **A**, **B** or **C**, has the highest boiling point?
Give reasons for your answer. (3 marks)

(Total 10 marks)
AQA specimen question

5 a An article in a newspaper contains the following statement:

'Ethanol may be used as a fuel in countries where there is plenty of spare fertile land and where the climate is hot and sunny. In these countries, ethanol is a very 'environmentally friendly' fuel. Where land is scarce and the climate is not very sunny, ethanol is not very commonly used as a fuel.'

i Why is ethanol more useful as a fuel where the climate is hot and sunny than where there is less sun? (1 mark)

ii Why must there be plenty of spare land if ethanol is going to be used as a fuel? (1 mark)

iii What method of producing ethanol is likely to be used in a hot sunny country where there is plenty of spare fertile land? (1 mark)

iv Why is ethanol produced in this way described as 'environmentally friendly'? (2 marks)

b Some data about ethanol and another fuel, octane (petrol), are given in Table 1.

		Ethanol	Octane
A	energy released when 1 mole of fuel atoms burns completely in air	1 367	5 470
B	mass of 1 mole of fuel (g)	46	114
C	density of fuel (g/cm³)	0.79	0.70

Table 1

i Copy and complete Table 2, using the information given in Table 1. (6 marks)

		Ethanol	Octane
X	mass in grams of 1 000 cm³ of fuel (calculated using the data in row C of Table 1)		
Y	number of moles of fuel molecules in 1 000 cm³ of each fuel (calculated using your answer in row X of this table and the data in row B of Table 1)		
Z	energy released when 1 000 cm³ of fuel burns completely in air (calculated using your answer in row Y of this table and the data in row A of Table 1)		

Table 2

ii One car runs on petrol (octane), while an identical car has been adapted to run on ethanol. The fuel tank of each car is filled with the correct fuel. Based on your calculations in Table 2, which car will travel further – the car fuelled by petrol or the car fuelled by ethanol? (3 marks)

(Total 14 marks)

Sulphuric acid is one of those chemicals which we use so regularly in the laboratory that it is easy to take it for granted. However sulphuric acid is an important industrial commodity, produced in vast quantities – and not just for use in school laboratories! It is needed, amongst other things, to provide the acid in the millions of car batteries in existence around the globe, to make fertilisers (see Section 11.2) and to make detergents.

↑ **Figure 1:** The numbers of motor vehicles all over the world is constantly increasing, even in remote areas like this – and every car battery contains sulphuric acid.

The Contact process

Sulphuric acid is manufactured from the raw materials sulphur, air and water. Sulphur is found in solid underground deposits, and is extracted using superheated steam to melt the sulphur which is then pumped to the surface.

In the Contact process sulphur is burned in air at very high temperatures (more than 1000 °C) to form sulphur dioxide:

$$S(s) \ + \ O_2(g) \ \longrightarrow \ SO_2(g)$$

The sulphur dioxide is then mixed with more air and the mixture of gases is passed over a catalyst (vanadium oxide, V_2O_5) at a high temperature (450 °C) and a pressure of between 1 and 2 atmospheres. Under these conditions the gases react to form sulphur trioxide:

$$2SO_2(g) \ + \ O_2(g) \ \rightleftharpoons \ 2SO_3(g)$$

The sulphur trioxide is dissolved in concentrated sulphuric acid to form fuming sulphuric acid or oleum:

$$SO_3(g) \ + \ H_2SO_4(l) \ \longrightarrow \ \underset{\text{oleum}}{H_2S_2O_7(l)}$$

This is then carefully diluted with water to make concentrated sulphuric acid again:

$$H_2S_2O_7(l) \ + \ H_2O(l) \ \longrightarrow \ 2H_2SO_4(l)$$

↑ **Figure 2:** The first step in the process of making sulphuric acid is to extract sulphur from the deposits below the Earth's surface. Here, piles of sulphur are being stored ready for use at a chemical plant.

Concentrated sulphuric acid is 98% H_2SO_4 and 2% water – 100% sulphuric acid is not used because it melts at 10.4 °C and so it would solidify in cool temperatures, making it harder to handle and use.

It might seem simpler to react sulphur trioxide with water rather than with concentrated sulphuric acid. However sulphur trioxide reacts very vigorously with water, heating the water up. This produces an acid mist of sulphuric acid which would be very difficult and dangerous to work with.

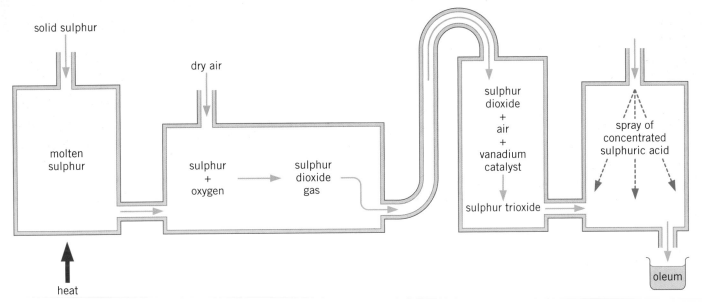

solid sulphur

dry air

molten sulphur

sulphur + oxygen → sulphur dioxide gas

sulphur dioxide + air + vanadium catalyst

sulphur trioxide →

spray of concentrated sulphuric acid

oleum

heat

↑ **Figure 3:** The Contact process for making sulphuric acid.

H Explaining the process

The conditions for the different stages of the Contact process vary quite considerably, because of the different reactions which are taking place.

⊙ The first stage where sulphur and oxygen react together to form sulphur dioxide is an oxidation reaction. A high temperature is needed to keep the sulphur molten and to ensure that the rate of the reaction is fast. The oxidation of the sulphur is an exothermic reaction, and the heat produced is used, through a heat exchange system, to melt more sulphur.

⊙ In the second stage sulphur dioxide is oxidised to sulphur trioxide. The catalyst vanadium oxide increases the reaction rate so it is economically viable. This reaction is reversible. Because the forward reaction which results in the formation of sulphur trioxide is exothermic, a low

temperature would increase the yield. However, the reaction would then be too slow, so the normal operating temperature of 450 °C is a good compromise. A high pressure would also increase the yield of the sulphur trioxide, but not enough to justify the additional expense of building and maintaining a high pressure plant, when the normal conditions give around a 97% yield of sulphur trioxide at 1–2 atm. Removing the sulphur trioxide as soon as it is formed ensures the formation of more sulphur trioxide.

⊙ When the sulphur trioxide is mixed with concentrated sulphuric acid and then mixed with water the reactions are exothermic, but it is much easier to control the rate at which energy is produced than if the sulphur trioxide is reacted directly with water.

? Questions

1 Why is sulphuric acid such an important industrial product?

2 Produce a flow chart summarising the different stages in the production of sulphuric acid.

H 3 Which of the conditions used in the Contact process for making sulphuric acid are expensive to maintain and why are they used?

4 At about 27 °C and a high pressure the yield of sulphuric acid in the Contact process would be almost 100%. Explain why these are not the operating conditions usually chosen when making sulphuric acid on an industrial scale.

O—m Key Ideas

⊙ Sulphuric acid is used as car battery acid and to make fertilisers and detergents.

⊙ Sulphuric acid is manufactured from sulphur, air and water.

H ⊙ The conditions used in the stages of sulphuric acid manufacture are those which will result in the best and most economical yield of the acid.

As we saw in the Section 11.1, the production of sulphuric acid is a major industry – about 150 million tonnes are produced worldwide each year. It is often said that the amount of sulphuric acid a country uses each year is a good measure of that country's economic success. Here we will look in a little more detail at some of the reasons why it is so important.

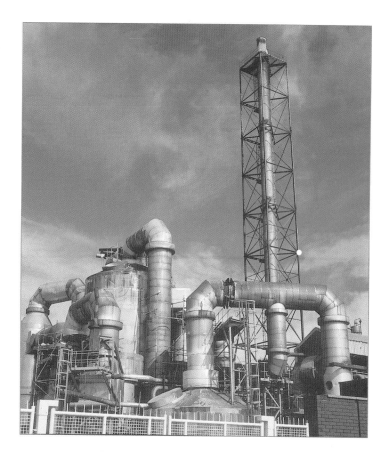

→ **Figure 1:** Sulphuric acid is produced in chemical plants like this. Huge amounts are made – and used – around the globe.

Commercial uses

Sulphuric acid has several advantages over other acids for use in industry. It is the cheapest of the strong mineral acids to make. It can be made and transported in an almost pure form, and at room temperature it is both stable and non-volatile. All of these things make it ideal for industrial use.

One important use of sulphuric acid is in car batteries. Its other main uses are in the manufacture of fertilisers and detergents. It is particularly important in the production of what are known as 'superphosphate' fertilisers – almost three-quarters of all the sulphuric acid produced worldwide is used in this way.

Plants need a number of different mineral ions to grow successfully and when farmers are trying to grow enough crops to provide relatively cheap food for everybody in the world, it is very important that all of these minerals are in place. Phosphate ions are one of the minerals needed by plants, but it is very difficult to extract them from the rocks where they are contained as they are very insoluble in water. However, if the phosphate-bearing rocks are reacted with sulphuric acid they form a mixture known as 'superphosphate' which is much more soluble in water and can be used to produce much needed phosphate fertilisers.

Chemical uses

Sulphuric acid has a multitude of uses in the laboratory, but one of the most dramatic is its action as a dehydrating agent. Dehydration is the removal of water, or the elements of water, from a compound. Concentrated sulphuric acid is a very powerful dehydrating agent. This can be seen very clearly in the reaction of concentrated sulphuric acid with some organic compounds like sugar. Ordinary granulated sugar is a chemical called sucrose, an organic chemical with the formula $C_{12}H_{22}O_{11}$. This can also be written as $C_{12}(H_2O)_{11}$. Concentrated sulphuric acid reacts vigorously with the sugar, removing the elements of water and leaving a great mass of black carbon:

$$C_{12}H_{22}O_{11}(s) \xrightarrow{\text{conc.H}_2\text{SO}_4\text{(aq)}} 12C(s) + 11H_2O(l)$$

It is not only organic compounds which can be dehydrated by concentrated sulphuric acid. The same thing can happen to inorganic compounds. For example, if concentrated sulphuric acid is added to blue copper sulphate crystals, the acid removes the water of crystallisation, leaving anhydrous, white copper sulphate:

$$\underset{\text{blue}}{CuSO_4.5H_2O(s)} \xrightarrow{\text{conc.H}_2\text{SO}_4\text{(aq)}} \underset{\text{white}}{CuSO_4(s) + 5H_2O(l)}$$

↑ **Figure 2:** The same quantity of sugar was in both of these beakers. The addition of sulphuric acid to the beaker on the right results in this spongy mass of elemental carbon as the water is removed when the acid dehydrates the sugar.

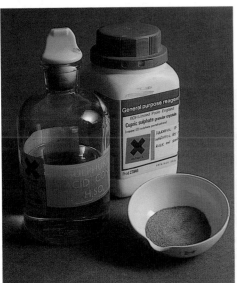

↙ **Figure 3:** The dehydrating action of concentrated sulphuric acid on blue hydrated copper sulphate crystals can be clearly seen by the white, dehydrated compound where the acid has been dropped.

Key Ideas

⊙ About 70% of the sulphuric acid manufactured is used to make fertilisers.

⊙ Dehydration is the removal of water or the elements of water from a compound.

⊙ Concentrated sulphuric acid is a powerful dehydrating agent. It will remove hydrogen and oxygen from organic compounds such as sugar, and the water of crystallisation from compounds such as hydrated copper sulphate.

? Questions

1 How is sulphuric acid important in helping to feed the world population?

2 Explain the difference between the action of sulphuric acid as a dehydrating agent with organic compounds like sugar and with inorganic compounds like hydrated copper sulphate.

3 Predict what will be formed when sulphuric acid reacts with the following compounds:

   a methanoic acid (HCOOH)

   b glucose ($C_6H_{12}O_6$)

   c ethanol (C_2H_5OH).

11.3 Using aluminium

In Sections 4.5 and 4.6 we looked at the way aluminium is extracted from its ore by electrolysis and examined the reasons why it is such as useful metal. Light and strong, with relatively plentiful supplies available in the Earth's crust, aluminium has another very important characteristic. Although it is a reactive metal it is nevertheless very resistant to corrosion. This is due to the formation of a layer of aluminium oxide when the metal first comes into contact with the air. This layer of aluminium oxide then protects the metal from any further oxidising attack.

Even more protection

For some uses of aluminium we actually want to artificially increase the thickness of the oxide layer. This is particularly true when we want aluminium to absorb colours or we need a particularly tough and scratch-resistant outer layer. The process by which aluminium is given this extra thick oxide coat is known as **anodising**.

The first step in the anodising process is **degreasing** – many of the aluminium pieces which are to be anodised have grease on them from the machinery which has shaped them, and this grease has to be removed before the process proper can begin.

The second step involves the removal of the natural oxide layer using concentrated sodium hydroxide (caustic soda) in a process known as **etching**.

The third stage in the process involves using the aluminium as the positive electrode (anode) in the electrolysis of dilute sulphuric acid. The aluminium object to be anodised is dipped into a lead-lined tank, with the lead sheets acting as the negative electrode (cathode). Oxygen forms on the surface of the aluminium as the sulphuric acid is split, and it reacts with the aluminium to form a thick oxide layer.

↑ **Figure 1:** Aluminium is a very useful metal around the home – for example in cooking pans, as foil for wrapping and storing foods, and more recently in disposable food trays like these, containing ready-prepared meals from the supermarket.

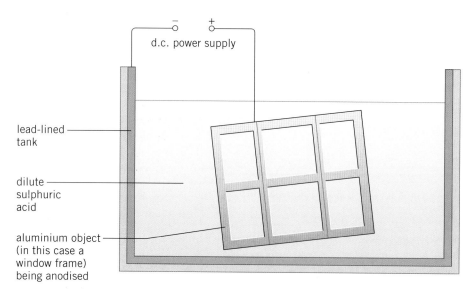

d.c. power supply

lead-lined tank

dilute sulphuric acid

aluminium object (in this case a window frame) being anodised

↖ **Figure 2:** The role of aluminium as the positive electrode means it reacts with the oxygen given up at the electrode to form a thick oxide film.

The thickness and toughness of the oxide layer depends on a number of things – including the length of time the electrolysis continues, the temperature at which the electrolysis takes place and the voltage used. Standard anodising, which gives an oxide layer about 0.01 mm thick, takes place at about 30 °C when low current is flowing and relatively low voltages are used. This is the process used when the aluminium is needed for decorative and protective purposes such as anodised aluminium window frames. 'Hard' anodising gives a much thicker oxide coat – between 0.02 and 0.05 mm – which is used for machine components where it is important that the protective layer will stand up to a great deal of wear and tear. To get the thicker oxide coat the electrolysis takes place at 0 °C and higher voltages are used.

Once the initial anodising is over, the oxide film has pores in it which can take up dyes, so at this stage of the process the anodised aluminium can be coloured to give a very durable colour finish. Then, whether the products have been dyed or not, the anodised aluminium is dipped in a cold chemical seal (or boiling demineralised water) and this seals the finish, closing the pores and leaving the aluminium coated with a very tough corrosion-resistant oxide layer.

Using the aluminium

Not only can anodised aluminium be dyed different colours, but the oxide film can be brushed, polished or etched to give a wide variety of decorative finishes for different uses. These vary from aluminium window and door frames through motor cycle exhaust cams to door handles. The protection against corrosion provided by the hard, tough oxide film which results from anodising helps make aluminium one of the most useful metals we have available to us in the 21st century.

↑ **Figure 3:** The ability of the oxide film to take up dyes immediately after anodising means that aluminium components like this anodised gear wheel can be visually attractive as well as long-lasting and functional.

Key Ideas

⊙ Aluminium is a reactive metal which is resistant to corrosion due to the formation of a protective oxide layer.

⊙ It is often desirable to increase artificially the thickness of the protective oxide layer as this makes the aluminium more versatile.

⊙ Anodising involves removing the natural oxide film using sodium hydroxide and then using the aluminium as the positive electrode in the electrolysis of dilute sulphuric acid. Oxygen forms on the surface of the aluminium and reacts to form a thick oxide layer.

Questions

1 Why is aluminium anodised?

2 Explain the purpose of the following steps in the process of anodising aluminium:

   a degreasing

   b etching with concentrated sodium hydroxide

   c electrolysing sulphuric acid.

H 3 Give half equations for the reactions at the positive and negative electrodes during the anodising of aluminium.

4 Design an internet web site for a company which anodises aluminium. Your site should inform the customer of what the company does, how they do it and why it is useful. (Take a look at www.mansfield-anodisers.co.uk to see how a real company set about the same task.)

Iron is the second most abundant metal in the Earth's core and is widely used in a variety of ways by people all over the world. Iron is extracted from its ores in the blast furnace (see Section 4.3) but the molten iron (pig iron) which is produced from the furnace is of limited use. It contains large crystals of carbon which make the metal very brittle. So before it can be used, another process is needed to remove the impurities or refine the metal.

Purifying iron and making steel

Although the metal iron is useful, the steel which can be made from it by adding small amounts of other metals and non-metals to it is even more useful. The majority of the iron which is extracted from iron ores is converted into steel before it is used.

The main way in which pure iron is produced ready for direct use or for steel production uses what is known as a **basic oxygen furnace.**

The molten pig iron containing impurities like silicon, sulphur and phosphorus is mixed with recycled scrap iron – the mixture is about 70% pig iron and 30% scrap. A tube called an **oxygen lance** is lowered into the furnace and pure oxygen is blown through it. The oxygen reacts rapidly with any carbon in the mixture, oxidising it to carbon dioxide. It also reacts with the other non-metal impurities and they are converted into acidic oxides (eg sulphur dioxide, phosphorus oxide). Powdered calcium carbonate (limestone) is then added to remove the acid impurities, forming a slag which floats on the top. The result of these reactions is pure iron.

At this stage, other elements can be added to the pure iron to produce steel, still within the same reaction vessel. Steels are alloys of iron – mixtures of iron with other metals and with carbon. Carefully calculated amounts of carbon along with specific quantities of other metals and non-metals produce a wide range of steels, each with the properties required for particular jobs (see Section 11.5). The properties of the original iron are altered by the addition of the other elements. The whole furnace then tilts to pour out the molten alloy at the end of the process.

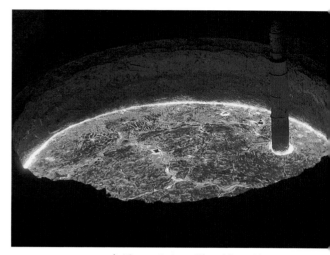

↑ **Figure 1:** Iron like this, which has just come out of a blast furnace, is known as pig iron. The carbon and other impurities in it mean that it is not much use without further refining.

→ **Figure 2:** The basic oxygen furnace is the most modern and fastest method of making exactly the sort of steel we want.

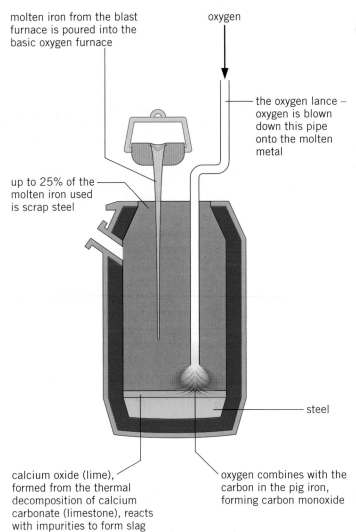

molten iron from the blast furnace is poured into the basic oxygen furnace

oxygen

the oxygen lance – oxygen is blown down this pipe onto the molten metal

up to 25% of the molten iron used is scrap steel

steel

calcium oxide (lime), formed from the thermal decomposition of calcium carbonate (limestone), reacts with impurities to form slag

oxygen combines with the carbon in the pig iron, forming carbon monoxide

↑ **Figure 3:** The basic oxygen furnace is a very rapid way of making steel of a very precise type – one furnace can make around 300 tonnes of steel in one hour.

 The chemistry of steel making

There is some interesting chemistry in the purification of pig iron and the making of steel.

⊙ Oxidation. The removal of the carbon and other impurities from the pig iron relies on oxidation reactions with the oxygen blown in through the oxygen lance. The impurities are oxidised to form acidic oxides. For example:

$$C(s) + O_2(g) \longrightarrow CO_2(g)$$
$$Si(s) + O_2(g) \longrightarrow SiO_2(g)$$
$$S(s) + O_2(g) \longrightarrow SO_2(g)$$
$$4P(s) + 5O_2(g) \longrightarrow P_4O_{10}(g)$$

⊙ Thermal decomposition. The powdered limestone (calcium carbonate) which is then added to the mixture undergoes thermal decomposition to form calcium oxide and carbon dioxide:

$$CaCO_3(s) \longrightarrow CaO(s) + CO_2(g)$$

⊙ Acid–base reactions. The calcium oxide is a base which reacts with the acidic oxides to neutralise them, forming a complex slag which contains a mixture of calcium compounds, such as calcium silicate and calcium phosphate:

$$CaO(s) + SiO_2(g) \longrightarrow CaSiO_3(s)$$
$$6CaO(s) + P_4O_{10}(g) \longrightarrow 2Ca_3(PO_4)_2(s)$$

? Questions

1 Explain the stages of the purification of pig iron, giving equations where possible.

2 The old method of purifying pig iron prior to making steel involved an open hearth with oxygen blown across the top of the molten metal. Explain why this method was so much slower than the basic oxygen furnace.

3 After using the basic oxygen furnace to get rid of impurities like carbon, carbon and other elements are then added to the pure iron. Why?

H 4 Compare the basic oxygen furnace with the blast furnace (Section 4.3) in terms of the redox reactions and acid–base reactions which take place.

Key Ideas

⊙ Pure iron is formed when oxygen is passed through molten pig iron and recycled scrap iron. The acid oxides formed are removed by the addition of limestone.

⊙ Calculated quantities of carbon and/or other elements are added to make a wide range of steels with particular properties.

H ⊙ Processes in the production of steel involve oxidation reactions and acid–base reactions.

What is steel?

Steel is not a single substance – there is a wide range of steels, all of them alloys of iron with carbon and/or other elements.

The simplest steels are the carbon steels, consisting of iron alloyed with small amounts of carbon (0.03–1.5%). These are the cheapest steels to make, and they are used in many products, like the bodies of cars, knives, machinery, ships, containers and structural steel for buildings. Often these carbon steels have small amounts of other elements in them as well. The precise quantities are added at the end of the process in the basic oxygen furnace. **High carbon steel**, with a relatively high carbon content, is very strong but brittle. On the other hand, **low carbon steel** is soft and easily shaped, not as strong but much less likely to shatter. Mild steel, one form of low carbon steel which contains less than 0.1% carbon, is very easily pressed into shape which makes it particularly useful in mass production.

Composition	Steel 1	Steel 2
max % carbon	0.20	0.22
max % silicon	–	0.55
max % manganese	1.50	1.60
max % sulphur	0.035	0.035
max % phosphorus	0.035	0.035

Property	Steel 1	Steel 2
tensile strength (N/mm^2)	410–560	490–630
yield strength (N/mm^2)	275	355
impact value (10 × 10 specimen at −20 °C)	27	27

↑ **Figure 1:** Different steels have different properties – and often the only difference between them is the tiny percentages of metals and non-metals mixed with the basic pure iron.

Low-alloy steels are more expensive than carbon steels because they contain between 1 and 5% of metals like nickel, chromium, manganese, vanadium, titanium and tungsten. Each of these metals gives a steel which is particularly well-suited for a particular use. Nickel steel alloys are used to build long span bridges, bicycle chains and military armour-plating because they are very resistant to tensile (stretching) forces, whilst tungsten steel operates well under very hot conditions so it is used to make high-speed tools.

↑ **Figure 2:** The qualities of nickel steel make it ideal for engineering structures such as the Humber bridge shown here.

Even more expensive are the **high-alloy steels**. These have a much higher percentage of other metals in their makeup. For example, chromium steels have between 12 and 15% chromium mixed with the iron, and often some nickel is mixed in too – this provides strength and chemical stability. These chromium–nickel steels are more commonly known as **stainless steel**. They are used to make cooking utensils and cutlery as well as chemical reaction vessels, because they combine hardness and strength with great resistance to corrosion – unlike most other steels, they do not rust!

Protecting steel – electroplating

Iron and most steels – with the exception of stainless steel – rust to a greater or lesser degree. The rusting can be slowed down or prevented by sacrificial protection using a more reactive metal like zinc or magnesium (see Section 4.3). Painting the metal can also slow down the beginnings of corrosion, but the paint needs frequent renewing. Adding chromium to the steel alloy reduces corrosion but adds to the price of the steel. However there is another way of protecting iron and steel from corrosion – **electroplating**. This involves covering the iron or steel with a thin layer of another, very unreactive, metal using electrolysis. The metals used to plate steel – and many other metals – are unreactive metals like gold, silver, nickel or chromium. This means that electroplating is not a cheap option, but for decorative pieces, cutlery and delicate machine parts it can be a very useful way of preventing corrosion.

The method used in electroplating is always the same. The object which is to be electroplated – for example a piece of cutlery – is made the negative electrode. The positive electrode is made of the pure plating metal. Both electrodes are dipped into a solution containing ions of the plating metal. When a current is passed through the system the positive ions of the plating metal move to the negative electrode where they gain electrons and are deposited as a layer of metal plated onto the steel.

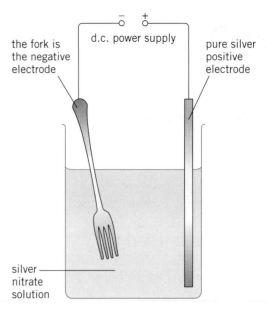

↑ **Figure 3:** The apparatus for electroplating a fork with silver.

↑ **Figure 4:** Many of the steel parts of this Harley Davidson motorbike have been chromium plated. This not only protects the bike against corrosion, it looks good too.

? Questions

1 Produce a table comparing the different types of steel. Include columns for the type of steel (eg high carbon steel), its composition, properties, and uses.

2 a Using the data in Figure 1 produce a bar chart to compare the composition (excluding iron) of the two steels.

 b If the maximum percentage of the other ingredients is present, what is the percentage of iron present in each type of steel?

3 a Display the data from Figure 1 to compare the properties of the two steels.

 b Which components of the steel do you think are affecting the tensile strength and the yield strength of the alloy? Explain your answer.

4 Explain how a steel kettle might be electroplated with copper to make it more decorative. Include a diagram to help your explanation.

🔑 Key Ideas

⊙ The addition of small quantities of carbon or other metals alters the properties of iron to form different steels.

⊙ Different types of steel have different properties.

⊙ Steel (and most other metals) can be electroplated with less reactive metals such as gold, silver, nickel and chromium to prevent corrosion.

11.6 Titanium

Titanium is a transition metal which has rapidly become increasingly important in high-tech engineering. It is a silvery white metal which is very strong and resistant to corrosion. Its density is only about 60% of that of iron, so its strength is combined with lightness. It also has a very high melting point – about 1660 °C – so it can withstand very high temperatures. It was first isolated in 1910, but has become increasingly widely used in the last 30 years or so.

What is it used for?

Titanium is a valuable resource because of its remarkable combination of properties. It is used instead of steel and aluminium in the bodies of aircraft and racing bikes because of its combination of lightness and strength. It is also used to make important components of jet engines because it maintains its strength at high temperatures. That property is also useful in nuclear reactors, where titanium is used to make the pipework and other components that must withstand high temperatures. Not only is titanium mechanically ideal under these conditions, but its lack of chemical reactivity provides resistance to corrosion. Other completely different uses for titanium are also based on its strength and resistance to corrosion – from replacement hip joints to the spectacular roof on the Guggenheim building in Bilbao, Spain.

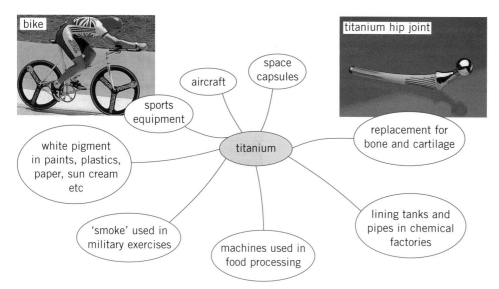

↑ **Figure 1:** Titanium rods like these are not something we see very often as titanium metal is very expensive – it is frequently used to form alloys.

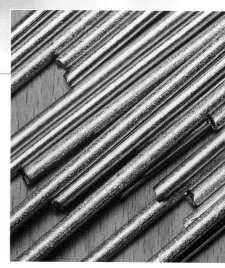

← **Figure 2:** The properties of titanium mean it is suited to a very wide range of uses.

Titanium is not only useful as an element. In alloys with other metals it imparts strength and resistance to corrosion, whilst the compound titanium dioxide is widely used as the pigment in white paint.

Extracting titanium

The main titanium ore is **rutile**, which is titanium dioxide. Titanium is the fourth most abundant metal present in the Earth's crust, and has become the ninth most commonly used industrial metal. Because titanium is not a particularly reactive metal, it can be extracted from its ore using a more reactive metal.

The first stage is to convert the titanium dioxide (TiO_2) into titanium chloride ($TiCl_4$) by reacting it with chlorine. The titanium chloride which is formed condenses as a colourless liquid.

↑ **Figure 3:** Like many other metal ores, rutile is not very exciting to look at. It is hard to imagine that this nondescript rock contains a highly valued metal resource.

The second stage of the extraction involves the reaction of titanium chloride with a reactive metal. Sodium or magnesium are the usual choices. The sodium or magnesium displaces the titanium, resulting in the formation of titanium metal and either sodium chloride or magnesium chloride. The reaction takes place in a closed iron chamber, in an atmosphere of argon (a noble gas) and at a temperature of around 800 °C:

$$TiCl_4 + 4Na \longrightarrow Ti + 4NaCl$$
$$TiCl_4 + 2Mg \longrightarrow Ti + 2MgCl_2$$

The sodium or magnesium chloride is removed from the reaction vessel, leaving titanium metal behind. The titanium is then melted and cast into ingots. The metal chloride can then be split by electrolysis, restoring the chlorine and the reactive metal needed to extract more titanium from its ore. This makes the extraction process very efficient and economically sound.

H The chemistry of extracting titanium

The extraction of titanium from its ore is based on a number of important chemical principles.

⊙ Reduction reactions. The conversion of titanium dioxide to titanium chloride is obviously a reduction reaction (in fact it is a redox reaction – see Section 4.2), as the titanium loses oxygen:

$$TiO_2 + C + 2Cl_2 \longrightarrow TiCl_4 + CO_2$$

Rather less obviously, the next stage, where $TiCl_4$ reacts with sodium or magnesium, is also a reduction reaction, as the Ti ions gain electrons to form titanium atoms:

$$TiCl_4 + 4Na \longrightarrow Ti + 4NaCl$$

⊙ The reactivity series. An element which is higher up the reactivity series will displace a metal lower in the reactivity series from its compounds. Like most other transition metals, titanium is below Group 1 and Group 2 metals. This is why sodium or magnesium are used to extract titanium from its ore.

⊙ Noble gases. Magnesium and sodium are both reactive metals which react with the oxygen in the air at temperatures of 800 °C (the temperature at which they react with titanium chloride). However noble gases such as argon are completely unreactive as they contain a complete outer shell of electrons. So by carrying out the extraction of titanium in an atmosphere of argon, any unwanted reactions with the gases in the atmosphere can be avoided.

? Questions

1 Select three different uses for titanium and for each one explain why the metal is so well suited to its function.

2 a Describe how titanium is extracted from its ore, giving word and chemical equations where appropriate.

   b Why do you think this method of extraction is used rather than electrolysis?

3 A lump of titanium ore (titanium dioxide, TiO_2) has a mass of 960 g.

   a How many moles of titanium dioxide are there in this lump of ore?

   b How many moles of titanium atoms are there in this lump of ore?

   c What mass of titanium could this lump of ore produce?

   d The ore is processed and 520 g of titanium metal are obtained. What percentage yield of titanium is this?

Key Ideas

⊙ Titanium is a transition metal which is strong, light and resistant to corrosion.

⊙ Titanium is extracted from the ore rutile (titanium dioxide) by reaction with a more reactive metal.

1 Sulphuric acid is made by the Contact process. A flow diagram for the process is shown below.

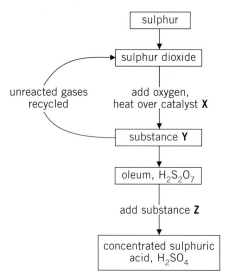

a Describe how sulphur dioxide is made from sulphur. (2 marks)

b Name catalyst **X**. (1 mark)

c Why are the unreacted gases recycled and not released into the atmosphere? (2 marks)

d Name substance **Y**. (1 mark)

e Name substance **Z**, which reacts with oleum to from concentrated sulphuric acid. (1 mark)

f Calculate the relative formula mass of oleum, $H_2S_2O_7$. Show clearly how you work out your answer.

(Relative atomic masses: H = 1, O = 16, S = 32) (2 marks)

g Give **one** use of concentrated sulphuric acid. (1 mark)

(Total 10 marks)

AQA specimen question

2 The table gives some information about steels.

Type of steel	Percentage (%) of carbon	Other elements present	Properties	
			strength	corrosion
high carbon	0.5–1.4	none		rusts quite easily
low carbon	0.04–1.15	none		
stainless	0.05–1.10	Cr, Ni	strong and hard	

a Copy and complete the table by choosing properties from the list:

- soft and easily shaped
- strong but brittle
- resistant to corrosion
- rusts easily.

b Steels are made from molten iron in a furnace.

The diagram shows the substances which are added to the molten iron during steelmaking.

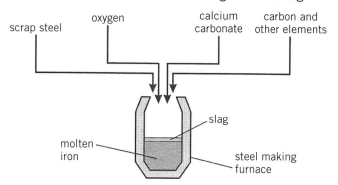

Give a reason why each of the following substances is added to the molten iron:

i scrap steel

ii oxygen

iii calcium carbonate

iv carbon and other elements. (4 marks)

c The following passage describes a method of preventing steel from rusting.

Some parts of the passage are missing. Copy the passage, choosing the correct words from the list to complete the sentences that have parts missing.

atoms	**electrolysis**	**ions**	**negative**
painted	**plated**	**positive**	**oxidation**

Steel can be .... with the metal nickel using the process of ....

The steel is made the .... electrode and pure nickel metal is the .... electrode. The steel is immersed in a solution of nickel .... (5 marks)

d Name the metal which is made more resistant to corrosion by increasing the thickness of the oxide layer on the surface of the metal. (1 mark)

(Total 13 marks)

AQA specimen question

3 Aluminium is a light, strong metal which reacts readily with oxygen.

a Unlike iron or steel, aluminium does not need protecting with a layer of paint or other material. Why not? (2 marks)

b The diagram shows how an aluminium object may be **anodised** by immersing it in dilute sulphuric acid and passing an electric current through it, making the aluminium object the positive electrode (anode).

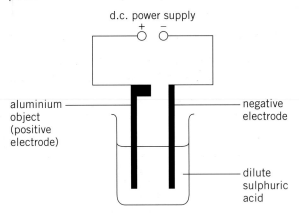

d.c. power supply

aluminium object (positive electrode)

negative electrode

dilute sulphuric acid

i What substance forms on the surface of the aluminium during this process? (1 mark)

ii What happens to the aluminium as a result? (1 mark)

iii Suggest a suitable substance that could be used for the negative electrode. (1 mark)

iv Object **A** is anodised at 30 °C using a low voltage, while object **B** is anodised at 0 °C using a higher voltage. How does this affect what happens to each object? (2 marks)

(Total 7 marks)

H **4** The table shows some properties of the metals aluminium, steel and titanium.

Metal	Melting point (°C)	Relative mechanical strength	Density (kg/m^3)
aluminium	660	70	2700
steel	~ 1650	200	7700
titanium	1660	116	4500

a What properties of titanium shown in the table make it ideal for use in applications like aircraft bodies and racing bicycles? (2 marks)

b Titanium is also used in nuclear reactors, chemical plants and for artificial hip joints. What **chemical** property of titanium makes it useful in these applications? (1 mark)

c Titanium is found combined with oxygen, as titanium dioxide. It is extracted by reacting it with chlorine to form titanium chloride. This is then reacted with a metal like sodium, leaving titanium metal and sodium chloride.

i Write a word equation for the reaction of titanium dioxide with chlorine. (1 mark)

ii Now write a balanced equation using chemical symbols for the reaction of titanium dioxide with chlorine. (2 marks)

iii Write a word equation for the reaction of titanium chloride with sodium. (1 mark)

iv Now write a balanced equation using chemical symbols for the reaction of titanium chloride with sodium. (2 marks)

v What kind of reaction is the reaction of titanium chloride with sodium? (1 mark)

(Total 10 marks)

Viewed from space, the Earth is a blue sphere with green and brown land masses arranged across the surface. The blue colour is water – the most abundant substance on the surface of our planet and essential for all life. Scientists think that life itself began in the water, and remained there for many millions of years before plants and animals finally colonised the land. So what exactly is water, and what is it about the chemistry of water that makes it so very important?

🔍 Ideas and Evidence

The water story

Water is a very simple chemical, a small molecule made up of one oxygen atom and two hydrogen atoms, which gives it the formula H_2O. At room temperature and normal atmospheric pressure water is a liquid. It freezes at 0 °C and boils at 100 °C. When it freezes, it behaves in a very unusual way, forming crystals of ice which are less dense than liquid water as a result of the unusually strong intermolecular forces between the water molecules in the liquid. As a result, instead of ice sinking to the bottom of the water when it forms, it floats on the top. This is enormously important for the success of life on Earth. The layer of ice which forms on the top creates an insulating layer, reducing the likelihood of the rest of the water freezing and therefore making sure that the animals and plants living in the water survive.

↑ **Figure 1:** This is perhaps the most spectacular water feature in the world – Angel Falls in South America – where the water drops 1000 m. Features like this are rare, but water is everywhere – it has formed our environment, surrounds our continents and islands and is an integral part of our everyday life.

The water in the rivers, lakes and oceans of the Earth evaporates in the heat of the sun. The water vapour which is formed rises into the atmosphere where it condenses as it cools and forms clouds. The clouds cool more as they rise further, until the droplets get too big and the clouds produce rain, replenishing the water in the rivers, lakes and oceans. This constant cycling of water between the Earth and the sky – sometimes passing through living organisms on the way – is known as the **water cycle**.

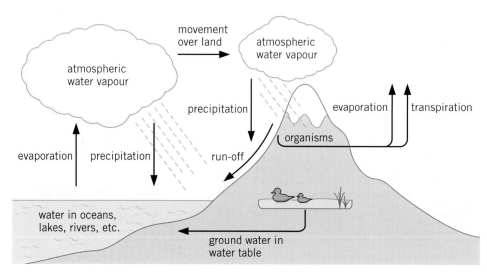

← **Figure 2:** The water cycle in nature maintains the levels of water on the surface of the Earth and in the atmosphere.

The uses of water

Water is an enormously useful substance – it would be impossible to list all of the ways in which it is used by people all around the world. Water is an important raw material, used in many industrial processes including the manufacture of sulphuric acid (see Section 11.1). It is also widely used as a solvent. Many substances will dissolve in water, which makes them useful for a wide range of purposes. For example, the fact that chlorine gas dissolves in water is useful in two ways – the solution which results can be used to bleach materials, while chlorine can be dissolved in water for drinking in order to kill any bacteria in it.

Many substances react with water to form solutions which are either acid or alkaline, and these too find a multitude of industrial uses.

Another important use of water is as a coolant. The specific heat capacity of water is high – in other words, it takes a lot of energy to warm water up. This means that water is an excellent coolant – circulating water can absorb a great deal of energy from exothermic reactions and transfer the heat elsewhere, where it may be useful.

Other uses of water worldwide are for washing and cleaning, and for drinking. Clean drinking water, uncontaminated by disease, sewage or chemicals, is a major issue all over the world. In the UK and other developed countries drinking water is treated by passing it over filter beds to remove any solid particles and then adding chlorine to kill bacteria. This system very efficiently supplies us with fresh water which is completely safe to drink.

↑ **Figure 3:** Water is used as a coolant in the production of electricity – the clouds of steam are dramatic evidence of the amount of energy it has absorbed.

? Questions

1 The graph shows the volume of 1 g of water at different temperatures, around its freezing point.

   a What volume does 1 gram of water occupy at 4 °C?

   b What volume does 1 gram of water occupy at 2 °C?

   c What volume does 1 gram of ice occupy at 0 °C?

   d Use this information to help you explain:

   i why ice floats on top of water

   ii why pipes burst when water in them freezes.

2 Produce a flow chart to show the water cycle in nature.

3 Draw a table with the headings 'raw material', 'solvent' and 'coolant'. Find out as many uses of water as you can and list them in the correct column of your table.

Key Ideas

⊙ Water is the most abundant substance on Earth and is essential for life.

⊙ Water vapour evaporates from water masses on the Earth into the atmosphere, where it forms clouds, and returns to Earth as rain in the water cycle.

⊙ Water is an important raw material and has many uses, both industrial and domestic.

In the developed countries of the world clean water – fresh from filtering and the addition of chlorine – is supplied to homes and industry through a system of supply pipes. The water which runs out of the taps in different areas of the country all looks very similar, but in fact there are some striking chemical differences in it. We may not be able to recognise these differences when we drink the water, but when we decide to get washed it is a different story.

The scum story

Some water readily forms a lather with soap when we wash ourselves – this is **soft water**. However, in other areas of the country it is not so easy to form a lather with soap and water – this is because these areas have **hard water**. Hard water not only makes it difficult to wash ourselves, it also makes it difficult to clean the bath or sink when we have finished. This is because hard water contains dissolved compounds which react with the soap to form **scum**, which floats on the water and sticks to the bath.

Most hard water contains dissolved calcium and magnesium compounds. It is formed when streams and rivers run over ground or rocks containing minerals which include calcium and magnesium compounds – like limestone for example, which contains calcium carbonate. As raindrops fall through the air, carbon dioxide dissolves in them. This dissolved carbon dioxide makes rain slightly acidic, even without pollutants like oxides of sulphur and nitrogen. The water in streams and rivers is therefore slightly acidic too, and minerals like limestone readily dissolve in it. These dissolved minerals are carried into the reservoirs and on into the domestic water supply – and it is the dissolved calcium and magnesium ions that react with soap to form scum.

It seems as if hard water actually benefits the people who drink it. The presence of dissolved compounds like calcium hydrogencarbonate ($CaHCO_3$) is actually very good for human health. The calcium ions taken in with the drinking water help in the development of strong bones and teeth. There is also evidence which suggests that hard water helps to reduce the incidence of heart disease (see Figure 1).

However, hard water isn't all good news. The same dissolved compounds which are good for human health are not so good for the health of plumbing systems. Using hard water increases household costs because much more soap and detergent are needed for cleaning. The soap first reacts with the dissolved calcium and magnesium ions in the water, forming compounds known as stearates (which we call scum). A lather can form only when all the calcium and magnesium ions have been removed by reacting with soap. In addition, hard water often leads to deposits known as **scale** forming in pipes, immersion heaters and other parts of the heating system. The same scale forms in domestic kettles, 'furring up' the heating elements and making them much less efficient, because scale is a very poor conductor of heat.

$$Ca^{2+}(aq) + 2HCO_3^-(aq) \longrightarrow CaCO_3(s) + H_2O(l) + CO_2(g)$$

lime scale

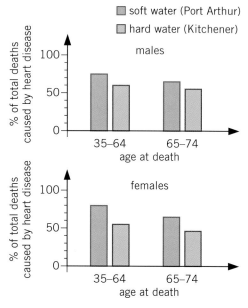

↑ **Figure 1:** These graphs show clearly that the number of people dying suddenly from heart disease in a Canadian town with a hard water supply is significantly lower than the numbers dying of heart disease in a town with soft water.

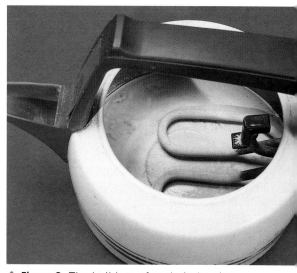

↑ **Figure 2:** The build-up of scale in heating systems and kettles not only makes them less efficient, but in time it can stop them working completely.

Softening things up

Hard water can be made soft by removing the calcium and magnesium ions which give it its 'hardness'. Whilst most people want to continue to drink hard water if it is available to them, many people both in domestic homes and in industry want to soften the water they use for heating, washing and manufacturing. There are two main ways in which this can be done.

⊙ The addition of sodium carbonate (known as washing soda) precipitates out calcium carbonate or magnesium carbonate and leaves soft water. Once they have been precipitated out, the hardness ions are no longer available to interfere with the soap! This is a similar reaction to lime scale formation, but it happens fast and when we want it to happen.

$$Ca^{2+}(aq) + CO_3^{2-}(aq) \longrightarrow CaCO_3(s)$$
from sodium carbonate

⊙ Ion exchange columns contain sodium ions – from salt – or hydrogen ions, and these 'change places' with calcium and magnesium ions in hard water when the water passes along the column (Figure 3). This is the basis of many domestic water softening units. Dishwashers have a similar water-softening system, and this is why they need regular topping up with salt. The salt keeps the ion exchange column working by supplying it with sodium ions.

↓ **Figure 3:** Ion exchange columns, which contain a special resin, enable us to change hard water into soft water on an industrial scale or in our homes.

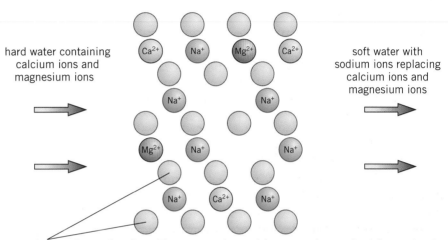

hard water containing calcium ions and magnesium ions

soft water with sodium ions replacing calcium ions and magnesium ions

Resin contains sodium ions. These are exchanged for magnesium and calcium as hard water passes through the resin. When all the sodium ions have been exchanged the column is flushed with water in which salt has been dissolved – so the magnesium ions and calcium ions in the resin are exchanged for sodium ions.

? Questions

1 What is the difference between soft water and hard water?

2 Using the graph in Figure 1:

  a Which city has soft water?

  b The apparent effect of hard and soft water on sudden deaths from heart disease can be seen in people of a wide range of ages and both sexes. Why does this make the data more significant?

  c This data looks to be convincing evidence that hard water helps to prevent heart disease. However, on its own it is not sufficient for firm conclusions to be made. Suggest one other study, or another type of evidence that would be important before a definite link between water hardness and heart disease could be made.

3 Using word and chemical equations, explain the difference between 'scum' and 'scale'.

4 Write an equation using both words and formulae to show the way washing soda softens water made hard by magnesium ions.

5 Design a leaflet to be distributed to people in an area of hard water, explaining the advantages and disadvantages of their situation and suggesting ways they might overcome the problems which hard water can cause.

🔑 Key Ideas

⊙ Soft water easily forms a lather with soap while hard water does not.

⊙ Hard water contains dissolved compounds – often calcium or magnesium compounds – which react with soap to form scum.

⊙ Hard water is good for the health of bones, teeth and the heart.

⊙ Hard water can cause problems in heating systems due to the build-up of scale, so methods of softening water are often needed.

Many gases are soluble in water, and so are most ionic compounds. However, the majority of covalent compounds do not dissolve in water, because they do not form ions.

Most of the reactions which take place in living organisms and many important laboratory and industrial reactions involve substances which are dissolved in water.

What affects solubility?

Many substances dissolve in water, but the amount which will dissolve is affected by a number of factors. The solubility of a solute in water (or in any other solvent) is given in grams of solute per 100 g of water (or solvent) at a given temperature. The solubility of most solutes increases as the temperature increases.

A **saturated solution** is one in which no more solute will dissolve at a given temperature. If the solution is heated, then more solute will be dissolved until the solution becomes saturated again. As a hot saturated solution cools down, it will hold less solute again and so some of the solute will separate out from the solution – it will crystallise out. The effect of temperature on the solubility of solutes can be seen by looking at **solubility curves**. A solubility curve shows the amount of a solute which is needed to give a saturated solution at any given temperature.

We can use these solubility curves to help us understand the way solutes crystallise out of hot solutions as they cool down. For example, from Figure 2 we can see that at 80 °C 150 g of potassium nitrate will dissolve in every 100 g of water, but at 40 °C only about 70 g will dissolve. This means that as we cool our solution down from 80 °C to 40 °C we can expect 80 g of potassium nitrate to crystallise out of every 100 g of water.

Gases can also dissolve in water. The two main factors which affect their solubility are temperature and pressure. Gases are the opposite to solid solutes in the way they are affected by temperature changes – as the temperature increases, the amount of gas dissolved in 100 g of water decreases. On the other hand, if the temperature is kept constant but the pressure increases, then the solubility of a gas increases.

↑ **Figure 1:** Citron pressé is a popular drink in France. It is a mixture of lemon juice and cold water, with sugar added. Even with lots of stirring you are often left with some undissolved sugar. The same amount of sugar in hot tea would dissolve very quickly.

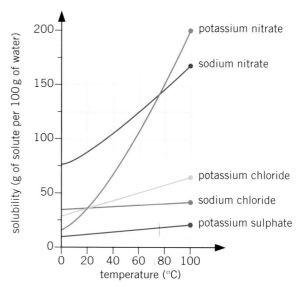

↑ **Figure 2:** These solubility curves show us the effect of temperature on five different solutes – in each case, the solubility increases as the temperature increases.

Gas	Solubility (g of gas per 100 g of water):			
	at 0 °C	at 20 °C	at 50 °C	at 100 °C
nitrogen, N_2	0.0029	0.0019	0.0012	0
oxygen, O_2	0.0069	0.0043	0.0027	0
carbon dioxide, CO_2	0.335	0.169	0.076	0
ammonia, NH_3	89.9	51.8	28.4	7.4

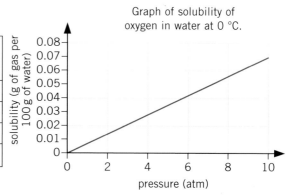

↖ **Figure 3:** These data show the effect of temperature and pressure on the solubility of gases in water.

How does solubility affect us?

There are lots of examples of the way the solubility of different substances affects our everyday life.

The solubility of nitrate ions and ammonium ions from artificial fertilisers means that they dissolve in rainwater, contaminating rivers, lakes and reservoirs. Nitrate ions can have harmful effects on babies (see Section 4.9) and so nitrate levels in drinking water must be carefully monitored.

Dissolved oxygen in the water is essential for the life of aquatic organisms, particularly the animals. When hot water from power stations is discharged into rivers and lakes, it contains no chemical pollutants but the increased temperature of the water reduces the amount of oxygen dissolved in the water and this can damage aquatic life.

Another, more frivolous, example is the fizzy drinks that many people enjoy. The carbonated water used to make them is produced by dissolving carbon dioxide in water under high pressure. When the pressure is released the gas bubbles out of the solution, providing us with 'fizz'! Warm drinks are not very fizzy – because they do not contain very much dissolved carbon dioxide.

↑ **Figure 4:** Some aquatic organisms, like this salmon, can only survive with high levels of oxygen in the water. They are particularly badly affected if the temperature of the water is raised.

Questions

1 From the solubility curves in Figure 2, how many grams of each of the solutes could be dissolved in 100 g of water at 40 °C?

2 Using the graph in Figure 2:

  a 100 g of sodium nitrate is dissolved in 100 g of water to form a saturated solution. What is the temperature?

  b How much more sodium nitrate could be added to give a saturated solution at 100 °C?

  c How much sodium nitrate would you expect to crystallise out of the solution in part **a** if it was cooled down to 0 °C?

3 Draw a graph to represent the data in the table (Figure 3) and explain what it shows about the effect of temperature on the solubility of gases.

4 Using the graph in Figure 3:

  a What mass of oxygen is dissolved in water at

    i 1 atm   **ii** 4 atm   **iii** 6 atm?

  b What effect would you expect an increase in temperature to have on the amount of gas dissolved at any given pressure?

Key Ideas

- Most ionic compounds are soluble in water.

- The solubility of most solutes increases as the temperature increases.

- Many gases are soluble in water.

- The solubility of gases increases as the temperature decreases and the pressure increases.

Acids and bases are essential to our understanding of chemistry and they play a vital part in the working balance of living organisms too. Water must be present for a substance to act as an acid or a base.

What are acids and bases?

When an acid dissolves in water (forming an aqueous solution) it produces hydrogen ions (H^+). The H^+ ion is a hydrogen atom which has lost its electron – in other words, it is simply a proton. A proton produced as an acid dissolves in water becomes surrounded by water molecules which keep it in solution – it is said to be **hydrated**. Hydrated hydrogen ions are represented as $H^+(aq)$. Because they act a source of protons, acids are sometimes referred to as **proton donors**.

An alkali is a base which dissolves in water. When it does this it produces hydroxide ions (OH^-). These hydroxide ions combine readily with protons to form water:

$$OH^-(aq) + H^+(aq) \longrightarrow H_2O(l)$$

Because they behave like this, bases are sometimes referred to as **proton acceptors**.

↑ **Figure 1:** Acids and bases are all around us – in our bodies, in products like these around our homes, in our laboratories and in our industries.

👤 *Science people*

Developing the acid–base theory

Acids are very difficult to define. For many years chemists knew them as substances which tasted sour and which caused certain indicator substances to change colour. It was not until late in the 19th century that the first truly scientific definition of acids and bases was suggested, by the Swedish chemist Svante Arrhenius in his PhD thesis. First published in 1884, Arrhenius's theory states that when acids, bases and salts dissolve in water they separate either partly or completely into charged particles called ions in a process known as **dissociation**. Acids are substances which dissolve in water to produce hydrogen ions, H^+. According to Arrhenius, all the similarities seen between acids with very different formulae were due to the hydrogen ions they produce when dissolved in water. Similarly he thought that the common properties of bases are due to the fact that they all produce hydroxide ions in solution.

Arrhenius's ideas were seen as revolutionary at the time. The University of Uppsala was very reluctant to give him his doctorate, and finally gave him a fourth rank pass – a disgrace which meant he could not get a professorship. Arrhenius kept passing his ideas on to other scientists, but all the older chemists completely rejected his ideas – they were convinced that molecules could not split up and

↑ **Figure 2:** Svante Arrhenius taught himself to read by the age of three, produced his radical new ionic theory on electrolytes, acids and bases by the time he was 25 but had to wait until he was 44 before he received his well-deserved Nobel prize. ⬇

certainly could not carry an electric charge. Fortunately some of the younger men in the field began to see that Arrhenius's ideas could help explain the results they were getting from their experiments. More and more data built up supporting the new theory and eventually Arrhenius was given credit for the great breakthough he had made. In 1903 Arrhenius was finally awarded the Nobel prize for his work.

Arrhenius's theory has been and still is extremely useful, but it has some limitations. His definition of acids and bases is limited to the situations in which water is present. However, many reactions which appear to be acid–base reactions occur in solvents other than water or even when there is no water present at all.

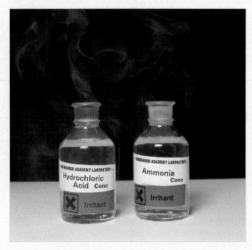

← **Figure 3:** When hydrogen chloride gas reacts with ammonia gas a neutralisation reaction occurs and white fumes made up of tiny crystals of ammonium chloride appear:

$$HCl(g) + NH_3(g) \longrightarrow NH_4Cl(s)$$

By the Arrhenius definition of an acid the reaction between hydrogen chloride and ammonia is not a neutralisation because it does not take place in aqueous solution, yet it is clearly the same reaction as if the two liquids were mixed. This problem was recognised in 1923 by the Danish chemist Johannes Brønsted and the British chemist Thomas Lowry. They both came up with a much more general definition of acids and bases – that an acid is a proton donor and a base is a proton acceptor. This definition explains reactions like the one above as well as aqueous acid–base reactions. The ideas of Lowry and Brønsted were accepted very quickly, because they built on the foundation of Arrhenius's theories which were by now well accepted, and because they also helped to explain observations which Arrhenius's ideas did not explain.

? Questions

1 a List at least eight acids, both from the laboratory and from everyday situations.

   b What do all these acids have in common?

2 a List at least eight bases/alkalis.

   b What do all these bases have in common?

3 Arrhenius, Brønsted and Lowry all made major contributions to our understanding of acids and bases.

   a Summarise their ideas.

   b Explain why Arrhenius's ideas took so much longer to be accepted than those of Brønsted and Lowry.

Key Ideas

⊙ Acids in aqueous solution produce H^+ ions.

⊙ An acid can be defined as a proton donor.

⊙ Alkalis (bases) in aqueous solution produce OH^- ions.

⊙ A base can be defined as a proton acceptor.

12.5 Acids, bases and salts

Arrhenius's model of acids and bases shows them ionising in water to give hydrogen ions and hydroxide ions respectively. This same model helps us to understand why some acids are so strong that they will eat away human flesh and etch metal, whilst others are relatively weak and can safely be eaten .

Strong and weak acids

Acids and alkalis can be classified by the extent to which they ionise in water. A **strong** acid or alkali is one that is 100% ionised in water. Hydrochloric, sulphuric and nitric acids are all examples of strong acids, whilst sodium hydroxide and potassium hydroxide are examples of strong alkalis.

On the other hand, a **weak** acid or alkali is only partly ionised in water. Examples of weak acids are ethanoic, citric and carbonic acid, whilst weak alkalis include ammonia solution.

How can we tell if an acid is weak or strong? There are two main ways. The pH scale is in effect a measure of the number of hydrogen ions in a solution. If we measure the pH of two acids of the same concentration – for example, the molecular weight in grams of each acid dissolved in a litre of water – then their pH will tell us if all or only some of the acid molecules are ionised. The more free hydrogen ions there are, the lower the pH will be. This means that the strongest acids have the lowest pHs, whilst weaker acids have higher pHs.

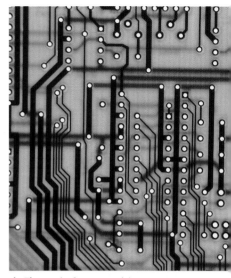

↑ **Figure 1:** Strong acids are used to etch printed circuit boards like this, removing all the copper which is not needed from the surface.

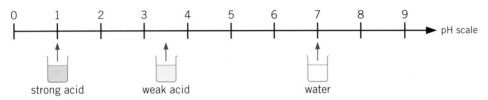

← **Figure 2:** When two acids of the same concentration are compared, the stronger acid will have the lower pH .

Another way of distinguishing between weak and strong acids of the same concentration is to observe the rate of reaction when a metal is added to the acid. If a piece of metal such as magnesium or zinc is added to a certain concentration of a strong acid there will be a vigorous reaction, with lots of bubbles of hydrogen gas produced quickly and a metal salt will be formed. For example:

hydrochloric acid + magnesium $\longrightarrow$ magnesium chloride + hydrogen

$2HCl(aq)$ + $Mg(s)$ $\longrightarrow$ $MgCl_2(aq)$ + $H_2(g)$

If a similar piece of magnesium or zinc is added to the same concentration of a weak acid there be a similar but much less vigorous reaction, with hydrogen given off relatively slowly as a metal salt forms. For example:

ethanoic acid + magnesium $\longrightarrow$ magnesium ethanoate + hydrogen

$2CH_3COOH(aq)$ + $Mg(s)$ $\longrightarrow$ $Mg(CH_3COO)_2(aq)$ + $H_2(g)$

These reactions, between a metal and an acid, can be used to make salts.

Making salts

There are a number of different ways of making salts.

⊙ The reaction of a metal with an acid gives a salt and hydrogen gas

(as seen in the examples above).

- The reaction of a soluble base with an acid gives a salt and water. Once the reaction is complete (no more bubbles of hydrogen gas are produced) the salt can be obtained from solution by evaporation. For example:

sodium hydroxide + hydrochloric acid $\longrightarrow$ sodium chloride + water

(see Section 7.3).

- The reaction of an insoluble base with an acid gives a salt and water. The salt can be obtained from solution by evaporation. For example:

copper hydroxide + nitric acid $\longrightarrow$ copper nitrate + water

(see Section 7.4).

- Mixing two solutions may form an insoluble salt. The formation of an insoluble salt is known as **precipitation**. Once the precipitate of insoluble salt has formed it can be obtained from the solution by filtering and washing. For example:

lead nitrate + sodium chloride $\longrightarrow$ lead chloride + sodium nitrate

$Pb(NO_3)_2(aq) + 2NaCl(aq) \longrightarrow PbCl_2(s) + 2NaNO_3(aq)$

- In some cases elements can be directly combined to form anhydrous salts. The best examples of this type of salt formation are the reactions between aluminium and chlorine to form aluminium chloride and between iron and chlorine to form iron chloride. In both cases the metal is heated in an atmosphere of chlorine gas:

aluminium + chlorine $\longrightarrow$ aluminium chloride

$2Al(s) + 3Cl_2(g) \longrightarrow 2AlCl_3(s)$

iron + chlorine $\longrightarrow$ iron(III) chloride

$2Fe(s) + 3Cl_2(g) \longrightarrow 2FeCl_3(s)$

Key Ideas

- A strong acid or alkali is 100% ionised in water.

- A weak acid or alkali is only partially ionised in water.

- A strong acid has a lower pH than a weak acid.

- Strong acids react more rapidly than weak acids with a metal to release hydrogen and produce a metal salt.

- There are a number of ways of making different salts.

? Questions

1

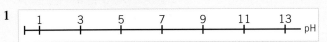

Copy the pH scale and mark on it the positions of the pH of these substances:

a vinegar (a weak acid)

b pure water

c caustic soda (a strong alkali)

d hydrochloric acid

e toothpaste (a weak alkali).

2 A student carried out an investigation in which she dropped a piece of magnesium into a weak acid. She measured the amount of gas produced in the reaction and plotted it on a graph:

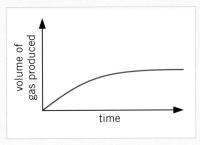

a What gas was produced?

b What test could you use to show this?

A second student carried out a similar experiment using a strong acid in place of the weak acid.

c Copy the graph and add a line to it showing the results that the second student might have obtained.

d What other factors would have to be controlled in order for this experiment to be a fair comparison of the strengths of the two acids?

3 Write chemical equations to describe the following reactions in which a salt is formed in each case:

a zinc oxide (an insoluble base) + hydrochloric acid

b sodium hydroxide (a soluble base) + nitric acid

c calcium metal + ethanoic acid

d aluminium + iodine

4 Using words and diagrams, describe how you would investigate the reaction of the metals copper, magnesium and zinc with hydrochloric acid (a strong acid).

If an acid solution is added to an alkaline solution they will react and neutralise each other, forming a salt. However, the resulting solution will be neutral only if acid and alkali are present in exactly the right quantities. If there is more acid than alkali, then although all the alkali will be neutralised the solution will remain acidic. On the other hand, if there is more alkali than acid, then all the acid will be neutralised and the solution will remain alkaline. The precise volumes of acid and alkali solutions which neutralise each other exactly can be measured by an important laboratory technique known as **titration**. The point at which the acid and alkali have been exactly neutralised is shown using a suitable **indicator**.

↑ **Figure 1:** Indicators such as these are needed for successful acid–base titrations.

Carrying out titrations

To carry out a titration in order to find the concentration of a solution containing a particular substance (for example, sodium hydroxide):

1 Put an accurately measured volume of the solution into a conical flask and place it on a white tile.

2 Add a coloured indicator solution – phenolphthalein is often used because of its distinctive colour change – it changes from pink in alkali solution to colourless in acid solution.

3 Put a solution of accurately known concentration (hydrochloric acid, for example) into a burette. (A burette is a long tube with a tap on one end. The tube has markings on it to enable the volume of liquid let out of the burette through the tap to be measured accurately – usually to the nearest $0.1\ cm^3$.)

4 Record the reading on the burette then open the tap to release small amounts of solution into the flask, swirling the flask to make sure the solutions are thoroughly mixed.

5 Eventually, the indicator changes colour, showing that the alkali in the flask has been neutralised by the acid added from the burette. Record the burette reading and calculate the volume of solution used.

6 Repeat the whole process at least three times, then calculate the average value to give the most accurate possible results.

7 The volumes of the two solutions used, together with the known concentration of one of them, can be used to calculate the concentration of the other solution (see Section 12.7).

A reminder of the mole

To be able to use the results of our titrations to calculate the concentration of unknown solutions we need to use a chemical concept introduced in Section 2.7 – the mole. The relative atomic mass of an element in grams or the relative formula mass of a compound in grams is equal to 1 mole of that substance. Remember that 1 mole of a substance contains the same number of particles as 1 mole of any other substance (Section 2.7). We can use these ideas to help us in our calculations.

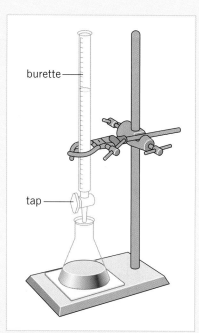

↑ **Figure 2:** The apparatus needed to carry out a titration.

If we are given a known quantity of a substance for which we know the formula, we can work out how many moles of that substance we have, using relative atomic or formula masses. For example:

⊙ We have 12 g of carbon. We know that the relative atomic mass of carbon is 12, so we can work out the number of moles of carbon: 12/12 = **1 mole.**

⊙ We have 80 g of sodium hydroxide. We know that the relative formula mass of sodium hydroxide is 23 + 16 + 1 = 40, so the number of moles is 80/40 = **2 moles.**

Similarly, if we are told that we have a given number of moles of a substance we can work out the mass of that substance in grams. For example:

⊙ We have 3 moles of magnesium chloride. We know that 1 mole of magnesium chloride contains one formula mass in grams of the compound, which is 24 + (2 × 35.5) = 95 g. From this we can work out that 3 moles of magnesium chloride in grams is 95 × 3 = **285 g.**

⊙ We have 1.5 moles of water. We know that 1 mole of water has a mass of 16 + (2 × 1) = 18 g. Therefore 1.5 moles of water would have a mass of 18 × 1.5 = **27 g.**

In Section 12.7 we will see how we can use calculations like these to make use of the results from our titrations to work out the concentrations of unknown solutions.

Key Ideas

⊙ The volume of acid and alkali solutions which neutralise each other can be measured by titration using a suitable indicator.

⊙ The relative atomic mass of an element or the relative formula mass of a compound in grams is equal to 1 mole of that substance.

? Questions

1 Describe how you would carry out a titration using 25 cm^3 of potassium hydroxide of unknown concentration and some sulphuric acid with a concentration of 0.25 mol dm^{-3}.

2 You are given a quantity in grams for each of the following substances. Calculate the number of moles of each compound present.

   a copper sulphate ($CuSO_4$) 318 g   **b** ammonia (NH_3) 68 g   **c** magnesium oxide (MgO) 20 g

3 How many grams of each of the following substances are present in the given number of moles?

   a 1 mole of calcium chloride ($CaCl_2$)   **b** 2.5 moles of sodium fluoride (NaF)

   c 0.33 moles of zinc nitrate ($Zn(NO_3)_2$)

4 Not all indicators change colour at the same pH. The table shows the names of some indicators. It also shows the colour changes which occur as the pH increases (the solution becomes more alkaline) and the approximate pH at which this happens.

Indicator	Colour change as pH increases	Approx pH at which change occurs
methyl orange	red ⟶ orange	4
litmus	red ⟶ blue	5
bromothymol blue	yellow ⟶ blue	7
phenolphthalein	colourless ⟶ pink	9

   a Copy the pH scale and add labelled arrows to show where the indicators change colour.

   | 1   3   5   7   9   11   13 → pH |

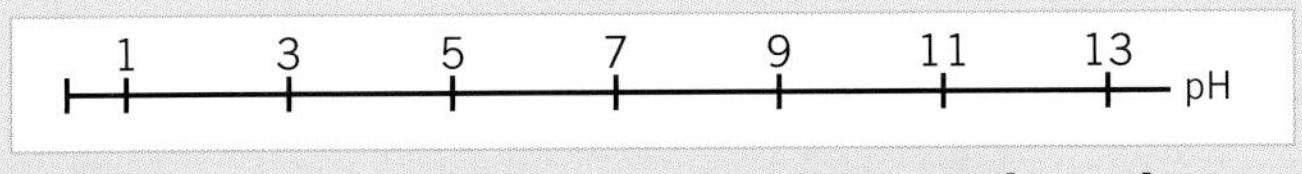

   b Which indicator could be used to distinguish a solution which is weakly acidic from a solution which is strongly acidic?

   c Which indicator could be used to distinguish a solution which is weakly alkaline from a solution which is strongly alkaline?

   d Which indicator could be used to distinguish a solution which is weakly alkaline from a solution which is weakly acidic?

12.7 Titrations and calculations

Moles and concentrations

The concentration of an aqueous solution is usually expressed in terms of moles per cubic decimetre, written as $mol\,dm^{-3}$ (or mol/dm^3) or M. If we know the amount of substance dissolved we can work out the concentration of the solution – sometimes called its molarity.

For example, 40 g of sodium hydroxide are dissolved in water to make $1\,dm^3$ of sodium hydroxide solution. We know that the formula mass in grams of sodium hydroxide (NaOH) is $23 + 16 + 1 = 40$, and that this is 1 mole of sodium hydroxide. This tells us that the concentration of the $1\,dm^3$ of solution which contains 40 g of sodium hydroxide is **$1\,mol\,dm^{-3}$**, or **1 M**. Another way of saying this is to describe it as a 1 molar solution of sodium hydroxide.

However, if the 40 g of sodium hydroxide was used to make $500\,cm^3$ of solution, the calculation would be rather different. To find the concentration of the solution, we have to work out how much sodium hydroxide would be present in $1\,dm^3$ ($1000\,cm^3$) of solution if the proportions of sodium hydroxide and water stayed the same.

This is how the calculation is done.

40 g of NaOH are dissolved in $500\,cm^3$ of water, so

$\dfrac{40}{500}$ g of NaOH would be dissolved in $1\,cm^3$ of solution and

$\dfrac{40}{500} \times 1000\,g = 80\,g$ would be dissolved in $1000\,cm^3$ of solution.

The formula mass of NaOH is 40, so 80 g of NaOH is $\dfrac{80}{40}$ moles = 2 moles.

So the concentration of the solution is **$2\,mol\,dm^{-3}$ or 2 M**.

On the other hand, if we know the concentration of the solution and the volume of that solution, we can work out the number of moles and so find the mass of substance in the aqueous solution.

How many grams of copper sulphate are there in $250\,cm^3$ of $1\,mol\,dm^{-3}$ copper sulphate ($CuSO_4$) solution, shown in Figure 1?

The concentration of the $CuSO_4$ solution is $1\,mol\,dm^{-3}$, so in $1\,dm^3$ of solution there will be 1 mole of $CuSO_4$.

1 mole of $CuSO_4$ has a mass of $63 + 32 + (4 \times 16) = 159\,g$.

In $1000\,cm^3$ ($1\,dm^3$) of solution there will be 159 g of $CuSO_4$,

so in $1\,cm^3$ of solution there will be $\dfrac{159}{1000}$ g of $CuSO_4$ and in $250\,cm^3$ of

solution there will be $\dfrac{159}{1000} \times 250\,g = 39.75\,g$ of $CuSO_4$.

There are **39.75 g** of $CuSO_4$ in $250\,cm^3$ of $1\,mol\,dm^{-3}$ $CuSO_4$ solution.

↑ **Figure 1:** In the flask are $250\,cm^3$ of $1\,mol\,dm^{-3}$ copper sulphate solution. How much copper sulphate does it contain?

← **The steps in the calculation are:**
⊙ Work out how much of the compound (in grams) is present in $1cm^3$ of solution.
⊙ Work out how much (in grams) is present in $1000\,cm^3$ of solution.
⊙ Change grams to moles.

← **The steps in the calculation are:**
⊙ Work out how much of the compound (in grams) is present in $1\,dm^3$ of solution.
⊙ Work out how much (in grams) is present in $1\,cm^3$ of solution.
⊙ Then work out how much is present in the given volume of solution.

← Notice that this is exactly 0.25 moles of $CuSO_4$. (Since $250\,cm^3$ is $0.25\,dm^3$ – by definition $0.25\,dm^3$ of a $1\,mol\,dm^{-3}$ solution must contain 0.25 moles.)

Calculations from titrations

In a titration there is always one solution of accurately known concentration, which is placed in the burette. The other solution, containing a known substance with an unknown concentration, is placed in a conical flask. The result from the titration is used to calculate the amount of the substance present in the solution in the conical flask.

Example

A student carried out a titration using 25.0 cm³ sodium hydroxide solution of unknown concentration, which was placed in a conical flask. The sodium hydroxide was exactly neutralised by 20.0 cm³ of 0.50 mol dm⁻³ hydrochloric acid added from a burette. What was the concentration of the sodium hydroxide solution?

The equation for this reaction is:

$$NaOH(aq) + HCl(aq) \longrightarrow NaCl(aq) + H_2O(l)$$

This tells us that 1 mole of NaOH is neutralised by 1 mole of HCl.

The concentration of the HCl is 0.50 mol dm⁻³,

so 0.50 moles of HCl are dissolved in 1000 cm³ of acid solution

and $\dfrac{0.50}{1000}$ moles of HCl are dissolved in 1 cm³ of acid solution.

Therefore $\dfrac{0.50}{1000} \times 20.0$ moles = **0.010 moles** of HCl are dissolved in

20.0 cm³ of acid solution.

The equation for the reaction tells us that 0.010 moles of HCl will exactly neutralise 0.010 moles of NaOH. This means that there must have been 0.010 moles of NaOH in the 25.0 cm³ of solution in the conical flask. To calculate the concentration of NaOH we need to find how many moles of NaOH would be present in 1 dm³ of solution:

0.010 moles of NaOH are dissolved in 25.0 cm³ of solution.

Therefore $\dfrac{0.010}{25}$ moles of NaOH are dissolved in 1 cm³ of solution

and $\dfrac{0.010}{25} \times 1000$ moles = **0.40 moles** of NaOH are dissolved in 1000 cm³

of solution.

So the concentration of the NaOH solution is 0.40 mol dm⁻³ (or **0.40 M**).

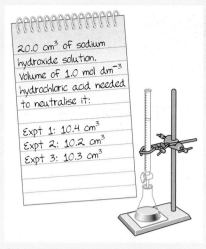

↑ **Figure 3:** From results like these we can work out the concentration of the unknown solution.

⊙— Key Ideas

- ⊙ The concentration of an aqueous solution is usually expressed in terms of moles per cubic decimetre (mol dm⁻³) or molarity (M).

- ⊙ Titrations can be used to find the concentration of an acid or alkali from the relative volumes used and the concentration of one of the two reactants.

? Questions

1 In a titration, 15.0 cm³ of hydrochloric acid reacted exactly with 10.0 cm³ of sodium hydroxide solution. The concentration of the acid was 0.10 mol dm⁻³.

   a Write down an equation for this reaction.

   b Calculate the number of moles of hydrochloric acid in the acid solution added to the sodium hydroxide solution.

   c Write down the number of moles of sodium hydroxide in the sodium hydroxide solution.

   d Calculate the concentration of the sodium hydroxide solution.

2 Vinegar contains ethanoic acid. A 20.0 cm³ sample of vinegar was titrated against 0.50 mol dm⁻³ sodium hydroxide solution. Exactly 25.0 cm³ of the sodium hydroxide solution was needed to neutralise the ethanoic acid in the vinegar.

   a Write down an equation for this reaction.

   b Calculate the number of moles of sodium hydroxide in the sodium hydroxide solution added to the vinegar.

   c Write down the number of moles of ethanoic acid in the vinegar.

   d Calculate the concentration of the ethanoic acid in the vinegar.

1 A sample of water taken from a lake was found to contain sulphuric acid.

A student carried out a titration to find the concentration of the sulphuric acid in this sample. $25.0\,cm^3$ of the sulphuric acid solution was neutralised exactly by $34.0\,cm^3$ of a potassium hydroxide solution of concentration $0.2\,mol\,dm^{-3}$. The equation for the reaction is:

$$2KOH(aq) + H_2SO_4 \longrightarrow K_2SO_4(aq) + 2H_2O(l)$$

a Describe the experimental procedure for the titration carried out by the student. (4 marks)

b Calculate the number of moles of potassium hydroxide used. (2 marks)

c Calculate the concentration of the sulphuric acid in mole per cubic decimetre ($mol\,dm^{-3}$). (3 marks)

(Total 9 marks)

AQA specimen question

2 This label has been taken from a bottle of mineral water.

Use the information on the label to answer some of the questions which follow.

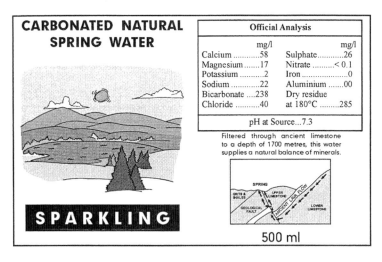

CARBONATED NATURAL SPRING WATER

Official Analysis			
	mg/l		mg/l
Calcium	58	Sulphate	26
Magnesium	17	Nitrate	< 0.1
Potassium	2	Iron	0
Sodium	22	Aluminium	00
Bicarbonate	238	Dry residue	
Chloride	40	at 180°C	285

pH at Source...7.3

Filtered through ancient limestone to a depth of 1700 metres, this water supplies a natural balance of minerals.

SPARKLING

500 ml

a This mineral water is hard.

　i Name an ion from the label which makes this mineral water hard. (1 mark)

　ii Describe and give the results of a test to show that this mineral water is hard. (2 marks)

b Describe some of the advantages and disadvantages of hard water. (3 marks)

(Total 6 marks)

AQA specimen question

3 A student carried out an experiment to measure the solubility of two different substances in water at different temperatures. One of these substances was a crystalline solid, the other was a gas.

The two graphs **A** and **B** show the student's results.

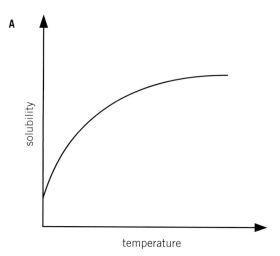

A

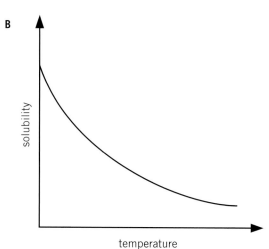

B

a Which graph, **A** or **B**, shows the results obtained by the student for the solubility of the gas? Explain your answer. (2 marks)

b Explain the shape of graph **A**. (2 marks)

c Warm water from a power station's cooling system is discharged into a river. Use graph **B** to explain why there are fewer fish in this part of the river than elsewhere along its length. (3 marks)

(Total 7 marks)

4 The diagram shows a box of washing soda.

Washing soda is used to soften water, making it easier to get clothes clean. It consists of crystals of sodium carbonate. Each crystal contains several water molecules in addition to sodium ions and carbonate ions.

a Name **one** ion which makes water hard. (1 mark)

b Write a balanced equation for the reaction of washing soda with this ion, showing how the washing soda makes the water soft. (2 marks)

c A student dissolves 2.5 g of Washo water softener in water in a conical flask. She carries out a titration to find the amount of hydrochloric acid needed to react exactly with the sodium carbonate in the water softener. She found that exactly 17.5 cm^3 of hydrochloric acid with a concentration of 1.0 mol dm^{-3} was required in the titration.

  i Suggest the name of an indicator that could have been used in this titration. (1 mark)

  ii Write a balanced equation for the reaction of hydrochloric acid with calcium carbonate. (2 marks)

  iii Calculate the number of moles of hydrochloric acid that reacted with the washing soda in the conical flask. (2 marks)

  iv How many moles of sodium carbonate was this equivalent to? (1 mark)

  v What mass of sodium carbonate was this? (2 marks)

  vi What mass of the water softener solution in the conical flask was water? (1 mark)

  vii How many moles of water is this? (2 marks)

  viii The formula of sodium carbonate can be written as Na$_2$CO$_3$.xH$_2$O.
  Use your answers to parts **iv** and **vii** of this question to calculate a value for x.

  (Relative atomic masses: H = 1, C = 12, O = 16, Na = 23) (1 mark)

  (Total 15 marks)

5 Sulphuric acid behaves as an acid.

Explain why, using the ideas of Arrhenius and Brønsted-Lowry.

To gain full marks you should write down your ideas in good English. Put them into a sensible order and use the correct scientific words.

(3 marks)

(Total 3 marks)

AQA specimen question

One of the problems we face in chemistry is that many substances – with many different properties – look very similar indeed to the naked eye. Even the elements themselves can be hard to distinguish – there are lots of shiny grey metals, and one colourless, odourless gas looks much like another! Once the elements are combined to form compounds the possibilities are simply enormous. The number of white solids alone is enough to cause problems – and white solids can range from harmless substances which we eat regularly to extremely toxic poisons. To identify unknown substances we have to become chemical detectives, and to make our task easier there are some tests which help us distinguish one substance from another.

Identifying metals – flame tests

Metals can be difficult to identify even when we have the element in front of us. It is even more difficult to know which metal is involved when the metal is part of a compound. But identifying some of the metals in Groups 1 and 2 of the periodic table is made much easier, because when they burn in air they produce flames with a characteristic colour. To carry out a flame test a small amount of the substance to be tested is placed in a wire loop, which has been dipped in concentrated hydrochloric acid, and held in the hot flame of a Bunsen burner. The Bunsen flame then shows the colour of the metal element involved.

↑ **Figure 1:** Sherlock Holmes was a famous fictional detective. Just as detectives investigating a crime nowadays have tests for fingerprints, fibres and paints, and DNA analysis to help them decide 'whodunnit', so chemists have some set procedures which throw light on the chemical make-up of an unknown substance.

→ **Figure 2:** The colours of the flame test help us identify some metals – in this photograph it is lithium.

Element	Flame colour
lithium	bright red
sodium	golden yellow
potassium	lilac
calcium	brick red
barium	green

Identifying metals – reactions with sodium hydroxide

Sometimes we can use the reactions of unknown substances with well known reagents to help with our identification. Aluminium ions, calcium ions and magnesium ions all form white precipitates with sodium hydroxide solution, so if we add sodium hydroxide to our unknown substance and a white precipitate forms we known it contains aluminium or calcium or magnesium ions. If we add more and more (excess) sodium hydroxide then the precipitate formed with aluminium ions dissolves away – the other two don't. This lets us identify aluminium ions precisely. Calcium and magnesium ions can be distinguished through a flame test – while calcium ions give a bright red flame, magnesium ions produce no colour at all.

Similarly, certain metal ions form coloured precipitates with sodium hydroxide. If sodium hydroxide solution is added to a substance containing copper(II) ions a light blue precipitate appears (see Figure 3). If the substance contains iron(II) ions a light green precipitate is produced when sodium hydroxide solution is added. This precipitate slowly turns a reddish brown colour. When sodium hydroxide solution is added to iron(III) ions, a reddish brown precipitate is produced immediately.

→ **Figure 3:** When distinctive precipitates like this copper(II) hydroxide are formed, it is easy to see why we use sodium hydroxide solution to help in our chemical detection.

Testing for carbonates

When we are acting as chemical detectives, we need to eliminate suspects all the time. There is a very useful general test which will tell us if an unknown substance contains carbonate ions. If a carbonate is mixed with a dilute acid such as hydrochloric or sulphuric acid then carbon dioxide is produced. So if an unknown substance produces a gas which turns limewater cloudy, we know that carbon dioxide has been given off and the substance is a carbonate.

In addition to the general test for carbonates, two metal carbonates in particular show distinctive colour changes when they undergo thermal decomposition. This means that if we have identified an unknown substance as a carbonate, and then heat some of that substance, we may be able to complete the identification.

For example, copper carbonate is a green substance which decomposes when heated to give black copper oxide and carbon dioxide.

Similarly, zinc carbonate is a white substance which decomposes to give zinc oxide when heated. Zinc oxide is also white, but when it is hot it is a lemon yellow colour – the only substance to show such a colour change.

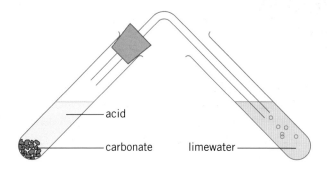

↑ **Figure 4:** The test for carbonates.

$$CuCO_3(s) \xrightarrow{heat} CuO(s) + CO_2(g)$$

green   black   turns limewater milky

$$ZnCO_3(s) \xrightarrow{heat} ZnO(s) + CO_2(g)$$

white   lemon yellow when hot, white when cold   turns limewater milky

? Questions

1 Copy and complete the following table:

Add sodium hydroxide solution	Flame test	Metal ion
nothing observed	lilac	
white precipitate	brick red	
		Fe^{3+}
white precipitate which dissolves as more sodium hydroxide solution is added	nothing observed	
light green precipitate which slowly turns reddish brown	nothing observed	
		Na^+

2 Four samples of chemicals have been found by detectives hunting a gang of international chemical thieves. Which of the four powders can be positively identified? Give your reasons.

Sample	Appearance	Add dilute acid	Effect of heat
Powder A	green	fizzes	green powder turns black and a gas is evolved which turns limewater milky
Powder B	white	nothing happens	no effect
Powder C	white	fizzes	white powder turns yellow while hot, cooling to white again, and a gas is evolved which turns limewater milky
Powder D	green	fizzes	no effect

⊙ Key Ideas

- ⊙ A range of chemical tests can be used for the detection and identification of elements and compounds.

- ⊙ Some metals can be identified using flame tests.

- ⊙ Reactions with sodium hydroxide allow different metals to be identified by the precipitates which form.

- ⊙ Carbonates react with dilute acids to give carbon dioxide.

- ⊙ Copper and zinc carbonates can be identified by heating them, when they both give off carbon dioxide and change colour in a distinctive way.

In Section 13.1 we saw how to identify some common metal ions and how to find out if carbonate ions are present. The tests below can help us to identify a wider range of negatively charged ions (anions).

Chloride ions

If an unknown solution contains chloride ions, a relatively simple test will reveal them. If dilute nitric acid and silver nitrate solution are added to the unknown solution, the appearance of a white precipitate (silver chloride) tells us that chloride ions are present.

Sulphate ions

Another common group which could be part of an unknown substance is the sulphate ion. Sulphate ions in solution produce a white precipitate when hydrochloric acid is added to them followed by barium chloride solution. (The precipitate is the insoluble salt barium sulphate.)

↑ **Figure 1:** A positive test for sulphate ions.

 ## Ammonia and ammonium ions

Ammonia is an alkaline gas that is readily soluble in water. Ammonia gas turns damp red litmus paper blue, since the gas dissolves in the water in the paper, bringing it into close contact with the indicator. Since ammonia is quite a pungent gas your nose is also quite a good guide to its presence – but damp red litmus paper will turn blue well before there is enough ammonia present for your nose to detect it.

The test for ammonia can also be used to help identify whether ammonium ions are present in an unknown substance. Ammonium ions react with sodium hydroxide solution to form ammonia and water:

$$NH_4^+(aq) + OH^-(aq) \longrightarrow NH_3(aq) + H_2O(l)$$

So, to test for ammonium ions, sodium hydroxide solution is added to a solution of the unknown substance. If ammonium ions are present, ammonia is formed. Gently warming the solution then drives off the ammonia as a gas, which can be detected using damp red litmus paper.

Nitrate ions

Detecting the presence of nitrate ions in an unknown substance also makes use of the test for ammonia. As before, sodium hydroxide solution is added to a solution of the unknown substance and gently warmed. If no ammonia is detected, aluminium powder is added. The aluminium powder reduces the nitrate ions to ammonium ions. These then react with the sodium hydroxide solution to form ammonia gas, which is given off and detected using damp red litmus paper.

$$3NO_3^-(aq) + 5OH^-(aq) + 2H_2O(l) + 8Al(s) \longrightarrow 8AlO_2^-(aq) + 3NH_3(g)$$

↑ **Figure 2:** Damp red litmus paper turns blue – a simple test for ammonia.

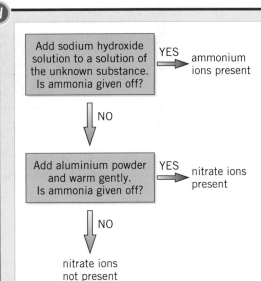

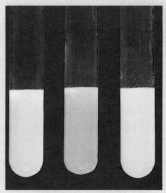

↑ **Figure 4:** One simple test can show us if we have chloride, bromide or iodide ions present.

Halide ions

On the opposite page we saw a test for chloride ions, which give a white precipitate with silver nitrate solution and nitric acid. The same test can be used to identify other halides, as both bromides and iodides give typical reactions with these reagents. Nitric acid and silver nitrate solution added to bromide ions give a creamy precipitate of silver bromide, whilst the same reagents added to iodide ions give a pale yellow precipitate of silver iodide.

↑ **Figure 3:** The steps in this test allow us to eliminate ammonium ions from our enquiry and demonstrate the presence of nitrate ions if they are there.

Key Ideas

⊙ Chloride ions produce a white precipitate with silver nitrate and nitric acid.

⊙ Sulphate ions produce a white precipitate with barium chloride and hydrochloric acid.

H ⊙ Ammonia gas turns damp red litmus paper blue. This can be used to test for the ammonium ion (with sodium hydroxide) and the nitrate ion (with sodium hydroxide and aluminium powder).

⊙ Silver nitrate and nitric acid give different coloured precipitates with different halide ions.

Questions

1 Compound A is a white solid which dissolves in water to produce a colourless solution. When this solution is acidified with nitric acid and silver nitrate is added, a white precipitate is produced. A flame test of compound A produces a bright red flame. Deduce the name of compound A and give your reasoning.

2 Compound B is a white solid which dissolves in water to give a blue solution. When this solution is acidified with hydrochloric acid and barium chloride is added, a white precipitate is produced. Deduce the name of compound B and give your reasoning.

H 3 Copy and complete the table.

Add dilute acid	Add sodium hydroxide solution and warm	Add sodium hydroxide solution and warm – then add aluminium	Flame test	Substance
nothing observed	nothing observed	gas evolved turns damp red litmus blue after aluminium is added	golden yellow	
fizzing – gas turns limewater milky	gas evolved turns damp red litmus blue	nothing observed	nothing observed	
				calcium carbonate

4 Copy and complete the table.

Add nitric acid and then silver nitrate solution	Flame test	Substance
creamy precipitate	golden yellow	
white precipitate	green	
yellow precipitate	lilac	

The sorts of tests described in Sections 13.1 and 13.2 have been used to identify unknown substances for many, many years, but they are time-consuming and use a lot of the substance being tested. However, in recent times technological developments have made it possible to identify unknown substances accurately, sensitively and rapidly using a variety of instrumental methods of analysis. What is more, instrumental methods can often be used even when only a very small sample of the unknown material is available – in fact it is in these circumstances that they are particularly useful.

Identifying elements

One important type of instrumental analysis used for identifying elements is based on the same principles as the simple flame test for metals in Section 13.1. **Flame photometry** is a very fast, simple and sensitive analytical method which can be used to determine the presence of metal ions in a solution. It burns the sample, analyses the light produced by the flame and records the results on a flame spectrograph. The lines on the spectrograph can be then compared to the patterns given by known elements, so they can be used to identify an unknown metal element.

Flame photometry is also used to analyse water for the presence of aluminium ions. Aluminium salts are used in the process of purifying drinking water, yet aluminium ions can be very poisonous so it is important that levels are kept to a minimum in the water we drink. Analysing the water using flame photometry keeps us well informed about aluminium levels.

The disadvantages of flame photometry are that it does not work for all metals and it is no use for identifying non-metals or compounds. Another similar technique known as **atomic absorption spectroscopy** can be used in a similar way to identify metals, but this technique has the advantage that it can also be used to identify non-metal elements as well.

↑ **Figure 1:** This flame photometry apparatus is being used to identify metal ions in the sample of liquid in the beaker. The technique is particularly useful for demonstrating the presence of ions such as sodium, potassium, calcium, rubidium, caesium, copper and barium.

🔍 *Ideas and Evidence*

Aluminium sulphate is usually used in carefully controlled amounts to purify drinking water in reservoirs. But in July 1988, a massive 20 tonnes of aluminium sulphate was accidently dumped into a reservoir at Camelford in Cornwall. Polluted water reached 20 000 homes and many local people suffered from aluminium poisoning (which causes brain damage). Since then, regular analysis of aluminium levels in drinking water has been carried out using techniques like flame photometry to make sure that there is no aluminium pollution in the water.

Identifying compounds

There is a wide range of chemical instruments used for identifying unknown chemical compounds. Again, these often include more sophisticated and automated versions of techniques used in the school laboratory. One example is **chromatography**, in which different compounds within a mixture are separated, depending on how well they dissolve in a particular solvent and consequently how far they travel on a substrate, such as a piece of chromatography paper.

Gas–liquid chromatography separates gases, gel permeation chromatography separates large molecules according to size, ion exchange chromatography separates charged particles, and liquid–liquid chromatography separates small neutral molecules in solution.

Once the compounds are separated out, they may be identified by comparison with the distance moved by known substances, or they may be fed into another very important instrument – the **mass spectrometer**. This can be used for identifying both elements and compounds – it measures the relative formula mass of the sample placed in it for analysis, which can then be used to identify the sample.

These techniques are very useful for measuring the make-up of the air, to test for air pollution. They are also widely used in medicine, for the analysis of blood and other body fluids. They also help to prevent cheating in sport – chromatography soon shows up any illegal substances present in an athlete's urine.

Despite their enormous power, instrumental techniques have disadvantages too – they are usually very expensive, it takes special training to use them and the results can often only be interpreted by comparison with already available known specimens.

← **Figure 2:** Gel electrophoresis – a type of chromatography – uses an electric field to separate compounds moving across a gel-covered plate. The bands shown here have been coloured with dyes.

→ **Figure 3:** Athletes train for years to reach the peak of their performance in the Olympic Games. Instrumental techniques which carry out rapid automated chromatography are used to test samples of athletes' urine for the presence of illegal drugs.

H Many of the instrumental methods of detecting and identifying elements and compounds are in great demand in a number of different industries. Many industries require rapid and accurate methods for the analysis of their products, to ensure that they are supplying a pure compound without any contamination by reactants or other by-products. Similarly, society has become increasingly aware of the risk of pollution of both air and water. Careful monitoring of the environment – such as using gas–liquid chromatography to analyse air quality – has become increasingly important.

Analysis and identification of different compounds and elements is also very important in health care. For example, in kidney dialysis machines aluminium can build up to dangerous levels, so no aluminium ions should be in the water used in these machines. The presence of alcohol or other drugs in the bloodstream can affect the way the body reacts to other treatments, so detecting their presence in the blood is very important too.

The development of modern instrumental methods has been aided by the rapid progress made in technologies such as electronics and computing. These advances have enabled us to develop machines which can carry out the analysis and rapidly compare and make sense of the results.

Key Ideas

⊙ Elements and compounds can be detected and identified using a variety of instrumental methods.

⊙ Some methods are suited to identify elements, others compounds.

⊙ Instrumental methods are particularly useful with small samples.

H ⊙ Industry requires rapid and accurate analysis methods, and so does society to monitor health and environmental issues.

? Questions

1 Name two instrumental methods, one for detecting elements and one for detecting compounds.

2 What are the main advantages and disadvantages of using instrumental analysis methods compared to traditional practical methods?

1 The flow diagram shows some reactions of iron.

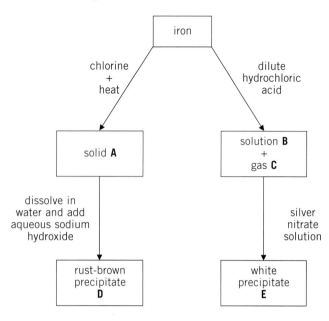

a Name the substances **A** to **E** shown in the flow diagram by choosing from the list:

hydrogen   iron(II) chloride
iron(III) chloride   iron(II) hydroxide
iron(III) hydroxide   oxygen
silver chloride   silver nitrate

  i Solid **A**   (1 mark)

 ii Solution **B**   (1 mark)

iii Gas **C**   (1 mark)

iv Rust-brown precipitate **D**   (1 mark)

 v White precipitate **E**   (1 mark)

b Today a variety of instrumental methods are used for detecting and identifying elements and compounds.

  i Name **one** instrumental method that might be used to detect the element iron.   (1 mark)

 ii Give **two** advantages of using instrumental methods for the detection and identification of elements.   (2 marks)

(Total 8 marks)
AQA specimen question

2 a A student had forgotten to label which of two test tubes contained a solution of aluminium nitrate.

Describe a chemical test using sodium hydroxide solution to show which test tube contained nitrate ions. Give the result of this test.   (3 marks)

b Name an instrumental method of analysis that might be used to detect a drug in the urine of an athlete.   (1 mark)

c Describe how advances in technology have assisted in the development of instrumental methods for the detection and identification of elements and compounds.   (2 marks)

(Total 6 marks)
AQA specimen question

3 A technique called **gel electrophoresis** is used to analyse DNA.

Analysis of DNA using this technique produces a plate which carries a series of bands, according to the composition of the DNA.

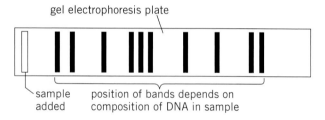

DNA from three suspects in a criminal investigation was analysed using this method and compared to the DNA from a sample found at the scene of a crime. The diagram shows the results that were obtained.

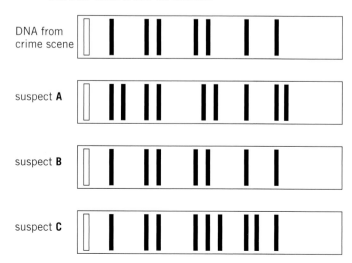

a How is evidence like this used to decide whether someone accused of a crime is guilty or not? (2 marks)

b According to the results in the diagram, which of the suspects, **A**, **B** or **C**, could have been present at the scene of the crime? Explain your answer. (2 marks)

c It might not be a good idea to rely on this kind of evidence alone when deciding if someone is guilty of a crime or not. Why? (2 marks)

(Total 6 marks)

H **4 a** A white powder dissolves in water to give a colourless solution. When a little hydrochloric acid is added to this solution, nothing happens. When sodium hydroxide is added and the solution is gently warmed, a gas is evolved which turns damp red litmus paper blue.

   i Suggest what the gas might be. (1 mark)

   ii Why must the solution be warmed? (1 mark)

   iii This test suggests which ion is present in the solution? (1 mark)

   If aluminium powder is now added to the solution and it is gently warmed again, a gas is evolved. This gas turns damp red litmus paper blue.

   iv This test suggests which ion is present in the solution? (1 mark)

   v What is the white powder? (1 mark)

b Describe how you would use a combination of sodium hydroxide solution and flame tests to distinguish between different solutions containing the following ions. Explain which tests you would use, in which order you would use them, and what results you would expect to see in each case.

   i Fe^{2+}

   ii Cu^{2+}

   iii Li^+

   iv Ca^{2+}

   v Fe^{3+}

   vi Al^{3+}

   vii Mg^{2+} (7 marks)

c **i** Name one instrumental technique which could be used to identify the ions in part **b**. (1 mark)

   ii What advantages do instrumental techniques have over techniques requiring a chemist to carry out test-tube reactions using many different chemicals? (3 marks)

(Total 16 marks)

Data

Reactivity series of metals

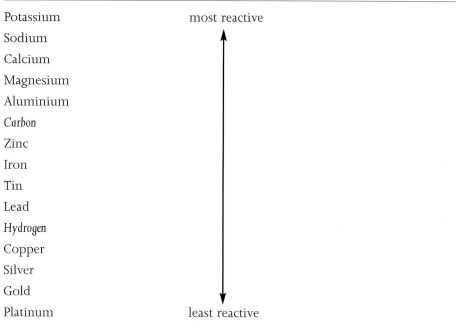

Potassium	most reactive
Sodium	
Calcium	
Magnesium	
Aluminium	
Carbon	
Zinc	
Iron	
Tin	
Lead	
Hydrogen	
Copper	
Silver	
Gold	
Platinum	least reactive

(Elements in italics, though non-metals, have been included for comparison.)

Formulae of some common ions

Positive ions

Name	Formula
Hydrogen	H^+
Sodium	Na^+
Silver	Ag^+
Potassium	K^+
Lithium	Li^+
Ammonium	NH_4^+
Barium	Ba^{2+}
Calcium	Ca^{2+}
Copper(II)	Cu^{2+}
Magnesium	Mg^{2+}
Zinc	Zn^{2+}
Lead	Pb^{2+}
Iron(II)	Fe^{2+}
Iron(III)	Fe^{3+}
Aluminium	Al^{3+}

Negative ions

Name	Formula
Chloride	Cl^-
Bromide	Br^-
Fluoride	F^-
Iodide	I^-
Hydroxide	OH^-
Nitrate	NO_3^-
Oxide	O^{2-}
Sulphide	S^{2-}
Sulphate	SO_4^{2-}
Carbonate	CO_3^{2-}

The periodic table of elements

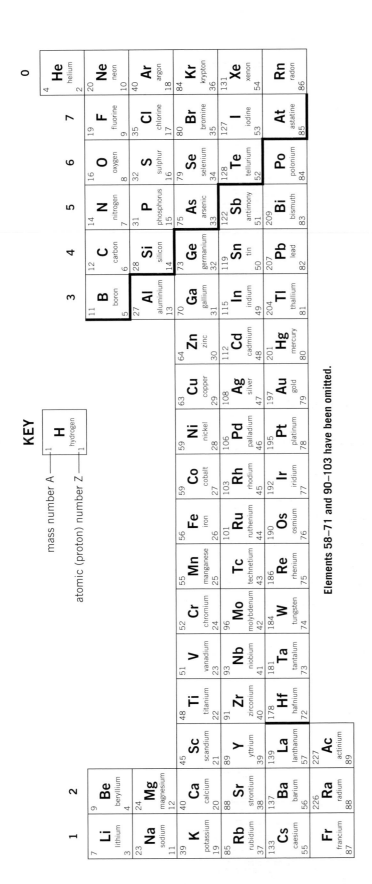

KEY

mass number A ——— H hydrogen
atomic (proton) number Z

Elements 58–71 and 90–103 have been omitted.

The value used for mass number is normally that of the commonest isotope, e.g. ^{35}Cl not ^{37}Cl.

Bromine is approximately equal proportions of ^{79}Br and ^{81}Br.

Index

A

acid–base reactions 179, 193
acid–base theory 192–3, 194
acid–base titrations 196–7
acid rain 43, 64, 109, 122
acids 106, 192–3
    household uses 108
    neutralisation of 108–9, 110, 136
    strong and weak 194
activation energy 122, 138
    and catalysts 140–1
addition polymerisation 48, 168
addition reactions 155
alcoholic drinks 128, 158–9
alcohols 158, 160–1
    oxidation of 163
    production of 160–1
    reactions 162–3, 165
    structure 160
    see also ethanol
algae 73
alkali metals 90–3
    electronic structures 89, 90, 91
    flame colours 92
    ionic radii 93
    properties 90–1
    reactions 92–3
        with chlorine 14, 23, 32, 93
        with oxygen 92–3
        with water 89, 92
alkalis 106, 192
    household uses 108
    neutralisation of 108–9, 110, 136
alkanes 46
    combustion of 46, 155
alkenes 46–7
    combustion of 47, 155
    hydrogenation of 155
    polymerisation of 44, 48
    test for 47, 155
aluminium 2, 60, 176
    anodised 176–7
    extraction of 60, 62, 63
    uses 176–7
aluminium alloys 61
aluminium ions, detection and analysis of 202, 206

aluminium oxide 60, 62
ammonia
    atomic structure 16
    manufacture of 66–7, 146–7
    reactions 68, 106, 110, 122
    test for 204
ammonium chloride
    dissolving in water 139
    formation of 110
    reversible decomposition of 144
ammonium hydroxide 106, 111
ammonium nitrate 111
ammonium salts 110–11
    test for 204
analytical techniques 206–7
animal fats 167
anode 58
anodising of aluminium 176–7
argon 9, 98, 99, 183
Aristotle 4
Arrhenius, Svante 192–3
ascorbic acid 165
aspirin 165, 167
Aston, Frederick 29
atmosphere 72–7
    changes 76–7
    composition 75
    early atmosphere 72, 74
atomic absorption spectroscopy 206
atomic mass 28
atomic models/theories 4–5
atomic number 6
    and periodic table 87
atoms 2
    structure of 3, 6–9
ATPase 141
Avogadro, Amedeo 34
Avogadro's number 34

B

baby foods 131
bacteria 73
balanced half equations 59, 62–3
balancing equations 24
    examples 25
barium, flame colour 202
basalt 78

bases 106, 192–3
    neutralisation of 108–9, 110
basic oxygen furnace 178–9
batch processes 132, 161
Becquerel, Antoine-Henri 113
Berzelius, Jöns Jacob 150
biodegradable plastics 45
blast furnace 56
bleach 33, 116
    supply and demand 117
boiling point 10, 11
    of hydrocarbons 156
bond energy calculations 142–3
bond formation and breaking 13, 138–9
boron, electronic structure 9, 88
Bosch, Carl 68
bread making 128
brine 114
    electrolysis of 114–15
bromine 2, 94, 96, 97
bromine water test 47, 155
Brønsted, Johannes 193
bronze 53, 101
Buchner, Eduard 127
burette 196
burning of fuels and organic compounds 46, 47, 136, 150–1
butane, isomers 156

C

caesium 90
calcium
    electronic structure 9
    flame colour 202
calcium carbonate 64
calcium chloride, formation of 15
calcium hydroxide 65, 109
calcium oxide 65
carbohydrases 131
carbon
    atomic structure 6
    electronic structure 6, 8, 88
    isotopes 6
    relative atomic mass 28
    see also diamond; graphite
carbon cycle 76
carbon dioxide
    in atmosphere 72, 74, 75, 76–7

from burning fossil fuels 43, 77, 153
from fermentation 128, 158
relative formula mass 32
removal from atmosphere 74, 77
sinks 76
test for 203
carbon monoxide 56, 143, 151
carbon steels 180
carbonates 77
    test for 203
    see also limestone
carboxylic acids 164–5
    everyday uses 165
    reactions 162, 164–5
    structure 164
cardiac chemistry 166–7
Carothers, Wallace 49
cast iron 56
cat cracker 42
catalysts 42, 125
    and activation energy 140–1
    biological see enzymes
    uses 42, 66, 103, 125
catalytic converters 103, 125
catalytic cracking 42
cathode 58
cement 65
cementation 79
Chadwick, James 5
Chain, Ernst 132
Chancourtis, Alexandre-Emile Beguyer de 86
cheese 129
chemical equations 24–5
chemical formulae 22
chemical reactions 12–13
    energy in 136–7
    quantities of reactants and products 32–3
    representing 23–5
chemical symbols 22
chlorides 110
    test for 96, 204
chlorine 94, 96, 97
    manufacture of 114–15
    reactions 14, 23, 32, 93, 96, 139
    uses 116, 187
cholesterol 166–7
chromatography 206–7

chromium–nickel steels 181
citric acid 164, 165
climate change 43
coke (fuel) 56, 143
collision of tectonic plates 81
collision theory (in reactions) 122
combustion
  incomplete 151
  of organic compounds 46, 47, 150–1
  see also burning
compounds 2, 12
  percentage of elements in 30–1
  representing 22
concentration, reaction rates affected by 122–3
concrete 65
condensation 10, 11
Contact process (for manufacture of sulphuric acid) 172–3
continuous processes 133, 161
convection currents, in Earth's crust 81
cooling curve 11
copper 101
  extraction of 52
  purifying of 61
  uses 101
copper bromide solution, electrolysis of 58, 59
copper carbonate 203
copper(II) sulphate 102, 112
  anhydrous 136, 144, 175
co-products 115
covalent bonding 13, 16–17
  halogens 95
covalent bonds, representing 16
covalent compounds
  giant structures 17, 18
  properties 16–17
cracking of hydrocarbons 42
crude oil 38, 154
  formation of 38, 39
  separation of 40–1
cryolite 60
cupro-nickel 101

D
Dalton, John 4, 5, 86
decomposition reactions
  photochemical 113
  thermal 65, 137, 144, 179
degreasing 176
dehydration 175
Demokritos 4
denaturation of proteins 126
denitrifying bacteria 75
deuterium 6
diamond 18
diesel oil 40
2,2-dimethylpropane 156, 157
displacement reactions 96
distillation 39
  fractional distillation 40, 158
dot and cross diagram 14
drinking water, nitrates in 69, 191
drug testing 207

E
earthquakes 83
Earth's crust
  elements in 54
  movements in 82–3
Earth's resources 52–69
economics 67, 115
electrodes 58
electrolysis 58–63
  of brine 114–15
electrolyte 58
electron 3
electron shells 8
electronic structures 8, 9, 14, 88
  of alkali metals 89, 90, 91
  of noble gases 8, 14, 98
electroplating 181
elements 2
  representing 22
empirical formula 35
endothermic reactions 136, 137, 138, 143
energy level diagrams 138
energy levels of electrons 8–9
energy transfers 138–9
  in reversible reactions 145

enzymes 126–33
  and activation energy 140
  advantages and disadvantages 130, 133
  denaturation of 126
  in fermentation 128, 158
  immobilised 133
  industrial uses 130–1, 141
  'lock-and-key' mechanism 127
  in milk processing 129
  pH sensitivity 127
  temperature effects 126
equilibrium in reversible reactions 145
  factors affecting 146
erosion of rocks 79, 82
esterification 162, 165
esters 162
etching 176
ethane 46, 154
  burning of 155
ethanoic acid 163, 164, 165, 194
ethanol 158
  production of 128, 158–9, 160–1
  reactions 162–3
  uses 158, 159, 160
ethene 46
  burning of 155
  from oil 42, 161
  polymerisation of 44, 48
eutrophication 69
evaporation 10, 11, 39
exothermic reactions 136, 138, 143, 173
extrusive igneous rocks 78

F
Faraday, Michael 58
fats 167
faults (Earth's crust) 82–3
fermentation 128, 158, 161
fertilisers 68, 69, 111, 174
filtration 39
fireworks 140
fizzy drinks 191
flame colours 92, 202
flame photometry 206
Fleming, Alexander 132
Florey, Howard 132
fluorine 94, 96, 97
folding of rocks 83
formula mass 29

fossil fuels 38, 150
  burning of 43, 77, 152–3
  consumption data 152
  formation of 38, 39, 74, 150
  pollution from burning 43, 77, 153
fossils 82
fractional distillation 40, 158
fracture in Earth's crust 82–3
francium 90
freezing point 10, 11
fructose 131
fuels
  burning of 46, 47, 136
  ethanol in 159
functional group 160

G
galvanised iron 57
gas oil 40
gases, solubility in water 190
gasohol 159
gasoline 40
gemstones 102
general formula 154
giant covalent structures 17, 18
giant ionic lattices 15, 18
giant metal structures 19, 100
glass 64, 65
gold 52
Gondwanaland 80
granite 78
graphite 18
Group 0 98–9
  see also noble gases
Group 1 90–3
  see also alkali metals
Group 7 94–7
  see also halogens
groups (in periodic table) 89

H
Haber, Fritz 66, 68
Haber process 66–7, 102, 125, 146–7
haematite 31, 56
Haigh, John 106
half equations 59, 62–3
halide ions, test for 96, 204, 205

Hall, Charles 60
halogens 94–7
  atomic radii 97
  covalent bonding 95
  ionic bonding 95
  properties 94
  reactions 96–7
  tests for 94
hard water 188
  'softening' of 189
hazard symbols 26–7
hazards
  in home 27
  in lab and industry 26
heating curve 11
helium 98, 99
high-alloy steels 181
Himalayas 80, 81
homologous series 154
hydrated hydrogen ions
  192
hydrated lime 65
hydrocarbons 38, 46–7
  burning of 46, 47, 154–5
  cracking of 42
  in crude oil 38, 40, 46
  properties 40
  saturated and unsaturated
    47, 154
hydrochloric acid 106,
  109, 194
  production of 116, 117
hydrogen
  electronic structure 6, 9
  isotopes 6
  manufacture of 114–15
  reactions 66, 96, 146–7,
    155
  uses 116
hydrogen chloride
  formation of 16, 95,
    116, 142
  reaction with ammonia
    122, 193
hydrogen peroxide 23
hydrogencarbonates 77
hydroxides 65, 92

I
identification tests 202–5
igneous rocks 78
immobilised enzymes 133
incomplete combustion
  151
indicators 106, 107, 196
industrial processes 160–1,
  172–85
inert gases see noble gases
intrusive igneous rocks 78
Io (moon of Jupiter) 72
iodine 94, 96, 97
iodine trichloride 144
ion 13
ion exchange columns 189

ionic bonding 13, 14–15
  halogens 95
ionic compounds
  giant structures 15, 18
  properties 15
iron 101
  corrosion/rusting of 56
  extraction of 53, 56, 178
  protection against rusting
    57, 181
  purifying 178–9
  quench hardening of 53
iron alloys 56, 57, 101
iron catalyst 66, 67, 103,
  125
iron ions, identification of
  202
isomerase 131
isomers 156–7
  naming 157
  numbers 156
  predicting 157
  properties 156
isotopes 6
  radioactive 7
  uses 7

K
kerosene 40
krypton 98

L
lactic acid 129
lactose 129
Laurasia 80
law of octaves 86
Le Chatelier, Henri 146
lead 101
lead bromide, molten,
  electrolysis of 58, 59
Leucippus 4
lime 65, 109
lime kiln 65
limestone 64–5, 78, 79
  processing of 65
  thermal decomposition of
    65, 179
  uses 56, 64, 178, 179
Lind, James 165
lipases 131
lithification 79
lithium 90
  flame colour 92, 202
  reactions 90, 92
lithium chloride 90, 93
litmus paper 94, 116, 204
low-alloy steels 180
Lowry, Thomas 193

M
magma 78
magnesium oxide
  empirical formula 35
  formation of 14, 35
magnetite 31

marble 78, 79
margarine 116, 167
mass number 6
mass spectrometer 29, 207
melting point 10, 11
Mendeleev, Dmitri 87
metal halides 95
  identification of 96, 205
metals 52–3
  extraction of 53, 54–5,
    60
  giant structures 19
  identifying 202
  purifying of 61
  reactivity 54–5
metamorphic rocks 78, 79,
  81
methane 16, 46, 142, 154
  combustion of 46, 150–1
methanoic acid 164
'meths' (methylated spirits)
  160
2-methylbutane 156, 157
2-methylpropane 156, 157
microorganism cultures
  132–3
mild steel 180
minerals 52, 53
mixing 12
mixtures, separation of 12,
  39
molecular formula 35
moles 34–5, 196–7, 198
monomers 44, 48
mountains, formation of 81

N
nanotechnology 141
neon 98, 99
neoprene 49
neutralisation of acids and
  bases 108–9, 110, 136,
  195, 196
neutron 3
Newlands, John 86
Newlands' octaves 86
nickel catalysts 103, 155
nickel steel 180
nitrates 66, 110
  pollution by 69, 191
  test for 204
nitric acid, manufacture of
  68, 125
nitrogen 66–7
  reactions 66, 146–7
  source in atmosphere 75
nitrogen-based fertilisers 69
  manufacture of 68, 111
nitrogen monoxide 68
noble gases 8, 88, 98–9
  electronic structure 8,
    14, 98
  properties 98

uses 99, 183
noble metals 52, 88
nucleus of atom 3
nylon 49

O
oil 38–51
  chemicals from 44–5
  composition 38
  formation of 38, 39
  prices 41
  see also crude oil
oleum (fuming sulphuric
  acid) 172
ores 52, 182
  extraction of metals from
    53, 55, 182–3
organic chemistry 46–7,
  150–69
organic compounds
  burning of 46, 47, 150–1
  sources 150
oxidation 55
  of alcohols 163
  in electrolysis 59
  of hydrocarbons 46, 47
  in iron/steel making 56,
    179
oxygen
  electronic structure 9, 88
  production by
    photosynthesis 73
  reactions 46, 47, 92–3
oxygen lance 178
ozone layer 75

P
Pangaea supercontinent 80
Pasteur, Louis 129
penicillin 132
pentane, isomers 156
pepsin (enzyme) 126, 127
periodic table 22, 86–9
periods 88
pH scale 107, 109, 194
phenolphthalein 196
photochemical
  decomposition 113
photographic film 113
photosynthesis 73, 137
plastics 44, 168–9
  disposal of 45, 169
  making 48
plate tectonics theory 80
platinum catalysts 103, 125
plutonic rocks 78
pollution
  from burning fossil fuels
    43
  by nitrogen-based
    fertilisers 69
poly(chloroethene) 168
poly(ethene) 44, 48, 168
polymerisation 48–9, 168

polymers 44, 48, 168–9
poly(propene) 44, 48, 168
polythene *see* poly(ethene)
potassium 90
    flame colour 92, 202
    reactions 92
potassium chloride 93
precipitation of insoluble
    salts 121, 195
pressure
    equilibrium position
        affected by 67, 146,
        147, 173
    reaction rates affected by
        122–3
    solubility of gases
        affected by 190
propane 46, 154
    burning of 46, 77
propene 46
    formation of 42
    polymerisation of 44, 48
proteases 131
proton 3
proton acceptors 192
proton donors 192
proton number 6, 87
PVC 168

Q
quicklime 65

R
radioactive isotopes 7
radioactivity, discovery of
    113
radon 98
reaction rates 120–35
    concentration/pressure
        effects 122–3
    effect of catalysts 125
    factors affecting 122–5
    measuring 120–1
        by change in mass 120
        by rate of precipitation
        121
        by volume of gas 121
    surface area effects 124
    temperature effects 122
reactivity series 54–5, 183
recycling of plastics 45
redox reactions 55, 59, 183
reduction 55
    in electrolysis 59
    in extraction of metals
        55, 56, 183
refinery gas 40
refining of oil 40–1
relative atomic mass 28
    using 30–3, 34, 63, 87,
    197
relative charge (of sub-
    atomic particles) 3
relative formula mass 29

using 30, 32, 33, 34,
    197
relative ionic mass 28
relative mass (of sub-atomic
    particles) 3
respiration 136
reversible reactions 144–5
    energy transfers in 145
    equilibrium in 145
rock cycle 78
rock salt 114
rocks 78–9
    folding of 83
    weathering and erosion
        of 79, 82
Röntgen, Wilhelm 113
rubidium 90
rusting 56
    prevention of 56–7, 181
Rutherford, Ernest 5
rutile 182

S
sacrificial protection 57
salt 114–15
    see also brine; sodium
        chloride
salts 93, 95, 108, 110–13,
    194–5
sandstone 78, 79
saturated fats 167
saturated hydrocarbons 47,
    154
saturated solution 190
scale (lime scale) 188
scum 188
sea water 114
seas and oceans, as carbon
    dioxide buffers 77
sedimentary rocks 78, 79
separation of mixtures 39
sherbert 137
silver halides 96, 112–13,
    205
silver nitrate test 96, 204,
    205
slaked lime 65
slate 78, 79
soap 108, 111, 188
sodium 90
    electronic structure 9,
        14, 89
    flame colour 92, 202
    reactions 14, 23, 32, 90,
        92, 93, 139, 163
sodium carbonate 189
sodium chloride
    formation of 14, 23, 32,
        93, 139
    relative formula mass 29,
        32
    structure 15, 18

sodium chloride solution,
    electrolysis of 114–15
sodium ethanoate 164
sodium ethoxide 163
sodium hydroxide 33, 106
    manufacture of 114–15
    reactions with metal ions
        202
    uses 116
sodium methanoate 164
soft water 188
solidification 10, 11
solubility curves 190
Sorensen, Soren 109
stainless steel 57, 181
standard atom 28
state symbols 25
states of matter 10–11
steel 56, 57, 178, 180–1
    protection against rusting
        181
strong acids 194
strong alkalis 194
strychnine 31
sub-atomic particles 3
sucrose (sugar),
    dehydration of 175
sulphates 110
    test for 204
sulphuric acid
    concentrated 175
    manufacture of 172–3
    uses 172, 174–5
superphosphate fertilisers
    174
surface area, reaction rates
    affected by 124

T
tectonic plates 80, 81
temperature
    enzyme-controlled
        reactions affected by
        126
    equilibrium position
        affected by 67, 146,
        147, 173
    reaction rates affected by
        122, 173
    solubility affected by
        190
thermal decomposition 65,
    137, 144, 179
thermosetting plastics 169
thermosoftening plastics
    168
Thompson, J. J. 5
titanium 182–3
    extraction of 182–3
    uses 182
titrations 196–9
    calculations 199

transition metal compounds
    102, 112
    coloured compounds 102
    naming of 102
transition metal oxides 110
transition metal salts 112
transition metals 88,
    100–3
    properties 100
    reactivity 101
    uses 101, 102–3
tritium 6, 7
trypsin (enzyme) 127
tungsten steel 180

U
universal indicator 107
unsaturated fats 167
unsaturated hydrocarbons
    47, 154
    polymerisation of 44, 48
    test for 47, 155
uplift (of rocks) 78–9

V
vanadium oxide catalyst
    172, 173
vegetable oils 116, 167
vinegar *see* ethanoic acid
vitamin C 165
volcanic rocks 78
volcanoes 72

W
washing powders,
    biological 131, 141
washing soda 189
water 186–7
    atomic structure 16
    hard and soft 188
    properties 186
    reactions involving 89,
        92, 172
    relative formula mass 29,
        32
    solubility in 190–1
    states of matter 10
    uses 187
water cycle 186
weak acids 194
weak alkalis 194
weathering of rocks 79, 82
word equations 23

X
X-rays 113
xenon 98

Y
yeast 128, 129
yoghurt 129

Z
zeugen (rock) 82
zinc carbonate 203
zymase (enzyme) 127, 128